FAITH DISCIPLESHIP

Faith Reaching Out to Cults

JOURNAL

Tal Davis, Bill Gordon, James Newman,
Jimmy Furr, Cky Carrigan, Sal J. Sberna

LifeWay Press
Nashville, Tennessee

ISBN 0-6330-0852-4

Dewey Decimal Classification: 248.5
Subject Heading: WITNESSING \ CULTS \ EVANGELISTIC WORK WITH CULTS

This book is the text for course CG-0607 in the subject area Evangelism in the Christian Growth Study Plan.

The FAITH Sunday School Evangelism Strategy® is an evangelistic venture of LifeWay Christian Resources of the Southern Baptist Convention and is endorsed by the North American Mission Board.

FAITH churches may obtain additional copies of this book by writing to
LifeWay Church Resources Customer Service, MSN 113;
127 Ninth Avenue, North; Nashville, TN 37234-0113; by calling toll free (800) 458-2772;
by faxing (615) 251-5933; or by emailing *customerservice@lifeway.com*.

For information about adult discipleship and family resources, training, and events,
visit our Web site at *www.lifeway.com/discipleplus*.

For information about FAITH, visit our Web site at *www.lifeway.com/sundayschool/faith*.

We believe that the Bible has God for its author; salvation for its end; and truth,
without any mixture of error, for its matter and that all Scripture is totally true and trustworthy.
The 2000 statement of *The Baptist Faith and Message* is our doctrinal guideline.

Printed in the United States of America

LifeWay Press
127 Ninth Avenue, North
Nashville, Tennessee 37234-0151

As God works through us, we will help people and churches know Jesus Christ and seek His kingdom by providing biblical solutions that spiritually transform individuals and cultures.

Contents

The Writers

Tal Davis is an associate on the Interfaith Evangelism Team, The North American Mission Board of the Southern Baptist Convention. He researches primarily cultic, sectarian, and new religious groups. Davis holds a bachelor-of-arts degree from Florida State University, a master-of-divinity degree from Southwestern Baptist Theological Seminary, and a doctor-of-ministry degree from New Orleans Baptist Theological Seminary.

Bill Gordon is an associate on the Interfaith Evangelism Team, The North American Mission Board of the Southern Baptist Convention. He researches primarily occultic and esoteric groups. Gordon holds a bachelor-of-science degree from Louisiana State University, a master-of-ministry degree from Criswell College, and master-of-divinity and doctor-of-theology degrees from New Orleans Baptist Theological Seminary.

James Newman is a retired national missionary for the western states and Canada on the Interfaith Evangelism Team, The North American Mission Board of the Southern Baptist Convention, and the pastor of a church in Bayfield, Colorado. He holds a bachelor-of-arts degree from Howard Payne University and a master-of-divinity degree from Southwestern Baptist Theological Seminary.

Jimmy Furr is a national missionary for the central and midwestern states on the Interfaith Evangelism Team, The North American Mission Board of the Southern Baptist Convention. Furr holds a bachelor-of-science degree from Delta State University and a master-of-divinity degree from New Orleans Baptist Theological Seminary.

Cky Carrigan is a national missionary for the Atlantic-coast and eastern states on the Interfaith Evangelism Team, The North American Mission Board of the Southern Baptist Convention, and North American missionary in residence at Wake Crossroads Baptist Church in Wake Forest, North Carolina. Carrigan holds a bachelor-of-arts degree from Criswell College and a master-of-divinity degree from Southeastern Baptist Theological Seminary, where he is also a candidate for a doctor-of-philosophy degree in theology.

Sal J. Sberna is the senior pastor of Metropolitan Baptist Church, a FAITH Originator Church, in Houston, Texas. He holds a bachelor-of-arts degree from Criswell Bible College in Dallas, Texas. Since Metropolitan began FAITH training, Sunday School enrollment has grown by more than 40 percent, and church membership has increased to six thousand. Metropolitan also hosted FAITH Clinics in 1998 and 1999 and is the May 2001 site of the National FAITH Institute. Sberna wrote A Quick Review, Your Discipleship Journey, and For Further Growth in each session and enlisted the writers of all FAITH at Work testimonies.

Expression of Commitment

FAITH Discipleship: Faith Reaching Out to Cults

I commit myself to continue **FAITH** Sunday School
evangelism training in my church.
I recognize **FAITH** training as a way to help my church and Sunday School,
to grow as a Great Commission Christian,
to be obedient to God's command to be an active witness,
and to equip others to share their faith.

Signed: ______________________________

Address: ______________________________

Phone number: ______________ Email address: ______________

I will faithfully attend and participate in this 16-week semester of FAITH training as a: ❑ Team Leader ❑ Assistant Team Leader ❑ Team Learner

My Team members: ______________________________

My Sunday School class/department: ______________________________

Dates of my *Faith Reaching Out to Cults* training: ______________________________

Introduction

Congratulations for completing semesters of FAITH evangelism training and for making a commitment to further growth as a Great Commission Christian through FAITH Discipleship. FAITH Discipleship grows from solid biblical principles like Jesus' Great Commission: " 'Go and make disciples of all nations, baptizing them in the name of the Father and of the Son and of the Holy Spirit, and teaching them to obey everything I have commanded you. And surely I am with you always, to the very end of the age' " (Matt. 28:19-20, NIV). Notice Jesus' dual emphasis on going and making disciples. In FAITH Basic and Advanced you concentrated a great deal on going to the lost, and you learned many skills and biblical teachings that are important for disciples to know and practice. In FAITH Discipleship courses you learn more about what it means to be a disciple of Jesus Christ and to make disciples of others.

Here are some specific ways FAITH Discipleship courses equip you further as a Great Commission witness.

- By teaching you important biblical truths you need to understand and exemplify as a growing disciple
- By equipping you to respond to difficult questions you may encounter in witnessing
- By helping you develop as a life witness for Christ, taking advantage of daily opportunities to share God's love
- By giving you opportunities to practice what you have learned in witnessing situations
- By helping you develop as a Team Leader
- By suggesting ways you can disciple others

This stop on your FAITH Discipleship journey is *Faith Reaching Out to Cults*. This course was designed to equip you to become a competent witness to those who have become ensnared in false teachings. The growth of cults and new religions is exploding across our nation. Estimates of the number of cults in America range from seven hundred to as many as three thousand, involving nearly 20 million people. These cults are directly opposed to Christianity; yet many of them present themselves as viable Christian churches. Only through a study of their belief systems, illuminated by the pure doctrine of the Word, can we begin to understand their differences and formulate witnessing strategies to reach their misguided followers.

The growth of cults confirms the fact that millions of people are seeking spiritual truth and a relationship with God, but in their search for truth, they have been deceived by the enemy to believe lies. Christians have a responsibility to learn how to reason from Scripture in ways that shed light on this encroaching darkness and rescue those who have been taken captive. This FAITH Discipleship course will help you accomplish that goal.

Here are the specific purposes of *Faith Reaching Out to Cults*.

1. *You will increase your understanding of historic biblical doctrines*. All cults use a little truth and a lot of error to seduce seekers. You will identify the biblical doctrines they pervert and will

learn how to use historic biblical teachings to present the truth to cult members. Here are some of the biblical doctrines you will use to refute cultic teachings.

- The deity of Jesus Christ
- The nature of God
- A biblical understanding of the Trinity
- The sole authority of the Bible
- The nature of humanity
- The reality and effects of sin
- Salvation by grace through faith
- The nature of the church
- The afterlife
- Characteristics of a true prophet of God

2. *You will gain confidence in confronting cult members with the truth of the gospel.* Maybe you are intimidated by cult members because of your lack of experience in countering their false teachings and their methods of seduction. Following is some of the practical information you will learn to increase your confidence in confronting cult members.
   - The history of individual cults
   - Ways cultic teachings violate biblical truth
   - A biblical response to specific cultic beliefs
   - Cults' deceptive use of Christian terminology
   - Cults' use of isolation, feelings, and psychological manipulation to recruit and control members
   - Why cults believe that they are the only true church
   - A witnessing strategy for encountering each cult

3. *You will develop Christian compassion for cult members.* Cult members are deceived to believe lies and are then trapped in the cult's system. The majority of these members have never had anyone with a loving heart and an equipped mind to point out, in the power of the Holy Spirit, the fallacy of their beliefs. You will be such a person. There can be no more pitiful scenario than the picture of persons who seek God and express their need for Him, only to be caught in a web of deception spun by the false teachings of a cult. Although they face death without Christ's salvation, they are taught that Christians are the enemy. How refreshing and revealing it will be for cult members who discover that Christians genuinely care for their souls.

Faith Reaching Out to Cults will help you, as a growing disciple, anchor your Christian life deeper in the eternal truths of God's Word. You will also grow as a Great Commission witness by learning how you can shine the light of God's truth in the lives of those who are lost in the dark world of cults. Your investment of 16 weeks will make an eternity of difference in the kingdom of God.

FAITH Visit Outline

Preparation

INTRODUCTION
INTERESTS
INVOLVEMENT

Church Experience/Background

- Ask about the person's church background.
- Listen for clues about the person's spiritual involvement.

Sunday School Testimony

- Tell general benefits of Sunday School.
- Tell a current personal experience.

Evangelistic Testimony

- Tell a little of your preconversion experience.
- Say: "I had a life-changing experience."
- Tell recent benefits of your conversion.

INQUIRY

Key Question: In your personal opinion, what do you understand it takes for a person to go to heaven?
Possible Answers: Faith, works, unclear, no opinion
Transition Statement: I'd like to share with you how the Bible answers this question, if it is all right. There is a word that can be used to answer this question: FAITH (spell out on fingers).

Presentation

F is for FORGIVENESS

We cannot have eternal life and heaven without God's forgiveness.
"In Him [meaning Jesus] we have redemption through His blood, the forgiveness of sins"—Ephesians 1:7a, NKJV.

A is for AVAILABLE

Forgiveness is available. It is—
AVAILABLE FOR ALL
"For God so loved the world that He gave His only begotten Son, that whoever believes in Him should not perish but have everlasting life"—John 3:16, NKJV.
BUT NOT AUTOMATIC
"Not everyone who says to Me, 'Lord, Lord,' shall enter the kingdom of heaven"—Matthew 7:21a, NKJV.

I is for IMPOSSIBLE

It is impossible for God to allow sin into heaven.
GOD IS—

- LOVE
  John 3:16, NKJV
- JUST
  "For judgment is without mercy"—James 2:13a, NKJV.

MAN IS SINFUL

"For all have sinned and fall short of the glory of God"—Romans 3:23, NKJV.

Question: But how can a sinful person enter heaven, where God allows no sin?

T is for TURN

Question: If you were driving down the road and someone asked you to turn, what would he or she be asking you to do? (change direction)

Turn means *repent.*

TURN from something—sin and self

"But unless you repent you will all likewise perish"—Luke 13:3b, NKJV.

TURN to Someone; trust Christ only

(The Bible tells us that) *"Christ died for our sins according to the Scriptures, and that He was buried, and that He rose again the third day according to the Scriptures"—1 Corinthians 15:3b-4, NKJV.*

"If you confess with your mouth the Lord Jesus and believe in your heart that God has raised Him from the dead, you will be saved"—Romans 10:9, NKJV.

H is for HEAVEN

Heaven is eternal life.

HERE

"I have come that they may have life, and that they may have it more abundantly"—John 10:10b, NKJV.

HEREAFTER

"And if I go and prepare a place for you, I will come again and receive you to Myself; that where I am, there you may be also"—John 14:3, NKJV.

HOW

How can a person have God's forgiveness, heaven and eternal life, and Jesus as personal Savior and Lord?

Explain based on leaflet picture, FAITH (Forsaking All, I Trust Him), Romans 10:9.

Invitation

INQUIRE

Understanding what we have shared, would you like to receive this forgiveness by trusting in Christ as your personal Savior and Lord?

INVITE

- Pray to accept Christ.
- Pray for commitment/recommitment.
- Invite to join Sunday School.

INSURE

- Use *A Step of Faith* to insure decision.
- Personal Acceptance
- Sunday School Enrollment
- Public Confession

FAITH Participation Card

Name: ______________________ Semester dates: ____________

Address: ______________________ Phone: ____________

Sunday School department: ______________________ Teacher: ____________

Other Team members: ______________________________________

Check one: ❑ FAITH Team Leader ❑ FAITH Assistant Team Leader ❑ FAITH Team Learner

	1	2	3	4	5	6	7	8	9	10	11	12	13	14	15	16	Totals
Class Participation *Place a check to indicate completion for the appropriate session.*																	
Present																	
Home study done																	
Outline recited																	
Visitation *Indicate a number for the following areas.*																	
Number of tries																	
Number visits																	
Number of people talked with																	
Type of Visit *(Assignments)*																	
Evangelistic																	
Ministry																	
Follow-up																	
Opinion Poll																	
Gospel Presented																	
Profession																	
Assurance																	
No decision																	
For practice																	
Gospel Not Presented																	
Already Christian																	
No admission																	
Sunday School Enrollment																	
Attempted																	
Enrolled																	
Life Witness																	
Profession																	
Assurance																	
No decision																	

SESSION 1

Faith Reaching Out to Cults: An Orientation

In this session you will—

HEAR IT by learning the purpose of this course and the topics to be covered;

SAY IT by practicing the ***Preparation*** portion of the FAITH Visit Outline;

STUDY IT by overviewing Home Study Assignments.

NOTES

Where Your Journey in FAITH Has Led

Congratulations for completing semesters of FAITH evangelism training and for making a commitment to further growth as a Great Commission Christian through FAITH Discipleship. Perhaps your journey thus far has taken you to places you had never been before—into the lives of lost persons who need to know our Lord Jesus Christ. Although your way may have been difficult at times, we hope that your journey has also taken you to new heights in your relationship with God as you learned to rely on Him for power and boldness in sharing His love for people.

In *A Journey in FAITH* you learned to use the FAITH Visit Outline to present the gospel to lost persons. You also learned to use your Sunday School testimony in witnessing visits. You learned the value of making Sunday School ministry visits. You gained valuable experience in making witnessing visits, as well as in sharing FAITH in everyday situations.

In *Building Bridges Through FAITH* you learned the importance of following up with new Christians to lead them to their next steps of growth and commitment. You learned and practiced additional skills for connecting people with Christ, the church, and Sunday School. You saw how these vital connections occur in daily life, in intentional visits, in ministry actions, and in other ways.

The next phase of your journey is FAITH Discipleship.

Goals of FAITH Discipleship

FAITH Discipleship grows from solid biblical principles like Jesus' Great Commission: " 'Go and make disciples of all nations, baptizing them in the name of the Father and of the Son and of the Holy Spirit, and teaching them to obey everything I have commanded you. And surely I am with you always, to the very end of the age' " (Matt. 28:19-20, NIV). Notice Jesus' dual emphasis on going and making disciples. In FAITH Basic and Advanced you concentrated a great deal on going to the lost, and you learned many skills and biblical teachings that are important for disciples to know and practice. In FAITH Discipleship courses you learn more about what it means to be a disciple of Jesus Christ and to make disciples of others.

Discipleship has been defined as "a personal, lifelong, obedient relationship with Jesus Christ in which He transforms your character into Christlikeness; changes your values into Kingdom values; and involves you in His mission in the home, the church, and the world."[1]

Do you see the way FAITH Discipleship complements FAITH evangelism training? From your growing relationship with Jesus come motivation, skills, and knowledge for witnessing and ministering to others. Here are some specific ways FAITH Discipleship courses equip you further as a Great Commission witness.

- By teaching you important ______________ ______________ you need to ______________ and ______________ as a growing disciple
- By equipping you to ______________ to difficult ______________ you may encounter in witnessing
- By helping you develop as a ____________ ____________ for Christ, taking advantage of daily opportunities to share God's love
- By giving you opportunities to ______________ what you have learned in ______________ ______________
- By helping you develop as a ____________ ______________
- By suggesting ways you can ______________ others

Perhaps you have already studied the first FAITH Discipleship course, *Sharing a Living Faith*. If so, you formed a biblical belief system that serves as a foundation for your further growth as a disciple. You also learned ways to respond to difficult questions and to share your beliefs with others who are willing to listen. You strengthened your leadership skills as you practiced sharing your faith, discipled your Team members, and interacted with new Sunday School members.

If you studied the FAITH Discipleship course *Faith at Work in Your Relationships*, you learned a variety of skills for developing witnessing relationships with lost persons who are not initially open to the gospel. You also learned ways to take advantage of opportunities to witness to lost persons you encounter in the everyday patterns of life. In addition to relational skills, you were encouraged to grow further as a disciple of Jesus Christ, to disciple your fellow Team members, and to build up your Sunday School through loving fellowship and caring ministry.

This stop on your FAITH Discipleship journey is *Faith Reaching Out to Cults*.

Purposes of Faith Reaching Out to Cults

This FAITH Discipleship course was designed to equip you to become a competent witness to those who have become ensnared in false teachings. The growth of cults and new religions is exploding across our nation. Estimates of the number of cults in America range from seven hundred to as many as three thousand, involving nearly 20 million

NOTES

NOTES

people. These cults are directly opposed to Christianity; yet many of them present themselves as viable Christian churches. Only through a study of their belief systems, illuminated by the pure doctrine of the Word, can we begin to understand their differences and formulate witnessing strategies to reach their misguided followers.

The growth of cults confirms the fact that millions of people are seeking spiritual truth and a relationship with God, but in their search for truth, they have been deceived by the enemy to believe lies. Christians have a responsibility to learn how to reason from Scripture in ways that shed light on this encroaching darkness and rescue those who have been taken captive. This FAITH Discipleship course will help you accomplish that goal.

Let's overview the specific purposes of *Faith Reaching Out to Cults*.

1. *You will increase your understanding of historic __________ ____________.*

All cults use a little truth and a lot of error to seduce seekers. You will identify the biblical doctrines they pervert and will learn how to use historic biblical teachings to present the truth to cult members. Here are some of the biblical doctrines you will use to refute cultic teachings.

- The deity of Jesus Christ
- The nature of God
- A biblical understanding of the Trinity
- The sole authority of the Bible
- The nature of humanity
- The reality and effects of sin
- Salvation by grace through faith
- The nature of the church
- The afterlife
- Characteristics of a true prophet of God

2. *You will gain ______________ in confronting cult members with the truth of the gospel.*

Maybe you are intimidated by cult members because of your lack of experience in countering their false teachings and their methods of seduction. Following is some of the practical information you will learn to increase your confidence in confronting cult members.

- The history of individual cults
- Ways cultic teachings violate biblical truth
- A biblical response to specific cultic beliefs
- Cults' deceptive use of Christian terminology
- Cults' use of isolation, feelings, and psychological manipulation to recruit and control members
- Why cults believe that they are the only true church
- A witnessing strategy for encountering each cult

3. *You will develop Christian* ________________ *for cult members.*

Cult members are deceived to believe lies and are then trapped in the cult's system. The majority of these members have never had anyone with a loving heart and an equipped mind to point out, in the power of the Holy Spirit, the fallacy of their beliefs. You will be such a person. There can be no more pitiful scenario than the picture of persons who seek God and express their need for Him, only to be caught in a web of deception spun by the false teachings of a cult. Although they face death without Christ's salvation, they are taught that Christians are the enemy. How refreshing and revealing it will be for cult members who discover that Christians genuinely care for their souls.

Name cults with whose members you have had contact.

____

How did you respond? ______________________________

Write ways you would like the Lord to change and equip you to reach cult members with the truth of the gospel.

____

Faith Reaching Out to Cults will help you, as a growing disciple, anchor your Christian life deeper in the eternal truths of God's Word. You will also grow as a Great Commission witness by learning how you can shine the light of God's truth in the lives of those who are lost in the dark world of cults. Your investment of 16 weeks will make an eternity of difference in the kingdom of God.

The Roles of a Team Leader

While you are meeting for this *Faith Reaching Out to Cults* orientation, Team Learners are overviewing many important ingredients of FAITH. They will learn to depend on you to interpret and reinforce many of the things they are discovering for the first time. *Faith Reaching Out to Cults* was intentionally designed for someone who has already learned the FAITH Visit Outline. Everything is planned to help you encourage and train individuals who are learning the outline for the first time. Although every participant in this course may not be a Team Leader, the importance of this role will be evident in this course.

If you are participating in this training as a Team Leader, you will

NOTES

learn specific ways to lead your Team through training. If you are participating in another way, you will still focus on actions you can take to enhance your skills in leading persons to faith in Christ. God may be preparing you for the time when you will lead a Team of Learners through FAITH.

If you are a Team Leader, you will fill several important roles.

1. *You are a __________ __________.*

You will serve as a role model in FAITH training by—
- demonstrating how to make a FAITH visit;
- being on time for Team Time;
- learning and demonstrating what you have learned and are learning in FAITH training;
- keeping up with all Home Study Assignments;
- making sure the Team has positive Visitation Time experiences;
- participating in Celebration Time.

You will also serve as a role model in Sunday School by—
- taking leadership roles;
- participating in weekly Sunday School leadership meetings;
- assimilating people, especially new members, into the class or department;
- looking for ways to disciple new believers through Sunday School.

2. *You are an ______________________ and a ______________________.*

As a Team Leader, you are responsible for—
- recognizing Learner needs;
- helping class and department members know about and want to be a part of the FAITH strategy;
- letting Learners know that you are praying for them;
- getting to know Learners and helping them feel comfortable with you during training sessions and throughout the week;
- assisting Learners as they memorize various parts of the FAITH Visit Outline during the week;
- encouraging Team members in things they are doing well before, during, and after visits;
- helping Learners during Team Time recite memory work and share experiences from home study;
- being sensitive to pressure points for Learners during the training;
- recognizing dropout signals;
- celebrating what Learners have memorized and completed by signing off on their assignments during Team Time;
- gently persuading Learners, when they are ready, to take the lead in specific parts of the visit.

NOTES

WHAT LEARNERS NEED

Learners need a Team Leader who will—
- hear them recite the FAITH Visit Outline every week during Team Time;
- contact and pray for them during the week;
- gently persuade them to share what they have learned in actual visits;
- motivate and encourage them;
- check off memory work every week;
- model the outline in visits;
- use the Opinion Poll correctly in visits;
- know how to adjust the pace of training to meet Learner needs/abilities;
- be with them and encourage them to attend Celebration Time.

3. *You are a ________________ __________________.*

Everything you do as a Team Leader assumes that you are growing in your faith. It will be obvious if you are not doing this. Everything done in FAITH Discipleship—witnessing, ministry, mentoring, Bible study, prayer—requires you to grow. Making yourself available to be used by God in these ways is essential.

NOTES

The Process

Faith Reaching Out to Cults follows the format of FAITH Basic and Advanced courses.

1. Team Time (15 mins.)
   - CHECK IT—Leading Team Time
2. Teaching Time (45 mins.)
   - KNOW IT—review of the previous week's material
   - HEAR IT—presentation of the current week's material
   - SEE IT—video segment supporting the week's material (selected sessions)
   - SAY IT—practice of the FAITH Visit Outline (selected sessions)
   - STUDY IT—preview of Home Study Assignments
3. Visitation Time (110 or more minutes, depending on your church's schedule)
   - DO IT
4. Celebration Time (30 mins.)
   - SHARE IT

What Happens During Team Time

Team Time is a very important part of the schedule for FAITH Learners. During these 15 minutes Learners debrief, practice, and recite the portion of the FAITH Visit Outline they have been assigned to learn up to that point. Since learning the entire FAITH Visit Outline is such a significant part of FAITH training, Team Time becomes a time of accountability.

If You Are a Team Leader

Your job is to help Learners rehearse the outline so that they feel more comfortable and natural in making a visit. Although Team Time is only 15 minutes during most sessions, Learners will increasingly see it as a much appreciated checkup and practice time.

Each session of this resource provides help to prepare for and lead Team Time. Although Team Leaders are responsible for conducting Team Time each week, everyone who has completed FAITH Basic will have an important role.

Team Time begins in session 2. Because good use of time is extremely

NOTES

important throughout this training, it is vital that you begin and conclude on time each week. (Session 12 is an extended Team Time, in which Learners spend the entire session practicing material they have learned.)

Each week ask Learners to recite the assigned portion of the FAITH Visit Outline as designated in the Team Time portion of *A Journey in FAITH Journal*. Hold the Learner's FAITH Journal and follow the outline as each person recites it.

Notice that these same assignments are capsuled in your resource in the section Leading Team Time, which begins each session. This feature will make you aware of what Learners are expected to know. Your copy of the FAITH Visit Outline is on pages 8–9 in this resource.

During the first few sessions you will likely have adequate time for both Team members to recite. Be aware that the longer the recitation, the greater the likelihood that only one person will be able to complete the outline during the 15 minutes before Teaching Time. Some of this work can continue in the car as the Team travels to and from visits.

In early sessions ask the person who feels most comfortable reciting to share first. Try not to put a Team member on the spot.

As a general rule and especially in later sessions, try to call on the person who most needs practice to share first. Do so with sensitivity and gentleness.

As a Team member correctly recites each line or phrase of the outline, place a check mark in the box beside the phrase. If the Learner has difficulty, does not recite it appropriately, or overlooks any portions, write notes in his copy of the FAITH Journal for his review. Be prepared to answer any questions the Learner might have about the outline and suggest ways to strengthen sharing the outline. When a Team member has successfully recited the assigned portion of the outline, sign off by writing your name or initials in the space provided in the member's Journal.

Overview the Learner's Home Study Assignments from the previous week. Feel free to raise questions and to discuss any aspect of the assignments. Doing so can help reinforce many important concepts taught through these assignments—concepts that may have been only introduced during the session. Again, sign off in the Learner's Journal any assignments that have been completed and that call for your approval.

As you debrief assignments or answer questions about the previous session, highlight ones that will appear on the final written review (ses. 16). Weekly, help reduce Learners' concerns about the final review.

Although you will not read the Learner's Your Journey in Faith pages, it will be significant to check to see that the Learner is keeping a written journal of his experiences throughout FAITH. It is easy to overlook this important aspect of home study.

However, journaling brings an enriching dimension to FAITH training. Suggest that Team members record their experiences and reflections on the Bible study. Encourage Learners to review previous journaling pages, particularly during times of discouragement. At the end of this semester both you and your Learners will be asked to write testimonies of what FAITH has meant personally, so your Journal is a wonderful record.

If You Are Not a Team Leader

Even if you are not a Team Leader, you will still need to participate in Team Time by being prepared to recite the FAITH Visit Outline, review the Home Study Assignments, and discuss ways to strengthen a visit. You may be asked to assist the Team Leader by working with a Team member who needs help and encouragement in learning and reciting the FAITH Visit Outline.

As Team members ride together to and from the visits, Learners can continue to practice sharing the outline and to discuss ways to strengthen a visit.

What Happens During Teaching Time

During Teaching Time you and Team Learners will go in separate directions for a focused time to learn new information. While Teaching Time for Team Learners presents the concepts in FAITH Basic, you will study the content in this course, *Faith Reaching Out to Cults*. You will spend 45 minutes each week focusing on a different cult. You will overview the history of each cult, examine its beliefs system, and identify ways the group departs from biblical teachings. You will also receive practical, biblical suggestions for reaching out to cult members with the good news of Jesus Christ.

The following format will be used for Teaching Time.

A Quick ______________

The first segment of Teaching Time, A Quick Review, is a five-minute period of accountability. Principles from the previous session will be reviewed. Some of the material in A Quick Review will appear on the final review (ses. 16).

Session ________________

The session content, which the Facilitator presents in about 35 minutes, identifies cultic teachings, presents a biblical response, and suggests ways you can share the truth of Jesus Christ with cult members. As the Facilitator presents the content, you will fill in the blanks in your Journal. Sometimes the session content is enhanced by a video segment.

What Happens During Visitation Time

This period of 110 or more minutes, depending on your church's schedule, is the vital time when you and your Team come back together to practice what you have learned through prayer and training.

NOTES

NOTES

FAITH Teams

Three persons are on every FAITH Team. In addition to the Team Leader, who has been trained in the FAITH strategy, two Team Learners have been enlisted to be trained and to visit together. Each Team represents a designated Sunday School division, department, or class.

Write the names of your Team members. If a Team member has already received training but is not participating as a Team Leader, write that member's name and role on the Team (for example, Assistant Team Leader).

____________________ ____________________ ____________________

Team Leader

FAITH Participation Card

One of the first things Team members are doing is preparing their FAITH Participation Cards. You will remember that this card is used each week as a name placard and to record numbers and types of visits attempted and made by the Team. If you have not already completed the top portion of your Participation Card, do so now. Make sure your name is printed in large letters on the reverse side of your name placard.

Review the categories of the Participation Card. You will be responsible for helping your Team members understand the categories identified on the card. You will also be responsible for helping them complete their cards following visits that begin with session 2.

The Participation Card is the basis for information on the FAITH Report Board. Remember that reports from the visits are summarized here. Your job is to orient your Team members to this process so that they can eventually report during Celebration Time.

Types of Visits

In all visits you should be ready to share the message of the gospel, as well as to invite unsaved persons to saving faith in Christ. You will look for opportunities to represent Christ by ministering to individuals in need, by enrolling some people in Bible study, and by helping others grow in their journey of faith. Each Team will make four types of visits.

1. Teams will make visits to Sunday School prospects, some of whom have had contact with your church as visitors to Sunday School, worship, or a special event. Some have been referred by a member, and others were discovered through a People Search opportunity. Generally, prospects are those who are open to a contact from or a relationship with your church.
2. Teams will make ministry visits to Sunday School members.
3. Teams will make visits using the Opinion Poll.

4. Teams will make follow-up visits to persons who have made significant decisions: to trust Christ, join the church, or enroll in Sunday School.

Although you will discover many new experiences when you make visits, Learners will be interested in knowing about each of these types of visits when they receive their assignments. Your experience, as well as what is taught during Teaching Time, will be particularly helpful as Learners determine ways to participate in each type of visit.

NOTES

Visitation Folder

Each Team will have a visitation folder that has been prepared for that week's visits. Be prepared to explain the significance and use of each item before, during, and after visits.

Contents of the visitation folder may include these and other items designated by the church.

Visitation assignment forms. Each week you should have several of these forms. Some assignments will be to a specific person or family indicated as a prospect. Other forms might be for visits to members. Some forms will indicate the assignment as a follow-up visit. Each form should indicate the general nature of the assigned visit.

If the card does not indicate that the person is a Sunday School member, assume that you are visiting to cultivate a relationship on behalf of the church and the Sunday School. Approach the visit assuming that you may have an opportunity to share the gospel.

Lead your Team to make as many visits as are feasible during the designated time. If you are unable to make assigned visits and/or have extra time, use the Opinion Poll to identify opportunities for evangelism and ministry.

Information about the church and Sunday School. A diagram, list, or information sheet should include a basic overview of Sunday School so that you can help family members identify with and know where Sunday School classes meet.

A *Step of Faith*. Use this leaflet when sharing the gospel with a person and issuing an ***Invitation***. Also use it to enroll a person in Sunday School and to record decisions made during a visit.

My *Next Step of Faith*. In session 3 of FAITH Advanced you received detailed help in using this leaflet to help a new believer take a next step of obedience through believer's baptism.

Opinion Poll cards. Use these forms to ask and record responses when making Opinion Poll visits.

Bible-study material used by your class. During a visit give a copy of current material to new enrollees and to nonattending members.

Believe magazine. This devotional magazine helps new believers understand who they are in Christ and become grounded in their faith.[2]

Church promotional information about upcoming special events and opportunities.

NOTES

Identify the items in your packet that are unique to your church. How can these items help you make better visits?

____

____

You will be responsible for demonstrating how to use each item in the visitation folder. Until Learners overview how to use these items and complete the forms, you will be responsible for training them in how to use them. Remember that you are the Learners' model, and they will follow the example you set. Whatever you do correctly or incorrectly will be multiplied by them in the future.

Let's briefly review what is expected in completing the visitation forms. No matter what type of record form is used by the church, you need to take the following actions.

1. Fill in every applicable ____________ in which information is requested.
2. If an assigned person is not at home or is not willing to respond to selected questions for information, __________ the card (or blanks left incomplete) and indicate the __________ of the attempted visit and the ____________ information was not recorded.
3. ____________ information ______________.
4. Write information discovered from the visit that will help in making any __________________ _______________.
5. Record information about all other ___________________ discovered in the home.
6. Turn in the detachable __________________ __________ portion of *A Step of Faith*.

Prayer and Practice

If you have a sufficient number of Teams participating in FAITH visits, the work of several Teams will be coordinated by a FAITH Group Leader. For the purposes of Prayer and Practice, one group of Teams will remain in the Teaching Time room each week to pray while other Teams make visits. This process will begin no earlier than session 3. Assignments for Prayer and Practice are made on a rotating basis and are noted in your weekly newsletter or in the visitation folder.

As soon as visiting Teams depart to make visits, the assigned Group Leader assembles Teams for prayer. Teams pray throughout Visitation Time specifically for the Team members visiting and for the individuals to be visited. They pray for divine appointments. The Group Leader might call the names of persons visiting and being visited.

During Prayer and Practice the Group Leader can also lead Teams to practice reciting the FAITH Visit Outline with one another. Team members can also spend time writing notes to prospects and members. When Prayer and Practice is over, the Group Leader leads participants to complete their session Participation and Evaluation Cards.

What Happens During Celebration Time

This is a 30-minute time to report Team and FAITH-strategy victories. Each week you will be responsible for leading your Team to report about visits attempted and visits made. This can become a very meaningful and motivational time. In addition to helping Team members update and submit their Participation Cards, Evaluation Cards, and visitation-assignment cards, help them know how to complete the Report Board.

Particularly during the first few weeks of training, Team members will look to you to share verbal reports during the report time. Even if a Team seemingly has not had a productive visit, Team members share in the ministry's victories during this period.

Keep these guidelines in mind as you lead and help your Team members verbally report.

1. *Be brief*. The amount of time needed will be determined by the number of Teams reporting.
2. *Be precise*. Do not give unnecessary details.
3. *Be positive*. Discuss problems or negatives in another setting, such as with your Group Leader.
4. *Be enthusiastic*. You and your Team have been attempting the greatest opportunity in the world!
5. *Be accurate*. Do not embellish what really happened.
6. *Be careful*. Do not report anything confidential that was shared with your Team. Use only the first names of the persons you visited.
7. *Be thankful*. Even if no decision was made or no one allowed you to share, be grateful for the opportunity to talk.
8. *Be affirming*. If Joe shared a Sunday School testimony for the first time in a visit and did a great job, tell the entire group. You not only encourage Joe but also motivate other Teams.

Your Testimony

By now you have been involved in FAITH training for at least two years, maybe longer. Many things can take place in that length of time.

Because Sunday School is an essential part of the FAITH process, it is important to keep your Sunday School testimony current. What changes do you need to make in your Sunday School testimony you developed for your first semester of FAITH to better describe what is happening in your class today?

NOTES

NOTES

____

____

You may also need to update your evangelistic testimony. What has God been teaching you in the past 18 months? How has your spiritual life changed? What adjustments do you need to make in your evangelistic testimony to make it current?

____

____

Growing as a Life Witness

While overviewing the Participation Card, you may have noticed the Life Witness line. One goal of FAITH training is to develop believers committed to sharing the gospel in today's world. This means sharing Christ more than the scheduled two hours a week. Sharing Jesus must become a part of your lifestyle if you are to be a true Great Commission Christian. You will be encouraged to grow as a life witness during *Faith Reaching Out to Cults* through the following expectations.

1. The ______________ as a ________ ______________ portion of your Home Study Assignments will remind you of your responsibility to witness and minister to others during the week, besides during FAITH visits.
2. In addition to your prayer partners in your Sunday School class or department, you will have an ______________________ ______________ throughout the semester who will—
   - ________ whether you have had witnessing and ministry opportunities during the past week, other than FAITH visits;
   - ________ for specific persons you identify, for your participation in FAITH Discipleship training, for your effectiveness as a Team Leader, and for your use by God in divine appointments;
   - ______________ problems or questions you may have in witnessing encounters or in completing Home Study Assignments and ways new concepts can be applied;
   - periodically ______________ the FAITH Visit Outline.

My accountability partner is ______________________

Phone number(s): ______________________

Your Resources

NOTES

Faith Reaching Out to Cults will enhance and reinforce your earlier FAITH training. Here are important resources you will use.

FAITH Visit Outline

There is no new memory work; you will continue to practice the FAITH Visit Outline.

Faith Reaching Out to Cults Journal

As was true in FAITH Basic and Advanced, the Journal will be your main resource. After you have filled in the blanks during each session's Teaching Time, it can be helpful during home study to reread that session to get the big picture. Besides the content studied during Teaching Time, the following sections are included in your Journal.

- *Leading Team Time*. The Leading Team Time suggestions each week will help you as a Team Leader debrief, practice, and review with your Team. Suggestions are based on Learners' *A Journey in FAITH Journal* Team Time agenda for each week.
- *Home Study Assignments*. Each week your Home Study Assignments reinforce the session by helping you apply what you have learned. Home Study Assignments consist of the following sections.

—*Your Discipleship Journey*. Assignments in this section focus on your development as a disciple.

—*Growing as a Life Witness*. This section reminds you of your responsibility to witness and minister to others during the week.

—*Your Weekly Sunday School Leadership Meeting*. This section allows you to make notes about the way your FAITH Team influences the work of your Sunday School class or department. As you and other leaders meet to plan for next Sunday's Bible-study time, identify actions that need to be taken through Sunday School as a result of prayer concerns, needs identified, visits made by the Team, and decisions made by the persons visited. You may also identify ways you can disciple others in your Sunday School class or department and in your church.

—*Discipling Your Team Members*. This section suggests ways you can disciple your Team members as you prepare to lead your FAITH Team's group time at the beginning of the next session and as you mentor and support members through the week. You will find reminders about the things the Learners have studied, as well as some tips to help you be a better Team Leader.

—*For Further Growth*. This section challenges you with optional long-term reading or discipleship activities.

—*FAITH Tip*. Selected sessions include optional readings that explore

NOTES

biblical teachings about a variety of doctrinal issues.

—*FAITH at Work*. Selected sessions include testimonies about the difference FAITH has made in participants' lives.

In-Session Training Resources

Your Facilitator will use these resources to help you learn.

- Videotape segments, in which you will see examples of FAITH participants who interact with cult members
- Computer presentation or overhead cels to help you fill in the blanks and understand that session's teachings

Sunday School Ministry

Your Sunday School class or department is a primary resource. Sunday School is the unique dynamic of FAITH. Your class/department can be a place where names become people, needs become visible, and assimilation becomes more than a term. Attending the weekly Sunday School leadership meeting creates this link.

Your Walk with God

Three components of your walk with God will provide essential spiritual direction as you participate in this course.

- *Your willingness to join God's work*. Evangelism is God's activity, and you must be willing to be on His agenda and timetable in this endeavor. Ask that His Holy Spirit will guide what you say and do; empower you for divine confidence, strength, and wisdom; and prepare each lost person's heart for the seeds you will sow. During the next 16 weeks, expect God to work in your life, in your Sunday School/church, in the lives of people you meet, and in your Team.
- *Bible study*. You will be exposed to a lot of biblical content during this course. Your Facilitator will not have time to cover in-depth each passage in your Journal. Spend time between sessions reading and reviewing the passages so that you will be better prepared "to give the reason for the hope that you have" (1 Pet. 3:15, NIV). Never underestimate the power of God's living and active Word to speak with an authority of its own (see 2 Tim. 3:15-17; Heb. 4:12).
- *Prayer*. Prayer is your most important and most powerful resource. The Lord has promised to hear us when we call on Him (see Matt. 18:19-20; 21:22; Luke 11:9-13). Call on Him throughout *Faith Reaching Out to Cults* and enlist faithful prayer partners to uphold you in prayer for the next 16 weeks.

Home Study Assignments

Home Study Assignments reinforce this session by helping you apply what you have learned.

Your Discipleship Journey

Journaling activities in Your Discipleship Journey are an important part of your development as a Great Commission Christian through FAITH training.

1. One purpose of FAITH Discipleship is to help you grow in your relationship with God. Each FAITH Discipleship course begins by asking you to assess your personal discipleship habits. Rate yourself in each area below, using the following scale.
   1 = never   2 = seldom   3 = sometimes   4 = usually   5 = always

I have a daily quiet time.	1	2	3	4	5
I make Christ number one in my life.	1	2	3	4	5
I stay close to the Lord throughout the day.	1	2	3	4	5
I read my Bible daily.	1	2	3	4	5
I study my Bible in depth.	1	2	3	4	5
I memorize a Scripture verse each week.	1	2	3	4	5
I keep a prayer list and pray for those concerns.	1	2	3	4	5
I recognize answers to my prayers.	1	2	3	4	5
I include praise, thanksgiving, confession, petition, and intercession in my prayers.	1	2	3	4	5
I live in harmony with my family and other believers.	1	2	3	4	5
I seek reconciliation when it is needed.	1	2	3	4	5
I attend worship services.	1	2	3	4	5
I attend Bible study.	1	2	3	4	5
I pray for lost persons by name.	1	2	3	4	5
I share my testimony with others.	1	2	3	4	5
I share the plan of salvation with others.	1	2	3	4	5
I witness each week.	1	2	3	4	5
I follow up on persons I have led to Christ.	1	2	3	4	5
I serve in my church.	1	2	3	4	5
I give at least a tithe through my church.	1	2	3	4	5
I minister to others.[3]	1	2	3	4	5

Examine your responses to the inventory and determine where you need to improve. Write one action you will commit to take to grow in discipleship.

____

____

2. Record goals you have for this semester of FAITH Discipleship.

A goal for your personal discipleship: ______________________________

____

____

A goal for witnessing: ______________________________

____

____

A goal for discipling Team members and Sunday School members:

____

____

Growing as a Life Witness

Growing as a Life Witness reminds you of your responsibility to witness and minister to others during the week.

1. Talk with your accountability partner and plan the way you will communicate each week during the semester.
2. Discuss any persons you are cultivating through ministry or witness.
3. Pray for each other's growth as disciples, as Team Leaders, and as witnesses.

Prayer Concerns	Answers to Prayer
____________________	____________________
____________________	____________________
____________________	____________________
____________________	____________________

Your Weekly Sunday School Leadership Meeting

A FAITH participant is an important member of Sunday School. Encourage Team members who are elected Sunday School workers to attend this weekly meeting. Use this section to record ways your FAITH Team influences the work of your Sunday School class or department. Use the information to report during weekly Sunday School leadership meetings. Identify actions that need to be taken through Sunday School as a result of prayer concerns, needs identified, visits made by the Team, and decisions made by the persons visited. Also identify ways you can disciple others in your Sunday School class or department and in your church.

1. Think back to your first day of FAITH training and recall as much as you can about your Sunday School class then. Who else from your class was in FAITH training?

____

____

2. Think about your class now. How has it changed? How many of the people in your class are new believers or new members of your church? Who has joined you in FAITH training? What role has FAITH played in these changes?

____

____

3. A new semester of FAITH is under way. How does the Team's preparation for every Sunday through this weekly leadership meeting need to consider the needs of individuals or families visited through FAITH?

____

____

4. This time together each week also can facilitate your growth as a disciple. Does your continuing commitment to FAITH training include a commitment to attend this important weekly meeting?

Discipling Your Team Members

This weekly feature suggests actions the Team Leader can take to support Team members, prepare for Team Time, and consider ways to improve visits. This work becomes part of the Team Leader's Home Study Assignments. Add any actions suggested by your church's FAITH strategy.

Support Team Members

❑ Contact Team members during the week. Explain to them that you will pray for them during this semester of FAITH. Discuss their orientation to FAITH. Emphasize the importance of being on time for Team Time. Briefly remind them of their role during Team Time.

- ❑ As you talk with Learners this week—
  - find out whether they understood their Home Study Assignments, especially the writing of their Sunday School testimonies;
  - ask whether they have a prayer partner from their Sunday School class;
  - suggest that they preview the FAITH Tip for session 2, "Helpful Visitation Tips," in *A Journey in FAITH Journal*.
- ❑ Remind members to bring a small Bible with them to take on visits. Teams will make visits after session 2, then return for Celebration Time.
- ❑ Record specific needs and concerns shared by Team members.

____

____

Prepare to Lead Team Time

- ❑ Review Team members' Home Study Assignments.
- ❑ Preview Leading Team Time for session 2.

Prepare to Lead Visits

- ❑ Review the FAITH Visit Outline.
- ❑ Be prepared to explain the contents of the visitation folder.
- ❑ Be ready to model a visit in which Team members are asked to share their Sunday School testimonies.

Link with Sunday School

- ❑ Prepare to share with other Sunday School workers a brief summary of what you will study during this semester of FAITH Discipleship. Ask that they pray for you as you continue to learn and grow in your witnessing skills.

For Further Growth

For Further Growth may include additional reading or activities that will enhance your growth as a disciple and a discipler of others. These assignments are intended to be long-term projects and do not have to be completed during this semester of study.

1. Participate in a group study of *MasterLife* by Avery T. Willis Jr. (LifeWay, 1996). This series of four six-week discipleship studies provides a comprehensive, biblical understanding of what is expected of a disciple of Jesus Christ.
2. Read 2 Timothy 3—4:5. Compare this picture of the last days with contemporary society and note Paul's instructions for the way believers should live.

---

[1]Avery T. Willis Jr., *MasterLife 1: The Disciple's Cross* (Nashville: LifeWay, 1996), 5.

[2]*Believe* and *essential connection* magazines are available by writing to LifeWay Church Resources Customer Service, MSN 113; 127 Ninth Avenue, North; Nashville, TN 37234-0113; by calling toll free (800) 458-2772; by faxing (615) 251-5933; by ordering online at *www.lifeway.com*; or by emailing *customerservice@lifeway.com*.

[3]Willis, *MasterLife 1*, 29–30.

SESSION 2

Defining Cults and Sects

BILL GORDON

In this session you will—

CHECK IT by engaging in Team Time activities;

KNOW IT by reviewing distinctives of this course from session 1;

HEAR IT by discovering characteristics that define cults and sects;

STUDY IT by overviewing Home Study Assignments;

DO IT by leading your Team in making visits;

SHARE IT by celebrating.

NOTES

Leading Team Time

All Team members participate in Team Time. They are primarily responsible for reciting the assigned portion of the FAITH Visit Outline and for discussing other Home Study Assignments.

As you direct this important time of CHECK IT activities with your Team, keep in mind that Learners look to you as a role model, motivator, mentor, and friend. Team Time activities can continue in the car as the Team travels to and from visits.

Lead CHECK It Activities

Since this is the first time for Team Time activities, provide any additional explanation that is needed. Make good use of the 15 minutes that begin each session.

✔ *FAITH Visit Outline*

- ❑ Team members should be ready to recite all aspects of ***Preparation*** up to INQUIRY and the key words in ***Presentation*** (FORGIVENESS, AVAILABLE, IMPOSSIBLE, TURN, HEAVEN) and ***Invitation*** (INQUIRE, INVITE, INSURE).
- ❑ Indicate your approval by signing or initialing Journals. Encourage Learners.

✔ *Sunday School Testimony*

- ❑ Ask Team members for their written Sunday School testimonies, due this session. Help evaluate each testimony to make sure it includes one or two of the following aspects: friendship/support received, assistance received during a crisis, personal benefits of Bible study through the class, or ways they have grown as a Christian through experiences in or through the Sunday School class. Discuss how benefits can and do change, reflecting different experiences.
- ❑ If the written testimony is acceptable, make sure each Team member understands the importance of learning to share it naturally, in his or her own words. Ask for permission to print the testimony in any church materials that publicize FAITH and/or that encourage persons to share their testimonies.

✔ *Other Home Study Assignments*

- ❑ Are Learners on track with Home Study Assignments? Provide any feedback or help they may need.

✔ *Session 1 Debriefing*

- ❑ Make sure major concepts from session 1 are understood, since this session provides an orientation to the course.

✔ *Help for Strengthening a Visit*

- ❑ This is the first session in which Teams will make home visits. Encourage members and try to ease any concerns. Explain that the Team Leader will take the lead in the INTRODUCTION portion of the visit(s) following this session.
- ❑ Identify a Team member(s) who would be prepared to share a Sunday School testimony at the Team Leader's prompting during a visit. Be sensitive to persons who are ready to share.

Notes

____

____

____

____

____

____

____

Actions I Need to Take with Team Members This Week

____

____

____

____

____

____

____

____

NOTES

NOTES

A Quick Review

Faith Reaching Out to Cults is a FAITH Discipleship course. Check the ways FAITH Discipleship courses equip you as a Great Commission witness.

- ☑ 1. By teaching you important biblical truths you need to understand and exemplify as a growing disciple
- ☐ 2. By surveying major themes in the Wisdom Literature of the Bible
- ☐ 3. By helping you identify and deal with destructive relationships
- ☑ 4. By equipping you to respond to difficult questions you may encounter in witnessing
- ☑ 5. By helping you develop as a life witness for Christ, taking advantage of daily opportunities to share God's love
- ☐ 6. By revealing cutting-edge opportunities for deacon ministry
- ☑ 7. By giving you opportunities to practice what you have learned in witnessing situations
- ☑ 8. By helping you develop as a Team Leader
- ☐ 9. By identifying ways to harass lost persons in the workplace
- ☑ 10. By suggesting ways you can disciple others

Identify the three purposes of *Faith Reaching Out to Cults*.

1. To increase your understanding of historic Biblical Doctrine
2. To give you Confidence in confronting cult members with the truth of the gospel
3. To encourage Christian Compassion for cult members

Characteristics of Cults and Sects

The phone rang at work, and a young mother picked up the phone. Her children asked permission to participate in a free Bible study being offered by some people who had come to their door. The mother thought: *I don't take the children to church as often as I should. They need to learn more about the Bible*. She gave the children permission to study the Bible with the people at the door. Years later she testified: "That was the worst decision I have ever made. Today all of my children and grandchildren are members of a cult because I let cult followers teach my children when they came to the door years ago."

Jesus warned His followers about false prophets and teachers who try to lead believers astray: " 'Beware of the false prophets, who come to you in sheep's clothing, but inwardly are ravenous wolves' " (Matt. 7:15). As you seek to share the true gospel of Jesus with people you meet, it is crucial that you know how to recognize and respond to those who have been misled by false teachers.

Many different definitions are assigned to the terms *cult* and *sect*. The media often reserve the term *cult* for groups that engage in violence or mass suicide, like the People's Temple in Guyana, the Branch Davidians in Texas, or the Heaven's Gate group in California. Sociologists define a cult as a religious group that deviates from the sociological norm of the larger culture. Evangelical theologians, on the other hand, use the term *cult* to refer to groups that claim to be Christian but reject the traditional Christian views of God and Jesus Christ. Theologians often refer to the doctrine of God as theology proper. The doctrine of Christ is known as Christology. The term *cult* is used in its theological sense to refer to a group that claims to be Christian but deviates from the traditional Christian understanding of theology proper and/or Christology. A sect is a group that does not deviate from the traditional Christian doctrines of the nature of God and Jesus Christ but nonetheless exhibits many sociological characteristics that are commonly associated with cults.

The Interfaith Evangelism Team of the North American Mission Board of the Southern Baptist Convention has identified four major characteristics of cults and sects. As a student executes the four basic math functions, cults use addition, subtraction, division, and multiplication to distort or deny Christian truth. Some cults use all four functions, while many sects use only division and/or multiplication. Cults and sects may use addition by adding to the inspired Scriptures. Many cults claim to have additional writings or scriptures that either supersede or supplement the Christian Bible. Some cults subtract from Jesus' deity or God's nature. Cults and sects may divide their followers from God. When this happens, devotion to the cult or sect becomes a test of faith and devotion to God. Cults and sects may also multiply the requirements for salvation by demanding works.

Let's look at some ways cults and sects might distort biblical teaching through addition, subtraction, multiplication, and division.

Cults Add to GOD'S WORD

Evangelical Christians accept the Bible as the only authoritative source of God's revelation. Although most cults derived from Christianity are willing to affirm that God inspired the Bible, they often add to it in a number of ways.

1. *Cults add to God's Word by using extrabiblical* WRITINGS.

Cults often assign authority to other scriptures or other written material they claim is necessary to understand the Bible. The cult may rationalize

NOTES

NOTES

this addition by claiming that the Bible is incomplete, corrupted, or mistranslated.

For example, the Church of Jesus Christ of Latter-day Saints (the Mormons) has three additional scriptures or standard works in addition to the *King James Version* of the Bible. Although Mormons accept the *King James Version* only as far as it is translated "correctly," they have complete confidence in their other scriptures: the *Book of Mormon, Doctrines and Covenants*, and *The Pearl of Great Price. The Book of Mormon* even claims that the Bible is missing plain and precious parts (see 1 Nephi 13:26). Many of the deviant doctrines that separate the Mormon Church from Christian denominations are found in *Doctrine and Covenants* and *The Pearl of Great Price*.

Although Jehovah's Witnesses believe that the Bible is a divinely inspired book, they have so corrupted the translation of the Bible in *The New World Translation of the Holy Scriptures* (NWT) that they have in effect added to the Scriptures. Wherever the Bible disagrees with Jehovah's Witnesses' teachings, they have changed the Bible to conform to the theology of the Watchtower Bible and Tract Society. For example, in John 1:1 Jehovah's Witnesses' NWT reads, "The Word was a god" instead of "The Word was God." This change was made so that Christ's full deity, which John affirmed in the original passage, is no longer apparent to readers.

In Colossians 1:16-19 Jehovah's Witnesses add the word *other* to the text even though no textual manuscripts support this reading.

> By means of him all [other] things were created in the heavens and upon the earth, the things visible and the things invisible, no matter whether they are thrones or lordships or governments or authorities. All [other] things have been created through him and for him. Also, he is before all [other] things and by means of him all [other] things were made to exist, and he is the head of the body, the congregation. He is the beginning, the firstborn from the dead, that he might become the one who is first in all things; because God saw good for all fullness to dwell in him (NWT).

In Colossians Paul affirmed that Jesus created all things. Logically, if Jesus created all things, then it is impossible for Him to be a created thing, because He could not create Himself. Because Jehovah's Witnesses teach that Jesus is a created being, they add the word *other* to the text to make it appear that Jesus is also a created thing.

2. *Cults add to God's Word by using other sources of* AUTHORITY *to interpret the Bible.*

Jehovah's Witnesses use this form of addition by requiring that their publications be used to interpret the Bible. Jehovah's Witnesses regard the Governing Body of their organization as the only accurate channel of biblical interpretation in the world today. For this reason the publications approved by the Governing Body are necessary to understand the Bible. *Watchtower* magazine claimed, "God has not arranged for that Word to speak independently or to shine forth life-giving truths by itself."[1]

The followers of Mary Baker Eddy, who founded the Church of Christian Science, believe that her book, *Science and Health with Key to the Scriptures*, is an inspired aid to understanding the Bible's true meaning. Mrs. Eddy claimed that the Bible can be understood properly only on the metaphysical level and that a literal reading of the Bible fails to discern the real meaning of the biblical text. Christian Scientists add to the Bible by requiring Mary Baker Eddy's writings as a metaphysical guide to understanding the "true" meaning of the Scriptures.

Scholars can point to textual and historical evidence that refutes cults' claims about the inaccuracy or corruption of God's Word. For example, the rules of Greek grammar argue against Jehovah's Witnesses' inaccurate translation of the New Testament. In contrast with Jehovah's Witnesses, other cults claim that the problem is not with the translation but that the biblical text itself has been corrupted. When they are asked when this corruption of the Bible occurred, they usually blame it on one of the early church councils. Fortunately, manuscripts of the Old and New Testaments exist that were copied long before any of the early church councils. Many of these manuscripts were already lost and buried by the time of the church councils. Christians can properly ask: How did the early councils change a manuscript when they didn't know that it existed? Also, how could they alter it in such a way that we cannot detect any tampering even with modern scientific instruments?

3. *Cults add to God's Word by claiming to be the only* TRUE CHURCH *or the* TRUEST CHURCH.

Jehovah's Witnesses, for example, believe that all other religious groups are false and that only their group has the truth that leads to eternal life on Paradise Earth. Christians know that the only way to eternal life is through faith in Jesus Christ, the eternal Son of God: " 'I am the way, and the truth, and the life; no one comes to the Father but through Me' " (John 14:6).

4. *Cults add to God's Word by claiming that their leaders are* DEVINELY INSPIRED.

Many cults believe that their leaders either are capable of receiving direct revelation from God or have a special, inspired ability to interpret the Bible. For example, Mormons believe that their president is a living prophet who can receive direct revelation from God. For groups that claim latter-day revelation, Christians can point out that the Bible has two tests for a true prophet of God.

NOTES

NOTES

1. Deuteronomy 18:21-22 states: "You may say to yourselves, 'How can we know when a message has not been spoken by the Lord?' If what a prophet proclaims in the name of the Lord does not take place or come true, that is a message the Lord has not spoken. That prophet has spoken presumptuously. Do not be afraid of him" (NIV). A true prophet of God is always 100 percent accurate when he prophesies in the name of the Lord. Seventy-five percent accuracy is not a passing grade for a prophet of God. Even a 99 percent accuracy rating is not sufficient for a biblical prophet. If a person claims to have a message from God and is wrong even one time, God's people are not to give him the reverence due a true prophet of God. Every cult leader who has claimed new prophecies from God has made predictions for the future that did not come true. Even one false prediction discredits these cult leaders as true spokespersons for God.
2. The second principle for recognizing a false prophet of God is found in Deuteronomy 13:1-4: "If a prophet, or one who foretells by dreams, appears among you and announces to you a miraculous sign or wonder, and if the sign or wonder of which he has spoken takes place, and he says, 'Let us follow other gods' (gods you have not known) 'and let us worship them,' you must not listen to the words of that prophet or dreamer. The Lord your God is testing you to find out whether you love him with all your heart and with all your soul. It is the Lord your God you must follow, and him you must revere. Keep his commands and obey him; serve him and hold fast to him" (NIV). A follower of God must have nothing to do with a prophet who advocates that people follow a deity other than the God of the Bible. Such a prophet can teach people to follow another god by altering God's nature or attributes as revealed in the Bible. For example, if a false prophet denies the doctrine of the Trinity or the deity of Christ, he is promoting a deity other than the God of the Bible.

Cults Subtract from the Nature of GOD and JESUS

The deity of Jesus Christ and the doctrine of the Trinity are two core Christian doctrines. Some cults and sects subtract either from Christ's deity or from the Christian understanding of God's triune nature. Jehovah's Witnesses, for example, deny Jesus' full deity. They claim that Jesus is a created being whom God used to create all other things. They teach that although Jesus is mighty, He is not Almighty God. If Jesus is not God, then He did not have the power to forgive sins, because only God has the power to forgive sins. If our sins are not forgiven, then we are still lost in our sins and doomed to receive God's judgment. Jesus' deity, therefore, has significant implications for our salvation.

Closely tied to Christ's deity is the Christian doctrine of the Trinity. The Bible teaches that there is one God; at the same time, Scripture reveals that the Father is God, Jesus is God, and the Holy Spirit is God. Yet the Bible also distinguishes the persons of the Father, Son, and Holy Spirit from one another. For example, when Jesus was praying to the Father, He gave His disciples the impression that He was praying to a person separate from Himself; He called this person His Father (see John 17). Jesus also referred to the Holy Spirit as a person separate from Himself when He promised His disciples that He would send another Comforter to be with them after He departed (see John 14:16). A belief that confuses the person of the Father with the person of the Son and the person of the Holy Spirit is referred to as the modalistic heresy.

Cults Divide People and God

Many cults place divisions between their members and God. Rather than encouraging their members to have a personal relationship with God through Jesus Christ, the cult becomes the mediator between God and humanity. For example, the Unification Church's training manual teaches that salvation is found in the Unification Church through Moon and his wife. Jehovah's Witnesses believe that personal faith in God is manifested by devotion to Jehovah's Witnesses' organization. Cults often claim to be the only true church, thereby placing divisions between their "true" group and all other churches, which they label false churches. Mormons, for example, teach that a great apostasy took place and that the true Christian faith disappeared from the earth until Joseph Smith reestablished the true church in 1830.

The Bible teaches that all Christian believers have direct access to God through faith in Jesus Christ. No church or priesthood is necessary for access to God. The only mediator between God and humans is Jesus: "There is one God, and one mediator also between God and men, the man Christ Jesus" (1 Tim. 2:5).

Cults that claim to be the only true church confuse the spiritual body of Christ with a physical manifestation. The church as the body of Christ is composed of all true believers in Christ, not just the members of a certain organization.

Cults Multiply the Requirements for SALVATION

Although many cults teach that faith is necessary for salvation, they often add some form of work that contributes to an individual's salvation. Mormons, for example, teach that the fullness of salvation, known as exaltation, can be achieved only through a series of work-related activities. Stephen Covey, a former Mormon bishop and a holder of the highest Mormon priesthood, labels the evangelical doctrine of salvation by grace alone a "false concept" and an "apostate doctrine."[2] He claims that one of Satan's lies to the world is that all God wants us to do is receive Christ Jesus through faith.[3] Mary Baker Eddy, the founder of

NOTES

NOTES

Christian Science, wrote, "Final deliverance from error, whereby we rejoice in immortality, boundless freedom, and sinless sense, is not reached through paths of flowers nor by pinning one's faith without works to another's vicarious effort."[4]

The Bible teaches that salvation comes solely through God's grace through faith in Jesus Christ. It denies the possibility that works can contribute in any way to salvation: "By grace you have been saved through faith; and that not of yourselves, it is the gift of God; not as a result of works, so that no one may boast" (Eph 2:8-9). When a cult multiplies the plan of salvation found in the Bible to include other requirements, it is preaching another gospel that is not the true gospel of Christ: "I am amazed that you are so quickly deserting Him who called you by the grace of Christ, for a different gospel; which is really not another; only there are some who are disturbing you and want to distort the gospel of Christ. But even if we, or an angel from heaven, should preach to you a gospel contrary to what we have preached to you, he is to be accursed. As we have said before, so I say again now, if any man is preaching to you a gospel contrary to what you received, he is to be accursed" (Gal. 1:6-9).[5]

Be Ready

Paul warned believers that "the time will come when they will not endure sound doctrine; but wanting to have their ears tickled, they will accumulate for themselves teachers in accordance to their own desires, and will turn away their ears from the truth, and will turn aside to myths" (2 Tim. 4:3-4). To recognize false beliefs, you must know true __doctrine__, which is presented only in __God's__ __Word__. As a growing disciple and a Great Commission witness, make sure that you are studying the Word daily and are participating in Bible study and discipleship training in your church. Paul admonished us to "preach the word; be ready in season and out of season; reprove, rebuke, exhort, with great patience and instruction" (2 Tim. 4:2) and to "be diligent to present yourself approved to God as a workman who does not need to be ashamed, accurately handling the word of truth" (2 Tim. 2:15).

As you talk with lost persons, begin to be aware of addition, subtraction, division, and multiplication that may be poisoning their understanding of the truth of Jesus Christ. This course will equip you to address specific false beliefs you encounter as you seek to dispel darkness with the light of the gospel.

Visitation Time

Do It

1. The Team Leader guides preparation for all visits. Remind Team members to stay alert during Sunday School to prospect and ministry needs.
2. Alert Team members in advance if they need to be ready to give Sunday School or evangelistic testimonies.
3. Team members have been introduced to the Key Question. Discuss responses to the question and emphasize the importance of the ***Preparation*** phase of the visit.
4. Keep in mind the visitation tips Learners have been asked to review (p. 35, *A Journey in FAITH Journal*). Highlight any you feel are especially helpful or needed.
5. Most of all, encourage Team members as they make their first home visits. Be prepared to take the lead in all visits. Model a visit and debrief what happened so that Team members can learn.

Celebration Time

Share It

1. Explain the purpose and importance of Celebration Time and encourage members to stay for this time each week.
2. Encourage Team members to listen carefully as reports are shared, especially about decisions made in visits; the information can be helpful in follow-up.
3. Take the lead in sharing reports.
4. Complete the necessary forms:
   - Evaluation Cards
   - Participation Cards
   - Visitation forms updated with the results of visits

NOTES

Home Study Assignments

Home Study Assignments reinforce this session by helping you apply what you have learned.

Your Discipleship Journey

Journaling activities in Your Discipleship Journey are an important part of your development as a Great Commission Christian through FAITH training.

1. Match the following Scripture references with the correct biblical teachings about the existence of false teachers.

   ____ 1. Matthew 7:15
   ____ 2. Acts 20:29-30
   ____ 3. 2 Corinthians 11:13-15
   ____ 4. 1 Timothy 4:1
   ____ 5. 2 Peter 2:1-2
   ____ 6. Jude 4

   a. Men will distort the truth and mislead the church.
   b. Godless men will change God's grace to a license for immorality and will deny Christ.
   c. Some will abandon the faith and follow demonic influences.
   d. Beware of deceptive false prophets.
   e. False teachers will introduce heresies and deny Christ.
   f. False apostles will masquerade as apostles of Christ.

2. Identify the goal of false teaching as stated in each of the following Scriptures.

   2 Timothy 4:3-4: ____

   ____

   ____

   2 Peter 2:2-3: ____

   ____

   ____

   Jude 4: ____

   ____

   ____

3. Match the following Scriptures with their instructions for responding to false teaching.

____ 1. 1 Timothy 4:6
____ 2. 1 Timothy 4:16
____ 3. 1 Timothy 6:3-5
____ 4. 2 Timothy 2:15
____ 5. 2 Timothy 3:14-17
____ 6. 2 Timothy 4:1-5
____ 7. Jude 3

a. Continue in the Scriptures you have learned. Let them equip you for good works through teaching, rebuking, correcting, and training in righteousness.
b. Point out the truths of the faith.
c. Present yourself to God as a workman who does not need to be ashamed and who correctly handles the word of truth.
d. Contend for the faith.
e. Doctrine should conform to the instruction of Jesus and to godly teaching.
f. Watch your life and doctrine closely and persevere in them.
g. Preach the Word. Be prepared. Correct, rebuke, and encourage. Keep your head, endure hardship, do the work of an evangelist, and discharge the duties of your ministry.

Growing as a Life Witness

Growing as a Life Witness reminds you of your responsibility to witness and minister to others during the week.

1. Talk or meet with your accountability partner and share ways you have cultivated a lost person or have witnessed or ministered on occasions other than FAITH visits.
2. Discuss ways you can apply the session 2 content.
3. Pray for lost persons by name and for each other.

Prayer Concerns	Answers to Prayer
____________________	____________________
____________________	____________________
____________________	____________________
____________________	____________________

Your Weekly Sunday School Leadership Meeting

A FAITH participant is an important member of Sunday School. Encourage Team members who are elected Sunday School workers to attend this weekly meeting. Use this section to record ways your FAITH Team influences the work of your Sunday School class or department. Use the information to report during weekly Sunday School leadership meetings. Identify actions that need to be taken through Sunday School as a result of prayer concerns, needs identified, visits made by the Team, and decisions made by the persons visited. Also identify ways you can disciple others in your Sunday School class or department and in your church.

1. FAITH Teams made or will make visits for the first time this week. If visits have been made, share reports and list any needs that affect your class or department.

___

___

2. Indicate any individuals/families who are expected to attend on Sunday and whether a FAITH Team member will greet them. Make specific plans to involve other class members in making guests feel comfortable when they attend, such as sitting with guests in the worship service, introducing guests to other class members, and so forth.

___

___

3. Discuss ways Sunday's Bible-study lesson can involve members and guests in transformational Bible study and discipleship.

___

4. Pray for FAITH Team members, teachers, and department directors.

Discipling Your Team Members

This weekly feature suggests actions the Team Leader can take to support Team members, prepare for Team Time, and improve visits. This work is part of the Team Leader's Home Study Assignments. Add any actions suggested by your church's FAITH strategy.

Support Team Members

❑ Call Team members and encourage them about their participation during the first home visits.

Prepare to Lead Team Time

❑ Preview Leading Team Time at the beginning of session 3.

Prepare to Lead Visits

- ❑ Review the FAITH Visit Outline to be able to model the entire process for Team members.
- ❑ Be prepared to explain the procedures in the car as you travel to and from the church, as well as the role of the Team Leader in making visits.
- ❑ Be prepared to model a visit in which Team member(s) are asked to lead in sharing a Sunday School testimony.
- ❑ Be prepared to model the use of the Opinion Poll in making visits.
- ❑ Be prepared to lead the Team to participate during Celebration Time.

Link with Sunday School

- ❑ Participate in your weekly Sunday School leadership meeting. Share pertinent information in this meeting, using Your Weekly Sunday School Leadership Meeting (pp. 43–44) and FAITH-visit results.
- ❑ Consider ways your Sunday School can ground members in the truths of the Word so that they recognize false teachings they encounter.

For Further Growth

For Further Growth may include additional reading or activities that will enhance your growth as a disciple and a discipler of others. These assignments are intended to be long-term projects and do not have to be completed during this semester of study.

1. Consult one of the following resources for more information on cults: *Encyclopaedia of Cults and New Religions: Jehovah's Witnesses, Mormonism, Mind Sciences, Baha'i, Zen, and Unitarianism* by John Ankerberg and John Weldon (Harvest House, 1999), *Understanding Sectarian Groups in America: The New Age Movement, the Occult, Mormonism, Hare Krishna, Zen Buddhism, Baha'i and Islam in America* (Revised) by George W. Braswell (Broadman & Holman, 1994), or *The Kingdom of the Cults* (Revised) by Walter Ralston Martin (Bethany House, 1997).
2. If you have not already done so, participate in a study of *FAITH Discipleship: Sharing a Living Faith* (LifeWay, 1999).
3. Using the Books of Acts, 1 and 2 Timothy, Titus, 2 Peter, and Jude, contrast the characteristics of a true follower of God and a false teacher.
4. Read the FAITH Tip on page 46.

---

[1]*Watchtower*, 1 May 1957, 274, as quoted in *Patterns in the Cults* (Alpharetta, GA: The North American Mission Board of the Southern Baptist Convention, n.d.).

[2]Stephen R. Covey, *Divine Center* (Salt Lake City, UT: Bookcraft, 1994), 68.

[3]Ibid., 271.

[4]Mary Baker Eddy, *Science and Health with Key to the Scriptures* (Boston, MA: The First Church of Christ, Science), 22.

[5]Session content adapted from *Patterns in the Cults* (Alpharetta, GA: The North American Mission Board of the Southern Baptist Convention, n.d.).

Answers to matching activity on page 42: 1. d, 2. a, 3. f, 4. c, 5. e, 6. b
Answers to matching activity on page 43: 1. b, 2. f, 3. e, 4. c, 5. a, 6. g, 7. d

FAITH TIP

Pulling the Weeds of False Doctrine

Before the seed of the gospel can find root in a cult member's heart, the theological weeds, or false doctrines the cultist believes, must be rebutted. A strategy of pulling weeds (refuting false doctrines) and planting seeds (sharing the gospel) needs to be practiced.

While visiting, I encountered a woman who was a Jehovah's Witness. A false doctrine held by Jehovah's Witnesses is that Jesus is a created being. They also teach that Jesus is known in the Bible as the created being called Michael the archangel. Knowing that Jehovah's Witnesses believe this, I asked the Jehovah's Witness, "Can you show me one Bible passage that teaches that Jesus is Michael the archangel?" She took off the shelf a book of Jehovah's Witness doctrine, turned to the index, and found Michael the archangel. The first passage the source book referred to was Daniel 10:13. The woman said: "Daniel 10:13 calls this angel Michael. The name Michael in Hebrew means *he who is like God*. Who is more like God than Jesus? Therefore, Michael must be Jesus, and Jesus must be Michael."

I asked the woman, "Do you believe that Jesus is unique? John 3:16 calls Jesus God's 'one and only Son' " (NIV). "Yes," she replied. "We believe that Jesus is unique." I then asked her, "If Jesus is unique, then how can He be Michael the archangel, since Daniel 10:13 reads, ' "Then Michael, one of the chief princes, came to help me" ' " (NIV). I continued: "If you are one of a group, then by definition you are not unique. Because Michael is "one of the chief princes," he cannot be unique. Because you agreed with me that John 3:16 teaches that Jesus is unique, then logically, Jesus cannot be Michael, and Michael cannot be Jesus. Isn't it interesting that the passage you read to me indicates that Jesus, in fact, cannot be the created angel named Michael? On the contrary, the passage you read confirms the Christian doctrine of the Trinity."

Witnessing to a follower of a cult or sect often requires a long-term commitment before you see positive results. Pulling the weeds of false doctrine and planting the seeds of truth can take time, often requiring that you cultivate a trusting relationship with the cult member. Don't get frustrated if you don't see immediate results.

SESSION 3

The Church of Jesus Christ of Latter-day Saints, Part 1

CKY CARRIGAN

In this session you will—

CHECK IT by engaging in Team Time activities;

KNOW IT by reviewing content from session 2;

HEAR IT by overviewing Mormon origins, by examining the Mormon concept of God, and by learning ways to witness to Mormons;

SEE IT by viewing a video segment;

STUDY IT by overviewing Home Study Assignments;

DO IT by leading your Team in making visits;

SHARE IT by celebrating.

NOTES

Leading Team Time

All Team members participate in Team Time. They are primarily responsible for reciting the assigned portion of the FAITH Visit Outline and for discussing other Home Study Assignments.

As you direct this important time of CHECK IT activities with your Team, keep in mind that Learners look to you as a role model, motivator, mentor, and friend. Team Time activities can continue in the car as the Team travels to and from visits.

Lead CHECK It Activities

✔ *FAITH Visit Outline*

- ❑ Be prepared to check off each Learner's memorization of all of ***Preparation*** (through Transition Statement) and the key words in ***Presentation*** and ***Invitation***.
- ❑ Indicate your approval by signing or initialing each Learner's Journal. Encourage Learners as you do and indicate any notes you have jotted down that might be helpful.

✔ *Other Home Study Assignments*

- ❑ Give as much time as needed to helping Learners understand different responses people might make to the Key Question and ways to answer those responses in love. Indicate that such answers will become clearer throughout FAITH training/visits.
- ❑ Discuss how FAITH Tips and/or other readings can provide specific help or answer some questions from sessions.
- ❑ Indicate specific content areas that may appear again on the session 16 written review.

✔ *Session 2 Debriefing*

- ❑ Answer any questions that remain from session 2. Emphasize the importance of a good beginning in building trust that can ultimately result in the gospel's being shared. Highlight ways the Sunday School testimony helps build bridges to people.
- ❑ Review Learners' written Sunday School testimonies.
- ❑ Indicate specific content areas that may appear again on the session 16 written review.

✔ *Help for Strengthening a Visit*

- ❑ Answer any questions that emerged from home visits following session 2.
- ❑ Review ways to begin a visit.

- ❑ Identify actions Team members took during last week's visits that were particularly effective and others that might need to be changed.
- ❑ Suggest ways Team members can improve sharing their Sunday School testimonies.
- ❑ Call attention to the evangelistic testimony you shared during last week's visit(s). Mention that Team Learners will be introduced during this session to ways to share their testimonies during a visit.

Notes

___

___

___

___

___

___

___

Actions I Need to Take with Team Members This Week

___

___

___

___

___

___

___

___

NOTES

NOTES

A Quick Review

Last week you learned how to recognize cults and sects. Try to define a cult and a sect by checking the correct responses.

A cult is a group that claims to be Christian but deviates from the traditional Christian understanding of—

❑ Christology (the doctrine of Christ) and/or theology proper (the doctrine of God);

❑ ecclesiology (the doctrine of the church) and/or eschatology (the doctrine of end times).

A sect is a group that does not deviate from the traditional Christian doctrines of the nature of God and Jesus Christ but nonetheless exhibits many sociological characteristics that are commonly associated with—

❑ governments;

❑ families;

❑ cults;

❑ colleges.

Identify each of the following false statements as *A*, *S*, *D*, or M.

A = Adding to God's Word
S = Subtracting from the nature of God and/or Christ
D = Dividing people and God
M = Multiplying the requirements for salvation

____ 1. To receive the fullness of salvation, you must devote a period of your life to missionary work.

____ 2. If you want to hear from the Lord, you must depend on someone else to mediate between you and God.

____ 3. You must believe other scriptures because the Bible neglects important truths.

____ 4. Jesus, though certainly a great prophet, was not God.

____ 5. Spiritual leaders are receiving new prophecies showing that God has qualities that are different from the ones described in the Bible.

____ 6. Jesus was a created being.

____ 7. Your salvation depends on your devotion to a group and its beliefs.

____ 8. Salvation by grace alone is a myth. It must be accompanied by works.

Solving the Mormon Puzzle

NOTES

"Just call the number on your screen for your free video. It is a free gift from the Church of Jesus Christ of Latter-day Saints." Martha picked up the phone. "That looks like a wonderful video on the life of Christ," she said to her husband as she dialed the number. Two days later the doorbell rang. Martha opened the door and found two young men dressed in white shirts and ties. "Good afternoon. We're here to deliver your free video. I'm Elder Carter, and this is Elder Douglas. We're from the Church of Jesus Christ of Latter-day Saints."

"You're Mormons, aren't you?" Martha asked. "Come in. I've always wondered what your church believes. It always seemed puzzling to me."

If Southern Baptists are serious about winning North America to the genuine Jesus, we will get more serious about doing interfaith evangelism. And if Southern Baptists are more serious about doing interfaith evangelism, we will get more serious about solving the Mormon puzzle. The Mormon Church, or the Church of Jesus Christ of Latter-day Saints, as they prefer to be called, is a major religious movement with a membership in need of salvation. The Mormon Church enjoys rapid worldwide growth and influence, ranking ninth in the world just behind Judaism. In North America Mormonism is in a virtual three-way tie for second place with Islam and Judaism. More than 10 million later, Latter-day Saints are in the world today, meeting in about 25,000 congregations called wards.[1] And North America is the home to more than 5 million Mormons, not all of whom reside in the western and southwestern United States. In fact, since 1980 Mormon membership growth in the southern United States has nearly doubled.[2]

About 60,000 Mormon missionaries around the world[3] help convert more than ______________ people each year from other religions, including thousands of Southern Baptists.[4] Perhaps the most revealing indicator of worldwide Mormon growth and influence is the rapid expansion of temple-construction projects around the world. Mormons had 68 temples in operation at the beginning of 2000, and 32 more were scheduled for opening by the end of that year. These temples are being constructed in anticipation of a boom in Mormon growth. If the Mormon Church continues to grow at its average rate since its inception, there will be about one hundred million Mormons 40 years from now. But if Mormonism continues to grow at its present rapid rate, there will be five hundred million Mormons by the year 2040.[5] In other words, by the year 2040, there may be as many as a half billion Mormons in desperate need of the genuine Jesus and the true way of salvation.

In this session we will seek to solve the puzzle of Mormon origins and the Mormon concept of God. In the next session we will attempt to solve the puzzle of more Mormon beliefs and Mormon terminology, and

NOTES

we will examine ways to use the Bible in witnessing to Mormons. As you complete these two sessions, keep in mind that God loves Mormons. Christ died a brutal death for them, and He charged us to make disciples among all peoples—even Mormons.

The Puzzle of Mormon ORIGINS

The beginning of Mormonism may be traced to the reported first vision of Joseph Smith Jr. (1805–44) at the age of 14. Smith claimed that this vision of the Heavenly Father and His Son came to him in what is now referred to as the sacred grove behind his family home outside Palmyra, New York. In 1820 he saw the two personages while he was seeking God's direction in prayer about which church he should join in Palmyra. Smith could not decide between the Baptist church, the Presbyterian church, or the Methodist church. One of the personages told him to join none of them, because all of them were "wrong … that all their creeds were an abomination … [and] that those professors [of those churches] were all corrupt."[6]

Three years later, when Smith was 17, he reportedly received his second vision while seeking God in prayer one night in his upstairs bedroom. Another personage, Moroni, appeared to Smith and told him that some golden tablets were hidden nearby in the Hill Cumorah. Moroni reportedly appeared to Smith on four other occasions during the next several years until Smith was finally permitted to retrieve the golden tablets from their secret location. Using special divining objects, Smith then began to translate the tablets, which he published as The Book of Mormon in 1830.[7]

Smith also claimed that in 1829 John the Baptist physically appeared to him and conferred the Aaronic priesthood on him and Oliver Cowdery. Smith and Cowdery baptized each other by immersion for the remission of sins in a river near Harmony, Pennsylvania. Reportedly, several months later, Peter, James, and John physically appeared to Smith and Cowdery and conferred the Melchizedek priesthood on them, as well.[8]

Smith officially organized and constituted his church with six men in April 1830. The original name of his church was the Church of Christ.[9] It was changed to the Church of Latter-day Saints in 1834, to the Church of Christ of Latter-day Saints in 1836, and to the Church of Jesus Christ of Latter-day SAINTS in 1838.[10]

Smith and his followers migrated from central New York to Kirtland, Ohio; Independence, Missouri; and Nauvoo, Illinois. Charges of polygamy among Mormon leaders began to circulate widely in the early 1840s. On June 7, 1844, the one and only issue of *The Nauvoo Expositor* was published by several former Mormons. It included an article leveling charges of polygamy against Mormon leaders. Smith, the lieutenant-general of the local militia, declared the *Expositor* to be a public nuisance and ordered the Nauvoo militia to destroy the *Expositor*'s printing press on June 10. Smith was arrested and taken to jail in Carthage, Illinois, where on June 27 the Warsaw militia killed Joseph and his brother, Hyrum Smith.[11]

A predictable struggle for Mormon leadership followed Joseph Smith's death. Brigham Young (1801–77) rallied support and conducted himself as the acting president of the church until an official church declaration in December 1847 confirmed his presidency. Young led the Mormon pioneers on a westward trek over the Rockies, through Immigration Pass, and into Utah's Wasatch Valley, where they founded Salt Lake City. After Young's death 13 Mormon presidents-prophets have led the Mormon people. The current Mormon president-prophet is Gordon B. Hinckley (1910–).[12]

Mormon origins provide knowledgeable Christian witnesses a number of opportunities to prepare the soil of the soul among Mormons they seek to influence. Most Mormons are fairly secure in Mormonism and see traditional Christianity as a flawed cousin of what they call their own restored gospel. The challenge for Christian witnesses is to create a crisis of belief about Mormon origins. The entire Mormon Church rests on the foundation of its history. If Joseph Smith's first vision actually happened as he reported it and if the Heavenly Father and His Son bodily appeared to him and told him that all existing churches were wrong, their beliefs an abomination, and their membership corrupt, then perhaps Mormonism is superior to Christianity. On the other hand, if the first vision was a fabrication or a realistic deception by the devil, then the entire system of Mormon beliefs and practices is fatally flawed and should be abandoned. A false prophet is no prophet at all. Even Mormon authorities concede this. Joseph Fielding Smith, the 10th Mormon president-prophet, wrote: "Mormonism, as it is called, must stand or fall on the story of Joseph Smith. He was either a prophet of God, divinely called, properly appointed and commissioned, or he was one of the biggest frauds this world has ever seen. There is no middle ground. If Joseph Smith was a deceiver … then he should be exposed … for the doctrines of an impostor cannot be made to harmonize in all particulars with divine truth."[13]

The same kind of argument is useful for cross-examining Smith's second vision, together with his claims that John the Baptist, Peter, James, and John physically appeared to him. Consider this example. If 17-year-old Smith was not physically visited by Moroni, someone who reportedly died in an epic battle between two Native American peoples of Hebrew origin about 1,600 years ago in upstate New York, and if Joseph was not told the secret location of the golden tablets, then there is no historical *Book of Mormon*. And if there is no historical *Book of Mormon*, then there is, of course, no Mormonism.

Use the following evidence to challenge confidence in the veracity of Joseph's first vision. This challenge may create a crisis of belief in Mormons you encounter.

NOTES

NOTES

1. Lack of Witness

There were no witnesses to Joseph's first vision. The Bible teaches that all matters shall be clearly established by the testimony of two or three credible witnesses (see Matt. 18:16; 2 Cor. 13:1). Historically, God's pattern has been to reveal something of doctrinal significance to several credible witnesses at the same time. Invite your Mormon friends to reflect on the major events of the Bible, like the Hebrew deliverance from Egypt; the giving of the Law; and Christ's birth, transfiguration, death, burial, resurrection, and ascension. Ask whether there were multiple credible witnesses to these historic events. Follow up by asking if it seems unlikely that God would orchestrate multiple witnesses for all of these doctrinally significant events but ask us to rely on a single witness's testimony to the bodily appearance of the Father and the Son in the sacred grove.

2. Unique CONTENT

Smith reportedly beheld in his first vision what no other person in the Bible or in all of recorded history has ever seen. Reportedly, he visibly beheld the faces and audibly heard the voices of the Heavenly Father and His Son. There is no biblical precedence for this. Ask your Mormon friend whether it seems strange that Smith claimed to see and hear what no other credible person has ever seen and heard: a Heavenly Father composed of flesh and bones.

3. Joseph Smith's Credibility

Several problems can be raised with the credibility of Smith's official account of his first vision. The first official history of the Mormon Church, written between 1834 and 1837, failed even to mention Smith's first vision. In addition, there are several different first-person written accounts of Smith's first vision. Discrepancies exist in their reports of the numbers of beings, the identities of the beings, and the beings' remarks. Smith did not publish the official account of the first vision until 1842, 22 years after the alleged event and 12 years after the restoration of the church. Also, the regional revival to which Smith referred in the 1842 account did not occur until 1824–25, 4 years after his alleged first vision and 1 year after his alleged second vision. Ask Mormons to investigate these historical facts for themselves. Ask whether it is reasonable for them to stake their eternal lives on Smith's inconsistent testimony about the founding event of the Mormon Church.

A careful look at Mormon origins is very useful to anyone wishing to share the genuine Jesus with Mormons. So much of the credibility of the entire Mormon program depends on accepting its origins. In addition to the previous evidence, consider asking your Mormon friend about the four-time name change of the church or the unlawful destruction of the *Nauvoo Expositor*'s press. If Joseph Smith or any subsequent president-prophet was of poor character, was a deceiver, or was mistaken about any feature of Mormons' distinctive teachings, then he was, by biblical definition, a false prophet. And a false prophet at any point is no prophet of God at all and should not be followed.

NOTES

The Puzzle of the Mormon ________

Why try to evangelize Mormons anyway? Aren't they already Christians? Don't they believe in God, worship Jesus Christ, go to church, and live a moral life? Aren't Mormons just another kind of Christian, like Methodists or Lutherans or Presbyterians? The answers to these questions will become self-evident when we look closely at the Mormon system of beliefs, especially the Mormon concept of God.

The Mormon concept of God is explained in official Mormon sources like *Gospel Principles* and *Doctrine and Covenants*. These documents reveal the Mormon God (Heavenly Father) as an exalted man named Elohim with a physical body of flesh and bone. Joseph Smith said that if God made himself visible to us, we would see him as a man in form: "Because we are made in his image (see Moses 6:9), we know that God has a body that looks like ours. His eternal spirit is housed in a tangible body of flesh and bones (see D&C 130:22). God's body, however, is perfected and glorified, with a glory beyond all description."[14] *Gospel Principles* records: "This is the way our Heavenly Father became God. Joseph Smith taught: 'It is the first principle of the Gospel to know for a certainty the character of God. ... He was once a man like us; ... God himself, the Father of us all, dwelt on an earth, the same as Jesus Christ himself did' (*Teachings of the Prophet Joseph Smith*, pp. 345–46)."[15] So the Mormon Heavenly Father has a body like that of a human male. He is the organizer of the matter of this world, but He did not create everything from nothing. His power is great but limited. His knowledge is great but growing. Because He has a body, He is necessarily localized in space. He is also changing from a man to a god. He is a contingent being, since His existence is derived from another, greater being. And finally, although He is the chief god of this world, He is only one of many gods among many worlds.

The Mormon concept of the Heavenly Father God is very different from the concept of God as described by traditional, biblical Christianity. Christians believe the following biblical teachings about God's nature.

- God is spirit (see John 4:24). Luke 24:39 tells us that spirit does not have flesh and bones. God has no body and is not localized in space (see Ps. 139: 7-10). Because God is spirit and spirit does not have flesh and bones, then God is not and never has been a man.
- God created everything that exists from nothing (see Gen. 1:1).
- God's power is unlimited (see Ps. 68:34-35; 1 Cor. 6:14).
- God's knowledge is complete (see 1 John 3:20).
- God is eternal (see Rev. 1:4,8).

NOTES

- God does not change (see Mal. 3:6).
- God is the only necessary being who exists anywhere. He is the only God of the only world (see Eph. 4:6).[16]

The Christian concept of God is in direct conflict with the Mormon concept of God. Both concepts cannot be correct. Prepare the soil of the Mormon soul to accept the genuine Jesus by creating a crisis of belief about the Mormon concept of God. Here are two ways to do that.

1. Point out conflicts with ________ ______________ ______ _______________________.

Many Mormons generally affirm the Mormon concept of God described, although evidence exists that some Mormons are not aware that their church teaches this concept. Mormons also believe that *The Book of Mormon* is the perfect companion to the Bible because the Bible is imperfect, having been corrupted and mistranslated. They generally have a higher view of *The Book of Mormon* than of the Bible.

First, ask your Mormon friends if they believe that *The Book of Mormon* is a perfect book that is designed to fill in the information gaps of an incomplete and corrupt Bible. Expect an affirmative response. Next, ask them if they think that the doctrine of the nature of God Himself is perhaps the key doctrine of any religious tradition. Expect an affirmative answer. Then ask them if they believe that the Heavenly Father is an exalted man. Expect another affirmative answer by most. Then ask them to show you where in *The Book of Mormon* you might find clear, convincing evidence to support the Mormon concept of God. Expect no response, because there is no evidence of any kind in *The Book of Mormon* to support the Mormon concept of God. Ask them whether they find it unsettling that the most perfect revelation known to humankind offers absolutely no evidence to support the distinctive Mormon concept of God, a key doctrine for every religious tradition. Joseph Smith's ideas about God evidently changed over the years after he wrote *The Book of Mormon*. Thus, the teaching that *The Book of Mormon* is God's perfect revelation must be false, or Mormon teachings about God are wrong. Logically, Mormons cannot have it both ways.

2. Clarify the claims of Mormon ____________________ about God.

There is another way to prepare the soil of the Mormon soul and create a crisis of belief about the Mormon concept of God. Don't be surprised if your Mormon friends do not believe you when you state the teachings of the Mormon Church on the nature of the Heavenly Father. Remember, every year thousands of people are converted from mainline Christian churches who are grounded in the Christian concept of God. Don't be surprised to discover that they have never heard any of these doctrines in their Mormon church. Yet these Mormon doctrines are presented in authoritative Mormon sources like *Gospel Principles* and *Doctrine and Covenants*. Perhaps by pointing out official Mormon teachings, you will have an opportunity to share the genuine Jesus with Mormons who question the Mormon concept of God.

You will learn more about Mormon beliefs in session 4.

NOTES

Witnessing to Mormons

Keep these principles in mind when talking with Mormons about matters of faith.

1. Get a clear understanding of basic ~~understanding of~~ biblical doctrines.

- The nature of God
- The Trinity
- The person and work of Christ
- Salvation
- Revelation and authority

2. Get a clear understanding of basic Mormon history ***and*** doctrines.

- The nature of God
- The person and work of Christ
- Revelation and authority
- Smith's first vision
- The names of the Mormon Church

3. Keep the intiative.

It will be difficult for you to stay focused on your point if you allow Mormons to constantly interrupt and challenge your position. Ask them to make notes for later discussion if they wish to raise objections or consult other passages.

4. Be very PATIENT.

Mormons are rarely won to Christ in one or two encounters. It will probably be necessary to maintain ongoing discussions. It will also be very important to build sincere, trustful relationships.

5. Clearly define your terms ***and ask Mormons to define theirs.***

Mormons use similar terms but ascribe very different meanings to them. Often, Christians and Mormons talk past one another during discussions.

NOTES

6. *Rely on the* HOLY SPIRIT *to lead you and to change your Mormon friends.*

Your goal is not to win an argument but to win a brother or a sister, to change a heart. Seek the Holy Spirit's direction through diligent prayer.[17]

7. *Follow the FAITH* VISIT OUTLINE.

Because your FAITH Visit Outline provides a scriptural gospel presentation, you can feel comfortable using it in a variety of situations. When the Holy Spirit leads you to do so, use the outline to present the truth of the gospel to the cult member. Generally expect Mormons to object to your arguments and to pose their own to convince you of the superiority of Mormonism. But if the Mormon offers no serious objections or rebuttals, immediately present the FAITH gospel presentation as you would to a non-Mormon.

In session 4 you will learn additional principles for witnessing to Mormons.

Visitation Time

Do It

1. Assign specific responsibilities to your Team Learners. Ask one to share a Sunday School or evangelistic testimony. Ask one to be the navigator to arrange the visitation schedule. Suggest that this person start with the prospect's home that is farthest away. Then work your way back toward the church. Assign another Team Learner to gather age-appropriate materials for your visit. This procedure will save time and will provide good training for Learners.
2. Pray before you go.
3. Review in the car. Share your evangelistic testimony and ask Learners to share what they would like to include in theirs.
4. Debrief each visit. Facilitate by asking specific questions.

Celebration Time

Share It

1. Hear reports and testimonies.
2. Complete Evaluation Cards.
3. Complete Participation Cards.
4. Update visitation forms with the results of visits.

Home Study Assignments

Home Study Assignments reinforce this session by helping you apply what you have learned.

Your Discipleship Journey

Journaling activities in Your Discipleship Journey are an important part of your development as a Great Commission Christian through FAITH training.

1. Match the following Scriptures with the statements that summarize what they teach about the nature of God.

____ 1. Genesis 1:1	a. God is spirit.
____ 2. Numbers 23:19	b. God is perfect.
____ 3. Deuteronomy 4:35; Ephesians 4:6	c. God is eternal.
____ 4. Psalm 18:30	d. God is present everywhere.
____ 5. Psalm 68:34-35; 1 Corinthians 6:14	e. God is the one true God.
____ 6. Psalm 139:7-10	f. God created the world.
____ 7. Romans 1:20	g. God is all-knowing.
____ 8. John 4:24	h. God is all-powerful.
____ 9. 1 Timothy 1:17	i. God has eternal power and a divine nature.
____ 10. 1 John 3:20	j. God is unchanging.
____ 11. Revelation 1:4,8	k. God is eternal, immortal, and invisible.

2. Mormonism teaches that it possesses the true gospel. Summarize what the following Scriptures teach believers about responding to false teachings and accepting the truth of the gospel.

Galatians 1:6-9: ____

____

1 Thessalonians 2:3-5,13: ____

____

2 Peter 1:16: ____

____

3. Mormonism teaches that God is limited in His power and is growing in His knowledge. Beside each of the Scriptures on the following page, write the characteristics of God that refute this idea.

Job 42:2: ______________________________

Psalm 139:1-6: ______________________________

Jeremiah 32:17: ______________________________

Matthew 19:26: ______________________________

Acts 17:24-26: ______________________________

Hebrews 4:13: ______________________________

Growing as a Life Witness

Growing as a Life Witness reminds you of your responsibility to witness and minister to others during the week.

1. Talk or meet with your accountability partner and share ways you have cultivated a lost person or have witnessed or ministered on occasions other than FAITH visits.
2. Discuss ways you can apply the session 3 content.
3. Pray for lost persons by name and for each other.

Prayer Concerns	Answers to Prayer
______________	______________
______________	______________
______________	______________
______________	______________
______________	______________

Your Weekly Sunday School Leadership Meeting

A FAITH participant is an important member of Sunday School. Encourage Team members who are elected Sunday School workers to attend this weekly meeting. Use this section to record ways your FAITH Team influences the work of your Sunday School class or department. Use the information to report during weekly Sunday School leadership meetings. Identify actions that need to be taken through Sunday School as a result of prayer concerns, needs identified, visits made by the Team, and decisions made by the persons visited. Also identify ways you can disciple others in your Sunday School class or department and in your church.

1. Share results of visits. Suggest opportunities to minister to persons who were visited.

2. List ways your class or department can minister to or assimilate new members.

3. Evaluate last week's Bible-study session. Discuss ways to make Sunday's lesson applicable to life. Indicate anyone visited by a FAITH Team who is likely to attend on Sunday.

4. Periodically consider actually making follow-up phone calls to prospects and new members during this meeting. (If this is not possible, make assignments.) In the calls communicate excitement about guests' participation in Sunday School.

5. In receiving the new list of absentees, share any information that can help in follow-up. Does this member need a Sunday School ministry visit? If so, by what date and by which FAITH Team?

6. Pray specifically for Sunday School plans and leaders this week.

____

____

Discipling Your Team Members

This weekly feature suggests actions the Team Leader can take to support Team members, prepare for Team Time, and improve visits. This work is part of the Team Leader's Home Study Assignments. Add any actions suggested by your church's FAITH strategy.

Support Team Members

- ❑ Call Team members and talk with them about their participation during the class training and visits. Discuss any observations they made during the visits and particularly about sharing their Sunday School testimonies.
- ❑ Discuss ways to prepare and share their evangelistic testimonies without revealing the answer to the Key Question.
- ❑ Encourage them as they memorize all of ***Preparation*** in the FAITH Visit Outline.

Prepare to Lead Team Time

- ❑ Preview Leading Team Time at the beginning of session 4.

Prepare to Lead Visits

- ❑ Review the FAITH Visit Outline in order to model the entire process for Team members.
- ❑ Be prepared to model a visit in which Team member(s) are asked to lead in sharing Sunday School and evangelistic testimonies.
- ❑ Be prepared to model the use of the Opinion Poll in making visits.
- ❑ Be prepared to lead your Team to participate during Celebration Time.

Link with Sunday School

- ❑ Participate in your weekly Sunday School leadership meeting. Share pertinent information in this meeting, using Your Weekly Sunday School Leadership Meeting (pp. 60–62) and FAITH-visit results.
- ❑ Use every opportunity to emphasize the true nature of God through Bible study, worship, and class discussions.

For Further Growth

For Further Growth may include additional reading or activities that will enhance your growth as a disciple and a discipler of others. These assignments are intended to be long-term projects and do not have to be completed during this semester of study.

1. Talk to persons who have left the Mormon Church and discuss the reasons for their leaving. Use these reasons to formulate a biblical response to Mormons who are seeking the truth.
2. Be better prepared to witness to Mormons by gaining a greater understanding of God's nature. A systematic-theology book will be helpful.

---

[1]"Key Facts and Figures," *Global Media Guide*, available at <*http://lds.org/med_inf/glo_med_gui/12Key_Facts_and_Figures.html*> (3 January 2000).

[2]Amy Frazier, "Mormons Flourish in the South," Associated Press, 20 November 1999, <*http://www.standard.net/stories/nation/11-1999/ftp0126@nation@21lds@ogden.asp*> (24 July 2000).

[3]"LDS Missionaries Number 60,000," *The Salt Lake Tribune*, 15 January 2000, <*http://www.sltrib.com/2000/jan/01152000/religion/17795.htm*> (21 January 2000).

[4]Walter R. Martin, *The Kingdom of the Cults, Revised*, ed. Hank Hanegraaff (Minneapolis: Bethany, 1997), 180.

[5]"Charts and Graphs," *Infobases Collector's Library* CD-ROM (Bookcraft, 1998).

[6]Joseph Smith, *History of the Church, Volume 1*, *Infobases Collector's Library* CD-ROM (Bookcraft, 1998), 1–20.

[7]Ibid., 27–54.

[8]Ibid., 66–75. Also see *Doctrine and Covenants* 13; 27:8, 12–13; 84:18; Moses 6:67-68.

[9]Joseph Smith, *Doctrine and Covenants* (Salt Lake City: The Church of Jesus Christ of Latter-day Saints, 1981), 20:1.

[10]Ibid., 115:4. Also see Susan Easton Black, "Name of the Church," in *Encyclopedia of Mormonism*, ed. Daniel H. Ludlow (New York: Macmillan, 1992), compiled in *Infobases Collector's Library* CD-ROM (Bookcraft, 1998).

[11]"History of the Church," in *Encyclopedia of Mormonism*, compiled in *Infobases Collector's Library* CD-ROM (Bookcraft, 1998).

[12]Ibid.

[13]Joseph Fielding Smith, *Doctrines of Salvation, Volume 1*, comp. Bruce R. McConkie (Salt Lake City: Bookcraft, 1992), 188, 322.

[14]*Gospel Principles* (Salt Lake City: The Church of Jesus Christ of Latter-day Saints, 1997), 9.

[15]Ibid., 305.

[16]Francis J. Beckwith, "Philosophical Problems with the Mormon Concept of God," *Christian Research Journal* 14.4 (Spring 1992): 25–29.

[17]*Latter-day Saints Interfaith Witness Resource Packet* (Alpharetta, GA: The North American Mission Board of the Southern Baptist Convention, 1996).

Answers to matching activity on page 59: 1. f, 2. j, 3. e, 4. b, 5. h, 6. d, 7. i, 8. a, 9. k, 10. g, 11. c

FAITH AT WORK

There was a time in my life when nothing made sense. Having grown up in a broken home, I carried around feelings of guilt and loneliness. Each day I would trudge through life searching for happiness in family, friends, and material possessions. I failed to realize that I was searching for happiness, security, and a sense of self-worth in all the wrong places. To try to counter my unhappiness, I was filling my life with more of the same earthly things. This only caused me to sink deeper into depression and loneliness.

I joined the Marine Corps when I was 17 to get away from it all. And in 1990 God began to work on me. In August of that year God broke through all the distractions I had used to stay away from Him by allowing me to serve in Operation Desert Storm. He led me to look deep into my life and myself, and I did not like what I saw. During this time I was writing to a woman and her brother back home, both of whom I had never met. They mentioned their assurance that when they died, they would go to heaven. Those letters began to hit home during the second week of December 1990, and I gave my life to Christ. The first week of January 1991 I was baptized in a wooden box lined with trash bags.

The woman I had been writing to back home eventually became my wife. We joined First Baptist Church in Snellville, Georgia, in October 1993 and have been serving in the Preschool/Children's Department most of the time since then. But I was still missing something in my life. I wanted a deeper relationship with God but could not seem to find the depth I was looking for. This past February I heard about the FAITH evangelism strategy, which was being offered on Tuesday nights. This training helped equip me to share the gospel with others and fulfill the Great Commission. After five weeks of FAITH training, God gave me the opportunity to lead to Christ a coworker, as well as a woman at the Gwinnett County Youth Detention Center. Sharing the gospel has given me the more meaningful relationship with God that I was looking for.

Frank Wright
First Baptist Church
Snellville, Georgia

SESSION 4

The Church of Jesus Christ of Latter-day Saints, Part 2

CKY CARRIGAN

In this session you will—

CHECK IT by engaging in Team Time activities;

KNOW IT by reviewing content from session 3;

HEAR IT by learning Mormon beliefs about authority, revelation, Christ, and salvation; by examining Mormon terminology; and by learning ways to witness to Mormons;

SEE IT by viewing a video segment;

STUDY IT by overviewing Home Study Assignments;

DO IT by leading your Team in making visits;

SHARE IT by celebrating.

NOTES

Leading Team Time

All Team members participate in Team Time. They are primarily responsible for reciting the assigned portion of the FAITH Visit Outline and for discussing other Home Study Assignments.

As you direct this important time of CHECK IT activities with your Team, keep in mind that Learners look to you as a role model, motivator, mentor, and friend. Team Time activities can continue in the car as the Team travels to and from visits.

Lead CHECK IT Activities

✔ *FAITH Visit Outline*

- ❑ Listen as each Learner recites the appropriate portion of the FAITH Visit Outline (all of ***Preparation***, adding the Key Question and Transition Statement, plus key words for ***Presentation*** and ***Invitation***).
- ❑ Indicate your approval by signing each Learner's Journal.
- ❑ Involve an Assistant Team Leader in this part of Team Time, if you have this Team member.

✔ *Evangelistic Testimony*

- ❑ Review the first draft of written evangelistic testimonies, due this session. Use the criteria from the session 3 FAITH Tip in *A Journey in FAITH Journal*. Explain why you are making your suggestions. Indicate that most testimonies undergo revisions. Be sensitive in helping Team members develop their testimonies, keeping their stories intact. As a reminder, these are the criteria Learners have used to develop their testimonies:
  - Define a specific event before (preconversion) and after your conversion (benefits).
  - Do not answer the Key Question in your testimony.
  - Keep your testimony brief (three minutes or less).
  - Do not give too many unnecessary details; instead, concisely reflect your experience.
  - Conclude your testimony with the assurance that you are going to heaven.

✔ *Sunday School Testimony*

- ❑ If possible, provide time for Team members to practice their Sunday School testimonies. Review of the evangelistic testimony, however, should be your priority.

✔ *Other Home Study Assignments/Session 3 Debriefing*

❑ Answer other questions Learners may have from session 3 or as a result of their Home Study Assignments.

✔ *Help for Strengthening a Visit*

❑ Identify ways Team members can improve sharing their evangelistic testimonies in a visit.

❑ Help your Team, especially Learners, know how to handle the following issues.

- Dialogue with someone who answers the Key Question with a faith answer by discussing his or her journey of faith in Christ.
- Briefly explain to a person who answers the Key Question with a works answer that many people feel that doing good things gets them into heaven. Discuss the various ways such a response might be verbalized.
- Look for opportunities to ask permission to share what the Bible says about how a person goes to heaven.
- Look for ways to get clarification or explanation if someone shares an unclear response to the Key Question.
- Prayerfully look for ways to talk with a person who indicates no opinion about the Key Question.

Notes

____

____

____

____

Actions I Need to Take with Team Members This Week

____

____

____

____

NOTES

NOTES

A Quick Review

Last week you studied the origins of the Mormon religion and Mormons' view of God. Based on that material, identify the following statements as true or false by writing *T* or *F* in each blank.

____ 1. Mormonism is also called The Church of Jesus Christ of Latter-day Saints.
____ 2. Since 1980 Mormonism membership has steadily declined.
____ 3. The beginning of Mormonism can be traced to a vision of Brigham Young.
____ 4. Joseph Smith claims to have been visited by the Heavenly Father and His Son in 1820 in a sacred grove.
____ 5. Joseph Smith supposedly translated *The Book of Mormon* from golden tablets revealed to him by Moroni.
____ 6. There were many witnesses to Joseph Smith's visions.
____ 7. Mormons believe that God, the Heavenly Father, is an exalted man with a physical body of flesh and bones.
____ 8. Mormons believe that God is all-powerful, having created the world from nothing.
____ 9. Teachings about God in *The Book of Mormon* contradict later writings by Joseph Smith and official Mormon doctrine.

Check principles you learned for witnessing to Mormons.

❑ 1. Get a clear understanding of basic biblical doctrines.
❑ 2. Get a clear understanding of basic Mormon history and doctrines.
❑ 3. Use the Bible as a bludgeon to get your point across.
❑ 4. Ask Mormon missionaries to get off your property.
❑ 5. Keep the initiative.
❑ 6. Be very patient.
❑ 7. Never turn your back on a Mormon.
❑ 8. Clearly define your terms and ask Mormons to define theirs.
❑ 9. Let the Mormon set the direction of the conversation.
❑ 10. Rely on the Holy Spirit to lead you and to change your Mormon friends.
❑ 11. Follow the FAITH Visit Outline.
❑ 12. Assure the Mormon that you accept Joseph Smith's claims as historical facts.

Solving the Puzzle of Mormon Beliefs

NOTES

Last week we examined Mormon origins and the Mormon view of God. In this session we will try to solve the puzzle of Mormon beliefs and terminology. Keep in mind that Mormons are not our enemy. They are God's precious creations who need to hear the truth.

The Puzzle of Mormon ____________ and ____________

Four standard works constitute the written authority for Mormon beliefs:

1. The ______ ______ ______ of the Bible "as far as it is translated correctly"[1]
2. ______ ______ ___ ______ *Another Testament of Jesus Christ*
3. ______ ______ ______
4. ______ ______ ______ ______ ______

Mormons consider all existing biblical texts to be corrupted and flawed, having been altered by the postapostolic church: "After the book hath gone forth through the hands of the great and abominable church that there are many plain and precious things taken away from the book, which is the book of the Lamb of God" (1 Nephi 13:28). Although Mormons claim that the *King James Version* is the official version for the Church, they do not believe that the Bible is accurate and trustworthy.

In contrast, Mormons regard *The Book of Mormon* as a historically accurate work about a people of Jewish descent who lived in Central America from the sixth century B.C. to the fifth century A.D. *Doctrine and Covenants* is a collection of 138 direct revelations of God given to Joseph Smith, plus two official church declarations. *The Pearl of Great Price* includes five documents: Selections from the Book of Moses, The Book of Abraham, Joseph Smith—Matthew, Joseph Smith—History, and The Articles of Faith. The Mormon Church also relies on continuing revelation from God through its prophets and other General Authorities as additional authority for Mormon beliefs. Modern Mormons disagree about what actually constitutes authoritative revelation by the prophets and other General Authorities, but they certainly agree that direct revelation from God continues through them.[2]

Biblical Christianity has historically affirmed that the canon of revelation is closed. The Old and New Testaments are faithful documents, and they are absolutely sufficient authorities for our beliefs. All other documents must be relegated at best to nonauthoritative commentary. Christians can affirm that the Bible is the authoritative Word of God and sufficient revelation for salvation, doctrine, and instruction. It was written by men inspired by the Holy Spirit and has been carefully

NOTES

preserved by God (see Ps. 119:89,105; Luke 21:33; Rom. 15:4; 2 Tim. 3:15-17; Heb. 4:12; 1 Pet. 1:25; 2 Pet. 1:19-21).

The Mormon contention that the present form of the Bible has been severely corrupted by scribes and translators has no basis in fact. Ask your Mormon friends to point out exactly where the Bible has been corrupted or poorly translated. Then ask them to present clear and convincing evidence to support their claims of corruption or poor translation. The vast majority of Mormons will not be able to field these questions. Asking these questions may help create a crisis of belief.

Christians can feel confident that existing Bible texts are within 1 percent of complete textual accuracy. The claim that Hebrew and Greek texts were seriously corrupted cannot be substantiated. In fact, scholars have confirmed textual evidence for the ______________ and ______________________ of both the Old and New Testaments. Many texts of the Old Testament date to several centuries before Christ, and some New Testament texts date as early as the second century after Christ. Biblical documents are the best attested of any ancient writings.

Contrary to Mormon claims, no clear and convincing archaeological evidence supports the historical accuracy of *The Book of Mormon*. No *Book of Mormon* ___________ have been located. No *Book of Mormon* ____________ have been found in New World writings. No ancient ___________ of *The Book of Mormon* have been located. No Reformed Egyptian _______________ have been discovered. No *Book of Mormon* __________, ____________, or _________ have been uncovered. No *Book of Mormon* _____________ have been located. Ask your Mormon friends whether they are a little concerned that no clear and convincing physical evidence supports the Mormon claim for the historicity of *The Book of Mormon*, especially compared to the thousands of pieces of evidence that have been located to verify other ancient documents.

The Puzzle of the Mormon Doctrine of ____________________

The Mormon Church also holds unbiblical beliefs about the Son of God. Mormons believe that Jesus was the firstborn _______________ _______________ of the Heavenly Father in the premortal realm. The Heavenly Father was also the parent of everyone else in the premortal realm. An official Mormon publication reads: "Every person who was ever born on earth was our spirit brother or sister in heaven. The first spirit born to our heavenly parents was Jesus Christ, so he is literally our elder brother."[3] Jesus was also the only begotten _________________ _________________ of the Heavenly Father in the mortal realm. The Heavenly Father, endowed with a physical body of flesh and bones, sired Jesus Christ in the same way all children are sired, or fathered. The 13th president-prophet of the Mormon Church, Ezra Taft Benson, wrote that the Son of God was "sired by that same Holy Being we worship as God, our Eternal Father. Jesus was not the son of Joseph, nor was He begotten by the Holy Ghost. He is the Son of the Eternal Father."[4]

The Christian view of the origin and nature of God's Son is vastly different. Jesus Christ is ________ ______________, the __________ Son of God. He has always existed with the Father and the Holy Spirit. The incarnate Son of God is one person who possesses two natures—__________ and __________[5] (see John 1:1-18; 8:56-59; Phil. 2:6-11; Col. 1:13-23; Heb. 1—2; 13:8). Ask your Mormon friend whether she believes the Mormon Church's teaching that Jesus was twice sired by the Heavenly Father. Responses will vary. If she appears uncomfortable about this Mormon teaching or is reluctant to affirm it, challenge her to consider the implications of disagreeing with the prophet of the church. If the prophet is wrong about something as important as the nature or origin of Christ, perhaps he is not a genuine prophet at all. The whole house of Mormonism rises and falls on the accuracy of its prophets.

The Puzzle of the Mormon Doctrine of ____________________________

The Mormon doctrine of salvation also differs significantly from Christian beliefs. In Mormonism Jesus' atonement occurred in the Garden of Gethsemane, on Calvary's cross, and in the resurrection, but the role of the cross is usually deemphasized.[6] His atonement provided immortality for _______ __________ without regard for their religious beliefs or practices, but it does not provide for complete salvation in the sense of eternal life with God.[7] Every individual is responsible for accruing enough merit to secure the fullest kind of salvation,[8] called ________________ (godhood). The Mormon temple rites of endowments and baptism on behalf of the dead may also secure the fullest salvation for those presently in the postmortal world.[9] Exaltation is available only to obedient Mormons who faithfully keep a rigorous code of belief and conduct.[10] There are three levels of heaven in Mormon doctrine. Only obedient, temple-worthy Mormons enter the Celestial Kingdom after the resurrection. The Terrestrial Kingdom and the Telestial Kingdom are reserved for almost everyone else. And only apostate Mormons and extremely vile sinners inhabit Outer Darkness.[11]

Biblical Christianity, on the other hand, teaches that complete salvation is entirely God's work in Christ. The Bible teaches that salvation is the result of God's work by __________ through __________ and is not produced by human ____________. Everyone who wishes to enter eternal life must be born again, repent, and believe. And all genuine believers must wholly rely on the work of Christ for salvation, not their own works (see Eph. 2:8-10). Ask your Mormon friends to demonstrate from the Bible clear and convincing evidence to support the Mormon doctrine of salvation. Expect a presentation from the Bible, but do not expect clear and convincing evidence. Gently show them

NOTES

NOTES

the flaws of their presentation in light of the totality of the Bible. Your FAITH gospel presentation includes essential biblical evidence of the true way of salvation. Explain that Christians value virtue and good works that are pleasing to God but that they are not needed to earn salvation.

Solving the Puzzle of Mormon Terminology

Sharing the genuine gospel with Mormons can be frustrating because they use many religious terms that are similar to Christian terms but assign them different meanings. Define your terms precisely and ask your Mormon friends to do the same. Contrast the following definitions.[12]

Term	**Mormonism**	**Christianity**
Atonement	The work of Christ from Gethsemane to the tomb that produces universal ________________ for everyone, though not complete salvation for anyone	The work of Christ on the cross that is sufficient to produce the complete salvation of all but is particularly efficient for the complete ________________ of everyone who repents and believes
Baptism	Live baptism and baptism on behalf of the dead are practiced. Baptism is ________________ to qualify for complete salvation and exaltation. It must be performed by the Mormon priesthood.	Baptism is not a requirement for complete salvation but is an act of ________________ symbolizing the believer's faith in Christ. There is no biblical support for baptism for the dead.
Eternal Life	Achieving ________________, or godhood, in the Celestial Kingdom	The state of all the redeemed in Christ in God's ____________ for all eternity
Gospel	________________ and ________________ of Mormon Church. The true gospel of Jesus Christ restored by Joseph Smith	The __________ __________ of the death, burial, and resurrection of Jesus Christ and His complete atonement for humankind's sins.

Heaven

Divided into __________ ______________________: Celestial, Terrestrial, and Telestial

All redeemed go to __________. All unredeemed go to ________. Different locations for types of redeemed people or divided realms of heaven are unbiblical.

Heavenly Father

Possesses a ____________ of flesh and bones and therefore is not present everywhere. The literal parent of all humanity and of the twice-sired Jesus Christ

One person of the eternal Trinity, which is three in person and one in being or essence. He is essentially _______, does not have a body, and does not sire children.

Holy Ghost

A ____________ person of God from the Father and the Son. Not the same as the Holy Spirit, which is not a person but an attribute or influence of the Heavenly Father

One person of the eternal Trinity, three in person and one in essence. The Holy Ghost and Holy Spirit are ____________—two English translations of a single Greek term.

Jesus Christ

Literally God's Son in the premortal spirit realm, like any other __________ _________ of God, and in the earthly realm through God's sexual union with Mary

The preexistent ___________, the one and only Son of God, fully and equally God, sharing the same divine essence with the Father and the Holy Spirit

Salvation

Salvation by grace is identical to the _____________ resurrection of all humankind. In Christ everyone has a kind of salvation.

Salvation is not universal, but ___________ salvation is enjoyed by those who repent and place faith in Christ's redemptive work.

Scripture

The *King James Version* of the Bible as correctly translated, *The Book of* ___________, *Doctrine and Covenants*, *The Pearl of Great Price*

The _________ __________ is authoritative Scripture.

Trinity

The three members of the Godhead are totally ___________ entities, united in purpose and love, not in essence.

God reveals Himself as Father, Son, and Holy Spirit, with distinct personal attributes but ___________ _______________ of nature, essence, or being.[13]

NOTES

NOTES

Witnessing to Mormons

Here are more principles for talking with Mormons about your faith.

1. Use the ________ ___________ _____________ of the Bible.

This is the only authorized version of the Bible recognized by the Mormon Church. Do not raise translation issues unnecessarily. When you have opportunities to use the FAITH gospel presentation with Mormons, memorize and use verses from the *King James Version*.

2. Determine the level of ______________________ to Mormonism.

Not all Mormons are thoroughly committed Mormons. The less active they are, the more likely they will be to set aside Mormonism in favor of genuine Christianity. You can gauge their commitment by discovering the following information.

- Determine whether they were converts to Mormonism or were born into a Mormon family.
- Determine whether they take the sacraments weekly in the ward house.
- Determine, if male, whether they have received the Melchizedek priesthood.
- Determine whether they are temple Mormons, those who are qualified to enter the temple.

3. Determine the level of adherence to Mormon ______________________.

Generally, faithful Mormons strongly affirm the following six unbiblical propositions. If your Mormon friends deny or question any of them, they may not be fully convinced of all Mormon claims.

- Mormonism is based on the Bible or agrees with it.
- *The Book of Mormon* is another witness to the Bible.
- The Mormon Church is the restored church founded by Christ.
- The Mormon Church is the only church with a valid priesthood.
- God was once a man and presently has a body of flesh and bones.
- Baptism for the dead must be performed.

4. Emphasize an objective method for discovering ________.

Remind Mormons that a claim for truth is not the same as evidence for truth and that a testimony to something does not necessarily make it so. Mormons characteristically offer their private, subjective religious experiences to confirm their doctrine.[14]

5. Proclaim the sufficiency of ________ ________.
Mormons need to hear that Jesus Christ is the sole and complete sacrifice for sin and that human works to achieve salvation are useless. Your FAITH gospel presentation provides Scriptures you can use to show that Jesus' death on the cross provides salvation for all who believe.

Visitation Time

Do It

1. Your visitation assignments will include evangelistic prospects, recent guests who visited the church and are already believers, and absentees from Sunday School. Approach evangelistic visits with the expectation that you will ask the Key Question. If the person gives a strong faith answer, your Team will have an opportunity for practice. If the prospect does not respond in faith, you as the Team Leader will have an opportunity to demonstrate how to present the gospel. Remember that you are there to fulfill God's divine purpose, whether in an evangelistic or a ministry role. Remember 2 Timothy 2:2.
2. Pray before you go.
3. Use the time in the car to review, allowing Learners to ask questions. Because they studied ministry visits in this session, ask them what ministry visits they think the Sunday School class needs. Remind them to listen to prayer requests and other discussions in Sunday School that might reveal ministry needs.
4. After each visit allow Learners to debrief it. Facilitate the debriefing by asking specific questions: What were their feelings about the visit? How could the visit have gone more smoothly? How does this visit compare with the previous week's visits?

Celebration Time

Share It

It is important that everyone attend Celebration Time. Emphasize this as an important part of the FAITH process. This is an opportunity to rejoice for decisions that were made. Demonstrate for your Team Learners how to do the following.

1. Hear reports and testimonies.
2. Complete Evaluation Cards.
3. Complete Participation Cards.
4. Update visitation forms with the results of visits.

NOTES

Home Study Assignments

Home Study Assignments reinforce this session by helping you apply what you have learned.

Your Discipleship Journey

Journaling activities in Your Discipleship Journey are an important part of your development as a Great Commission Christian through FAITH training.

1. The Mormon Church teaches that Jesus was sired by God and not born of a virgin. How do the following Scriptures refute that teaching?

   Isaiah 7:14: ______________________________

   ____

   Matthew 1:20-21: ______________________________

   ____

   Luke 1:30-35: ______________________________

   ____

2. The Bible claims that it alone is God's inerrant revelation to people. Match the following Scriptures with the correct statements summarizing the Bible's claim to authority.

   ____ 1. Psalm 119:89
   ____ 2. Isaiah 40:8
   ____ 3. Luke 21:33
   ____ 4. Romans 15:4
   ____ 5. 2 Timothy 3:16
   ____ 6. Hebrews 4:12
   ____ 7. 2 Peter 1:20-21

   a. Jesus' words will never pass away.
   b. Scripture was written by men who were led by the Holy Spirit.
   c. God's Word is eternal.
   d. Scripture teaches and encourages.
   e. God's Word is living and active, judging thoughts and attitudes.
   f. God's Word stands forever.
   g. Scripture is inspired and is useful for teaching, rebuking, correcting, and training in righteousness.

3. What do the following Scriptures teach about the guarantee of heaven for believers?

   John 14:1-4: ______________________________

Ephesians 2:6,19: ________________________________

Philippians 3:20: ________________________________

Colossians 3:3-4: ________________________________

Growing as a Life Witness

Growing as a Life Witness reminds you of your responsibility to witness and minister to others during the week.

1. Talk or meet with your accountability partner and share ways you have cultivated a lost person or have witnessed or ministered on occasions other than FAITH visits.
2. Discuss ways you can apply the session 4 content.
3. Pray for lost persons by name and for each other.

Prayer Concerns	Answers to Prayer
______________________	______________________
______________________	______________________
______________________	______________________
______________________	______________________
______________________	______________________

Your Weekly Sunday School Leadership Meeting

A FAITH participant is an important member of Sunday School. Encourage Team members who are elected Sunday School workers to attend this weekly meeting. Use this section to record ways your FAITH Team influences the work of your Sunday School class or department. Use the information to report during weekly Sunday School leadership meetings. Identify actions that need to be taken through Sunday School as a result of prayer concerns, needs identified, visits made by the Team, and decisions made by the persons visited. Also identify ways you can disciple others in your Sunday School class or department and in your church.

1. Share results of witnessing and ministry visits. Have Teams made Opinion Poll visits yet? Suggest opportunities to minister to persons who were visited.

____

____

2. Give or receive information appropriate for future FAITH Team assignments. Are additional prospect-discovery activities needed to keep FAITH assignments up-to-date?

____

____

____

3. Pray specifically for Sunday School plans this week. As a team, evaluate the previous session and discuss ways Sunday's Bible-study lesson can involve members and guests in transformational Bible study and discipleship.

____

____

Discipling Your Team Members

This weekly feature suggests actions the Team Leader can take to support Team members, prepare for Team Time, and improve visits. This work is part of the Team Leader's Home Study Assignments. Add any actions suggested by your church's FAITH strategy.

Support Team Members

- ❑ Call Team members and talk with them about their participation in class training and visits. Discuss any observations they made during the visits and particularly about sharing their Sunday School testimonies.
- ❑ Discuss ways to prepare and share their evangelistic testimonies without revealing the answer to the Key Question.
- ❑ Encourage them as they memorize all of ***Preparation*** in the FAITH Visit Outline.

Prepare to Lead Team Time

- ❑ Preview Leading Team Time at the beginning of session 5.
- ❑ Be prepared to evaluate Team members' written evangelistic testimonies, using these criteria:
  - Define a specific event before (preconversion) and after your conversion (benefits).
  - Do not answer the Key Question.
  - Keep your testimony brief (three minutes or less).
  - Do not give unnecessary details; instead, concisely relate your experience.
  - Conclude your testimony with the assurance that you are going to heaven.

Prepare to Lead Visits

- ❑ Review the FAITH Visit Outline in order to model the entire process for Team members.
- ❑ Be prepared to model visits in which Team member(s) are asked to lead in sharing Sunday School and/or evangelistic testimonies.
- ❑ Be prepared to model the use of the Opinion Poll in making visits.
- ❑ Be prepared to lead your Team to participate during Celebration Time.

Link with Sunday School

- ❑ Participate in your weekly Sunday School leadership meeting. Share pertinent information in the meeting, using Your Weekly Sunday School Leadership Meeting (pp. 77–78) and FAITH-visit results.
- ❑ Use examples from Mormon beliefs to warn Sunday School members about false beliefs when topics like the authority of Scripture and doctrines of Christ, salvation, and eternity arise in Sunday School lessons.

For Further Growth

For Further Growth may include additional reading or activities that will enhance your growth as a disciple and a discipler of others. These assignments are intended to be long-term projects and do not have to be completed during this semester of study.

1. Read *Mormonism Unmasked* by R. Philip Roberts (Broadman & Holman, 1998), which refutes Mormon theology from a Christian position. Pay particular attention to the biblical understanding of the person of Christ, salvation by faith alone, and the authority of the Bible.
2. Identify areas in your community that currently have or plan to have Mormon churches. Pray for the residents of these neighborhoods to be discerning and to search the Scriptures to prove the falsehood of Mormon claims. Begin to do Opinion Polls in these areas, as well.
3. Read the FAITH Tip on pages 80–81.

[1]*The Pearl of Great Price*, Articles of Faith, article 8.
[2]Ibid., articles 8–9.
[3]*Gospel Principles* (Salt Lake City: The Church of Jesus Christ of Latter-day Saints, 1997), 11.
[4]Ezra Taft Benson, *Come unto Christ* (Salt Lake City: Deseret, 1983), 4. Also see Bruce R. McConkie, *Mormon Doctrine*, 2nd ed. (Salt Lake City: Bookcraft, 1966), 546–47, 743.
[5]*The Baptist Faith and Message* (Nashville: LifeWay Christian Resources of the Southern Baptist Convention, 2000), 8.
[6]*Doctrines of the Gospel Student Manual: Religion 231–323* (Salt Lake City: The Church of Jesus Christ of Latter-day Saints, 1986), 22.
[7]*Gospel Principles*, 71–78.
[8]Ibid., 117–223.
[9]Ibid., 255–57.
[10]Ibid., 301–5.
[11]Ibid., 294–99.
[12]Adapted from Sandra Tanner, "Terminology Differences" (Salt Lake City: Utah Lighthouse Ministry).
[13]*The Baptist Faith and Message*, 7.
[14]Adapted from *Latter-day Saints Interfaith Witness Resource Packet* (Alpharetta, GA: The North American Mission Board of the Southern Baptist Convention, 1996).

Answers to matching activity on page 76: 1. c, 2. f, 3. a, 4. d, 5. g, 6. e, 7. b

FAITH TIP

Using the Bible to Challenge Mormon Doctrine

Establishing the Bible's Reliability

Most Mormons have a fair amount of respect for the Bible, but the level of confidence in the Bible varies among Mormons. When talking with Mormons about your beliefs, first determine their confidence in the Bible. Most Mormons will profess a high regard for the Bible until they are presented with biblical evidence that refutes a feature of Mormonism. Then they often retreat to the "translated correctly" clause from the Articles of Faith. To preempt this retreat, try asking your Mormon friend at the beginning to state his view of the Bible. Ask him to identify exactly where and how the Bible is corrupt or mistranslated, along with evidence to support his claims. He will probably not present a particular claim, having been taught only to offer a general objection. Tell him that you wish to establish what he believes to be the reliable parts of the Bible before you present biblical evidence. Offer not to use biblical evidence from what the person considers corrupted passages. In this way you avoid giving him the option of employing the "translated correctly" clause after you offer compelling biblical evidence that challenges Mormon doctrine.

It is also critical to establish the superiority of the Bible as a more reliable guide to truth than subjective feelings. Ask the Mormon if he thinks the Bible or his feelings are a more trustworthy guide when searching for truth. Ask him which he intends to follow when feelings and the Bible disagree. These steps establish that the Bible is reliable and that the Bible overrides feelings.

Challenging the Need for Modern-Day Prophets

To challenge the Mormon insistence that prophets are necessary in every era, use the Bible to demonstrate that Christ introduced a new age that concluded the Old Testament prophetic era. Consult Matthew 11:13; Luke 16:16; Acts 2:18; and Hebrews 1:1-2 for evidence that Jesus referred to John the Baptist as the last prophet. Indicate that the prophets spoken of in the New Testament were not sources for new truth or revelation but communicators and explainers of truth revealed in the Law and Prophets and in Christ's teachings.

Challenging Beliefs About the Stick of Ephraim

You can also use the Bible to reject the Mormon claim that *The Book of Mormon* is the stick of Ephraim mentioned in Ezekiel 37:15-20. Mormons claim that the stick of Judah is the Bible, written by Judah's descendants, and that *The Book of Mormon* is the stick of Ephraim, written by the Nephites, who were descendants of Ephraim. The text indicates that Ezekiel was told to write on two sticks (see v. 16). Ask your Mormon friend if he claims that Ezekiel wrote *The Book of Mormon*. He will probably concede that Ezekiel did not write it. Then state that whatever both sticks may be, they both must have been authored by Ezekiel. Because Ezekiel did not author *The Book of Mormon*, the stick of Ephraim cannot be identical to *The Book of Mormon*.

Challenging the Claim to Be the Restored Church

You can also employ the Bible to refute the claim that the Mormon Church is the restored church of Christ after 1,500 years of complete apostasy, or falling away, of the church. Ask your Mormon friend to show you evidence that 2 Thessalonians 1—2 says anything about complete apostasy. A falling away does not necessarily have to be complete. First Timothy 4:1 (KJV) clarifies 2 Thessalonians by stating that "some," not all, "will depart from the faith."

Challenging the View of the Aaronic Priesthood

Mormons claim that through Joseph Smith they have restored the Aaronic priesthood, which had been lost for centuries. The Bible presents a solid challenge to the Mormon practice of ordaining Mormon boys at about age 12. Mormons consider themselves to be Israelites, more specifically of the tribe of Ephraim. But according to Exodus 38:21 and Numbers 3 and 8, God appointed Aaron's descendants as priests, and Aaron was of the tribe of Levi. Ask your Mormon friend how an Ephraimite can hold the Aaronic-Levitical priesthood. Also ask him why the Mormon Church ordains Aaronic priests at the age of 12 when God set the age at 25 in Numbers 8:23-25.

Challenging the Teaching That God Has a Body

Mormons generally rely on Exodus 33:11 to prove that the Heavenly Father has a body: "The Lord used to speak to Moses face to face." However, Mormons use the title "the Lord" to refer only to the Son of God, not to the Heavenly Father. Another problem is that although in Deuteronomy 4:12—5:4 the Lord spoke to the people at Sinai face to face, the people saw no form of God. Mormons are forced to rely on revelations outside the Bible and *The Book of Mormon* to support their belief about the bodily form of the Heavenly Father.

Challenging the Practice of Baptism for the Dead

Mormons use 1 Corinthians 15:29 as the primary source for their teaching about baptism for the dead, but the context is the resurrection of the dead, not the baptism of the dead. Paul used *I*, *we*, and *you* everywhere else in this chapter, but he used *they* in verse 29, strongly suggesting that Paul excluded himself and his audience from those who practiced baptism for the dead. Jesus never mentioned baptism for the dead, nor is it mentioned anywhere else in the Old or New Testament, nor is it described as efficacious for salvation in either the Bible or *The Book of Mormon*. Ask your Mormon friend whether it seems strange that a doctrine so key and crucial to the entire Mormon way of salvation and temple works would not be supported by the two most important works of Mormonism—the Bible and *The Book of Mormon*.

FAITH AT WORK

I started participating in FAITH in August 1999. Most of my expectations were, I am ashamed to say, negative. Still a relatively new Christian, I had never shared my faith, the gospel, or my testimony. I had a fear of making mistakes, saying the wrong things, and embarrassing the others on my Team. The thing I am most ashamed of, though, was the fear I had for the potential ridicule I might receive for being associated with Jesus. It was easy to be a Christian inside the walls of the sanctuary. Outside them was a different story. Then God started working on me.

I went through that first semester with a wonderful Team Leader who helped me learn tremendously. I have gone through a second semester as a Team Leader with two great Team Learners who encouraged me and helped me through our visits. Through both semesters of FAITH I learned that all the power, all the strength, and all the courage come not from me and my weak mind and flesh but from God. As long as I am willing to go, God will do the work and take care of me in any situation.

Most important is the way God impressed on me that I don't need to feel embarrassed to be a Christian and a follower of the Lord Jesus Christ. How can I be ashamed of the one and only way to have salvation? How can I be ashamed of the one who died on that cross for me?

This period of my FAITH training has brought greater conviction to me than I have experienced at any other time in my life except for the time when I committed my life to Christ. I now have greater conviction for making sure that I am right with God every day and that I am striving to be obedient to His will for me. I have greater conviction to study His Word, understand it, and know how I should apply it to my life. I also have a greater burden for persons who are lost and a desire to share the gospel of Jesus with them.

My salvation was a life-changing experience. And being part of the FAITH strategy has been an experience of significant spiritual growth for me.

David Wells
Eastside Baptist Church
Paragould, Arkansas

SESSION 5

The Jehovah's Witnesses

JAMES NEWMAN

In this session you will—

CHECK IT by engaging in Team Time activities;

KNOW IT by reviewing content from session 4;

HEAR IT by examining the beliefs of Jehovah's Witnesses and by learning ways to witness to them;

SEE IT by viewing a video segment;

STUDY IT by overviewing Home Study Assignments;

DO IT by leading your Team in making visits;

SHARE IT by celebrating.

NOTES

Leading Team Time

All Team members participate in Team Time. They are primarily responsible for reciting the assigned portion of the FAITH Visit Outline and for discussing other Home Study Assignments.

As you direct this important time of CHECK IT activities with your Team, keep in mind that Learners look to you as a role model, motivator, mentor, and friend. Team Time activities can continue in the car as the Team travels to and from visits.

Lead CHECK IT Activities

✔ *FAITH Visit Outline*

- ❑ Call on each Learner to recite the assigned portion of the FAITH Visit Outline (all of ***Preparation***, plus key words in ***Presentation*** and ***Invitation***).
- ❑ Indicate your approval by signing each Learner's Journal. Be prepared to answer any questions Learners may have. Make suggestions for improvement.

✔ *Evangelistic Testimony*

- ❑ Call for final written copies of Learners' evangelistic testimonies. Congratulate Team members for achieving another important milestone.
- ❑ Make sure any revisions include criteria discussed in sessions 3 and 4. Ask for permission to print these testimonies in church materials that publicize the FAITH strategy or that encourage persons to share their faith.
- ❑ Emphasize to Team members the importance of sharing their testimonies naturally, in their own words, in actual visits.

✔ *Key Question/Transition Statement*

- ❑ Practice the Key Question/Transition Statement, helping Learners comfortably use their hands to spell the word *FAITH*.

✔ *Other Home Study Assignments*

- ❑ Look over Learners' Home Study Assignments. Are Learners on track? Clarify or emphasize key points from FAITH Tips and/or *Evangelism Through the Sunday School: A Journey of FAITH* as needed.

✔ *Session 4 Debriefing*

- ❑ Review the importance of and approach for making Sunday School ministry visits. Help Team members understand how such visits reconnect many inactive members to church life. Highlight ministry

visitation assignments and indicate why certain comments are made during different types of ministry visits (to absentees, nonattenders, members with ministry needs). As inactive members return to Sunday School or church, remind Team members they had a part.
- ❑ Ask any questions you feel would solidify Learners' understanding of session 4, including questions that will appear on the final written review (ses. 16).

✔ *Help for Strengthening a Visit*

- ❑ Be prepared to discuss ways to strengthen a visit, based on what has been discovered in previous sessions.
- ❑ Be prepared to model an Opinion Poll visit during Visitation Time.
- ❑ Identify which Team member(s) will take the lead in sharing a Sunday School testimony. Ask another Team member to be prepared to share his or her evangelistic testimony. With sensitivity to Learners and person(s) being visited, be prepared to resume the visit after Team members have shared.

Notes

____

____

____

____

____

Actions I Need to Take with Team Members This Week

____

____

____

____

____

NOTES

NOTES

A Quick Review

Last week you examined major Mormon doctrines to learn how they differ from biblical Christianity. Identify whether each statement represents a Mormon belief (M) or a Christian belief (C).

___ 1. God is continuing to give revelation to His prophets.
___ 2. Every person who was ever born on earth was our spirit brother or spirit sister in heaven.
___ 3. Jesus Christ is God incarnate, the eternal Son of God.
___ 4. The Heavenly Father physically sired Jesus Christ in the same way all children are sired.
___ 5. Jesus' atonement provided immortality for all people but does not provide for complete salvation.
___ 6. Salvation is entirely God's work by grace through faith.
___ 7. We experience eternal life by achieving a state of exaltation or godhood in the Celestial Kingdom.
___ 8. The gospel is the good news of the death, burial, and resurrection of Jesus Christ and His complete atonement for sin for all who repent and accept Him.
___ 9. God possesses a body of flesh and bones and therefore is limited and cannot be present everywhere.
___ 10. God is spirit and does not have a body; therefore, He is not limited by space and is eternal.
___ 11. Four standard works constitute the written authority for truth.
___ 12. The Bible alone is Scripture.

Check principles you learned for witnessing to Mormons.

❑ 1. Appeal to your common beliefs about the Trinity.
❑ 2. Realize that the Bible can be interpreted to support baptism for the dead.
❑ 3. Use the *King James Version* of the Bible.
❑ 4. Determine the level of commitment to Mormonism.
❑ 5. Hug the Mormon and call him or her your spirit brother or spirit sister.
❑ 6. Determine the level of adherence to Mormon doctrines.
❑ 7. Emphasize an objective method for discovering truth.
❑ 8. State that works are necessary to earn salvation.
❑ 9. Encourage the Mormon to judge truth by his or her feelings.
❑ 10. Proclaim the sufficiency of Jesus Christ.

Armageddon's Army

Rolling his lawnmower out of the garage, John noticed a well-dressed couple walking up the drive. The man, in a two-piece suit, carried a bag. The woman, in a fashionable midlength dress, held a magazine in her hand. "Good morning. We're in the neighborhood today sharing good news about Jehovah's kingdom."

"Oh?" John asked.

"Yes, would you be interested in reading one of our publications, *The Watchtower*? We ask for only a small donation."

"*The Watchtower*? Isn't that published by Jehovah's Witnesses?"

"Yes. We are Jehovah's Witnesses proclaiming His coming on earth."

Who are the people called Jehovah's Witnesses? Many people dismiss them as fanatics. They are ridiculed on television. Often, evangelical Christians slam doors in their faces, with no concern for their souls.

Still, Jehovah's Witnesses are a growing presence, numbering almost 6 million "publishers," those who faithfully go door to door with their message. The number of people who embrace their beliefs is much larger; 14 million attend their annual, gigantic Memorial gathering. They report more than 1 billion hours in door-to-door witnessing each year, subverting the faith of hundreds of thousands of unsuspecting Christians.

The movement known today as the Watchtower Bible and Tract Society (Jehovah's Witnesses) had its birth in the mind of a Pennsylvania haberdasher named Charles Taze Russell. Born in Old Allegheny (present-day Pittsburgh) in 1852, Russell joined both the Congregational Church and the YMCA as a teenager. With more zeal than understanding, young Russell attempted to dispute with an infidel acquaintance about Christianity and the existence of hell but lost the argument. The experience so disturbed him that he became obsessed with disproving the existence of hell, arguing that it was inconceivable that a loving God would make people in His own image and then create a hell in which to punish them forever.

Joining the Adventist movement, Russell devoted himself to Bible study, particularly seeking to disprove the existence of hell and to prove his opinions about Christ's second coming. He also set about to establish a chronology of biblical events from creation on. Armed with a substantial inheritance, Russell began to publish his opinions and to gather a group of followers. Significant among his early publications were *The Object and Manner of the Lord's Return*, which presented his view of the second coming, and *Zion's Watch Tower and Herald of Christ's Presence*. The latter attempted to prove that Christ had invisibly returned to the earth in 1874, contrary to the Bible's statement that at His return "every eye will see Him" (Rev. 1:7).

NOTES

NOTES

Russell also became fascinated with the Great Pyramid of Egypt. Defying historical evidence and simple logic, he concluded that the architect for the pyramid was Melchizedek, the priest of Salem, and that its structure was a clue to God's chronology of human history from Adam to the millennium. Assigning one inch in the pyramid passages to represent one calendar year, Russell presumed to discover the exact date of Adam's creation and the year 1874 as "the beginning of the period of trouble." Concluding that this year marked Christ's invisible return, Russell set dates for the battle of Armageddon and the millennial reign.

Since that time the Watchtower Society has repeatedly prophesied and reset dates for these events, none of which were fulfilled. Recently, the Watchtower Society, after repeated failed prophecies about the battle of Armageddon, announced that the date is unknown. However, Jehovah's Witnesses still believe it to be very near.

Jehovah's Witnesses' Beliefs

A fundamental tool Jehovah's Witnesses use to subvert the faith of those they approach is the book *Reasoning from the Scriptures*, which teaches Watchtower doctrines on a wide range of subjects Witnesses are likely to encounter as they visit from house to house. On some subjects the book agrees with historic evangelical understanding. On many the Scriptures are twisted to conform to the dogmas of the Watchtower. *Reasoning from the Scriptures* and the Watchtower's distorted and mistranslated version of the Bible, *The New World Translation of the Holy Scriptures*, give Jehovah's Witnesses dangerous and often formidable weapons, especially when confronting a naive and ill-equipped prospect.

1. Watchtower literature is placed above the BIBLE **.**
The Watchtower's declarations about the inspiration and authority of the Bible read much like those of Southern Baptists or other evangelical Christians. A grave and deadly difference lies in the Watchtower's assertion that it (more specifically, its Governing Body) functions as God's prophet.[1] Therefore, only interpretations of Scripture produced by this body in its official publications are allowed. Any Bible study undertaken by Jehovah's Witnesses quickly becomes a study of Jehovah's Witness literature about the Bible rather than a legitimate search of the Scriptures. Sound principles of biblical interpretation are dismissed. Only official Watchtower publications are approved for reading and study.

When Witnesses undertake a Bible study with prospective converts, it soon becomes apparent that they are not interested in studying the Bible as such but the Watchtower literature about the Bible. Further, the Watchtower maintains that only its own *New World Translation of the Holy Scriptures* is acceptable for proper study. This so-called translation was undertaken by a committee appointed by the Governing Body, none of whom, according to former Jehovah's Witnesses who were knowledgeable of the process, were academically qualified in the biblical languages. Arbitrary changes were made in numerous places to force a reading that conforms to the Watchtower's doctrinal bias.

For example, the *New American Standard Bible*'s translation of Romans 14:7-9 reads: "Not one of us lives for himself, and not one dies for himself; for if we live, we live for the Lord, or if we die, we die for the Lord; therefore whether we live or die, we are the Lord's. For to this end Christ died and lived again, that He might be Lord both of the dead and of the living." Four times in this passage the word *Lord* (Greek, *kurios*) is used. *The New World Translation* arbitrarily renders the first three instances *Jehovah*, a term not allowed by the Greek. Yet it correctly translates *kurios* in the last instance as *Lord*. Why the inconsistency? Obviously, if it had used *Jehovah* in verse 9, it would have read, "that He [Jesus] might be Jehovah." That would damage Jehovah's Witnesses' denial that Jesus is God. Changing the translation of *kurios* in verse 9 defies logic, departing from the sense of the passage. Similar methods have been used repeatedly in *The New World Translation*. According to *Reasoning from the Scriptures*, "the name Jehovah is used in both the Hebrew and the Christian Greek Scriptures in this [*New World Translation*], appearing 7,210 times."[2] This is done with no linguistic justification, only the determination to produce a Bible that agrees with Jehovah's Witnesses' beliefs.

This passion to deny that Jesus is God the Son causes Jehovah's Witnesses to ignore clear Bible passages affirming Jesus' deity or to flee to the Watchtower for explanations that keep them bound to their false belief in the lesser nature of Christ. Revelation 1:7-8 says that someone is coming, that the one who is coming is the Alpha and Omega, a term applied to God, "the one who is and who was and who is to come, the Almighty." Clearly this speaks of the Lord God. Yet the one speaking, employing all of these terms describing God to identify Himself, also says He is the one whom they pierced. Who was pierced? Jesus. Who is coming? Jesus. Who is Jesus? Jesus is God.

Jehovah's Witnesses and Baptists appear to agree on the inspiration and infallibility of the Bible. However, there is wide disparity in their approach to understanding the Bible. Jehovah's Witnesses depend on the official interpretations handed down by the Governing Body, believing that the Watchtower literature would be sufficient without the Bible but that the Bible could never be understood without the Watchtower literature. Their approach is to isolate passages from the body of Scripture, string verses together to force a viewpoint, apply false reasoning, and change the Bible's wording to make its message conform to their opinions.

NOTES

1 COR 8:7
TO PROVE THERE IS ONLY 1 GOD

But w/ second 1/2 OF THAT SCRIPTURE SAYS THERE IS ONLY 1 LORD

HEBREWS 1

JESUS VS. ANGELS

NOTES

Baptists and other Christians believe that the Bible is fully sufficient in all matters of faith and practice (see 2 Tim. 3:16-17), that passages must be understood in full context, and that human opinions must always give way to the clear teachings of the Bible (see 2 Pet. 1:20-21).

2. The view of ________ is limited.

Jehovah's Witnesses insist that the only acceptable name for God is *Jehovah*, and they deny the Trinity. *The New World Translation* inserts the term *Jehovah* 6,974 times in the Old Testament, 237 times in the New.[3] In contrast, in the *King James Version* the name *Jehovah* appears only four times in the Old Testament and not at all in the New Testament.

Christians counter that in addition to Jehovah, several names are used in the Bible to address God—Lord, Elohim, and Adonai, for example. Although the Bible does not use the word *Trinity*, it clearly depicts God as Father, Son and Holy Spirit.

3. Jesus' __deity__ is denied.

Jehovah's Witnesses assert that Jesus Christ is not God, instead contending that He is Michael the archangel, the first being created by Jehovah. He is called Son because as Jehovah's first creation He was like a son. However, He was not equal to His Father.[4] This Michael, they claim, lent his life force to be placed in Mary and born as Jesus. Jesus then lived a sinless life and at His baptism became Christ. When He died, Michael returned to heaven, retaining the title of Christ.[5] From there He will destroy the unbelieving world, including all who profess to believe in Jesus but have not joined the Watchtower as publishers, leaving a paradise earth for Jehovah's faithful Witnesses.[6]

Jehovah's Witnesses sometimes use 1 Corinthians 8:6 to prove that there is one God, the Father (Jehovah): "For us there is but one God, the Father, from whom are all things, and we exist for Him; and one Lord, Jesus Christ, by whom are all things, and we exist through Him." But the verse also says there is only one Lord, Jesus Christ. If Jehovah's Witnesses suggest that Jesus is not God, consistency dictates that this verse also teaches that the Father is not the Lord. Jehovah's Witnesses usually insert the name *Jehovah* wherever the word *Lord* is used, unless to do so contradicts their denial that Jesus is God. The differentiation they want to make in this verse between Jesus and God does not exist.

Hebrews 1 presents evidence to counter the Jehovah's Witnesses' claim that Jesus is not God's Son but the archangel Michael. This chapter distinguishes between Jesus and angels, clearly describing that Jesus is superior to the angels. In verse 6, for example, the angels are commanded to worship Him. Angels are not to be worshiped, only God. And here the angels worship Jesus! *The New World Translation* substitutes the word *obeisance* for *worship*. It is interesting to note, however, that prior to 1971 the translation used the word *worship* here.

Jehovah's Witnesses fail to grasp the distinction between the preincarnate Christ, God the Son, and the self-imposed limitations He accepted when "the Word became flesh and dwelt among us" (John 1:14). Jesus voluntarily subordinated Himself to the Father in earthly life (see John 14:28). In His complete humanity Jesus could pray to the Father and otherwise distinguish between Himself and the Father. But in His complete deity as God the Son, He could accept worship and truly affirm that " 'I and the Father are One' " (John 10:30). Jesus would not and could not misrepresent Himself.

The Bible states that Jesus is "the image of the invisible God, the firstborn of all creation" (Col. 1:15). Jehovah's Witnesses interpret *firstborn* to mean *first created* instead of *superior in station*. They fail to distinguish between the Greek terms *protoktistos* and *prototokos*. The former term would have been used if creation were meant. Instead, the latter is used, referring to station or rank.

Throughout the New Testament when references are made to the Son, He is presented with the attributes of the Father. Jesus was not merely a perfect creation; He was God incarnate: "In Him all the fullness of Deity dwells in bodily form" (Col. 2:9).

4. *The Holy Spirit is considered an impersonal* FORCE**.**

Jehovah's Witnesses deny the person of the Holy Spirit, or that the Holy Spirit is God. They consider the Holy Spirit an impersonal influence, Jehovah's invisible, active force, rendering the expression *holy spirit* in *The New World Translation* and in their literature. In contrast, the Bible depicts the Holy Spirit with the attributes of personhood and the qualities of the Father and the Son (see Luke 12:12; John 15:26; Acts 5:3-10; 13:2-4; 1 Cor. 12:11; Eph. 4:30; Heb. 3:7).

5. *Salvation is achieved by* Works**.**

According to Jehovah's Witnesses, Adam's disobedience brought physical death for the human race. When people die, they literally cease to exist. There is no hell. Jesus' death merely restored what Adam lost, since the transgression of the first perfect man, Adam, could be canceled only by the sacrifice of another perfect man, namely Jesus.

The Bible teaches that when people die, that is not the end of existence. A Christian enjoys a conscious fellowship with Christ prior to resurrection (see Matt. 22:32; Luke 16:22-23; 23:43; John 11:26; 2 Cor. 5:8; 12:2-4; 1 Thess. 4:14—5:10; 2 Pet. 2:9).

For a Jehovah's Witness, the instant of salvation is by grace (*undeserved kindness* in *The New World Translation*), but from that instant, salvation depends entirely on perfect obedience to Jehovah and maintaining favor in Jehovah's earthly organization, Jehovah's Witnesses. Appending works to grace plainly cancels the concept of grace, which is properly defined as *the undeserved, undeservable gift of*

NOTES

NOTES

God. This is entirely the work of Christ through faith, with good works purely the response to that saving grace (see Rom. 4:4-5; Eph. 2:8-10; Titus 3:5).

6. *Heaven is reserved for the faithful* ______________.

Jehovah's Witnesses believe that people cease to exist at death. Faithful Witnesses, however, will be raised, reconstituted with a re-created body, to live a probationary life in the millennium. Even in this Edenic life, it will be possible to fail God's demands and lose hope for immortality on a restored paradise earth.

At the end of the millennium, those who rejected the gospel of the Watchtower Society, even Jehovah's Witnesses who have failed at perfect obedience, will cease to exist here or hereafter. There is no hell. No one becoming a Jehovah's Witness after 1935 will be in heaven; no children will be there, nor will any of God's faithful who lived before Jesus, including Abraham, Moses, and John the Baptist. Only the faithful remnant will comprise the 144,000 who preside in heaven with Michael (Jesus), administering the affairs of paradise earth. All other Jehovah's Witnesses deemed worthy by their complete obedience will form the great crowd mentioned in Revelation 7:9 who will live forever on paradise earth.

Jehovah's Witnesses have been characterized by their preoccupation with the end times. They suggest that Jesus is not returning for His own but invisibly introduced His presence since 1914, a date determined by Russell's measurements of the Great Pyramid. Although Witnesses long ago rejected Russell's reasoning about the Pyramid, they nonetheless accept his conclusion about 1914.

Linked to these beliefs is a long history of setting and resetting dates for Armageddon, when all non-Jehovah's Witnesses will be annihilated and the millennial rule of resurrected Jehovah's Witnesses will begin. At the end of the millennium, the faithful composing the great crowd of witnesses will occupy a restored paradise earth, while the 144,000 witnesses born prior to 1935 will rule from heaven with Michael (Jesus).

The Bible clearly teaches that no one except God knows the day or the hour of Christ's return (see Matt. 24:36) and that His return will be visible to everyone (see Rev. 1:7). Setting dates is not only futile but also forbidden, and those who do so can be seen only as false prophets. Christians are to be ready for that moment whenever it comes (see Matt. 16:24-27; 24:14—25:30; Mark 13; Luke 21:5-16; John 5:28-29; 14:2-3; Acts 1:11; 1 Thess. 5:1-11).

Jehovah's Witnesses may deny the existence of hell, but the Bible clearly teaches that those who have trusted in Jesus for salvation will spend eternity in heaven with Christ and that those who have rejected Him will endure eternal suffering in hell (see Matt. 18:8-9; 25:41-46; Mark 9:43-48; 2 Thess. 1:9). The insistence that those who reject Him merely cease to exist and do not experience suffering has no basis in truth. In the Bible spiritual death is not the separation of the soul from the body; it is the separation of the soul from God. Someone living today who has not accepted Jesus is spiritually dead, being separated by his sin from God. That same person, in resurrection and judgment, will experience eternal separation. The Bible compares the consciousness of that separation to the pain of fire and the agony of dying without ever being dead to urge people to avoid that fate while they still have time.

NOTES

Witnessing to Jehovah's Witnesses

1. Bathe your encounter in ______________.
You are engaging in spiritual warfare. The battle is not yours but the Lord's.

2. Become familiar with Jehovah's Witnesses' ____________.
Know the way they interpret critical Bible passages and a proper understanding of those verses.

3. Be a better Bible ________________ than they are.
Know what you believe, why you believe it, and where in the Bible it is found. Be knowledgeable of the principles of proper interpretation so that you can recognize the abuse of Scripture.

4. Make ______________.
Prepare reference notes to place in your Bible so that you do not overlook important understandings you need to share or misinterpretations you need to refute.

5. Persuade Jehovah's Witnesses to consider only the ______________ in examining beliefs.
Refer to this quotation from one of Jehovah's Witnesses' resources: "Since many religions today are not doing God's will, we cannot simply assume that the teachings of the religious organization we are associated with are in agreement with God's Word. The mere fact that the Bible is used by a religion does not of itself prove that all the things it teaches and practices are in the Bible. It is important that we ourselves examine whether they are or not."[7] Read John 16:13, which identifies the Holy Spirit as the one who will guide us into all truth. *The New World Translation* of this verse can be used. Your goal is to get the Witness to examine the Bible for herself, without Watchtower literature.

NOTES

6. Control your ____________.

If you feel yourself getting tense or angry, it is better to discontinue the witness than to offend and lose the day. Jehovah's Witnesses believe that others' anger or rejection proves that they are right. Don't confirm their unbelief. Speak the truth in love.

7. Be ____________.

Jehovah's Witnesses will not be reached in a single, brief encounter. Take time to nurture an open relationship that will allow your witness to unfold.

8. Do not engage Jehovah's Witnesses unless you are confident of your __________________.

Even if you are confident of your witness, keep in mind that Jehovah's Witnesses have been memorizing, practicing, and role-playing in anticipation of engaging you. If you are not prepared, try to get their names and phone numbers so that you can contact them and set up a later meeting. If this fails, try to determine a time that is mutually agreeable. If you can get an address, you can take the initiative when you are better prepared. Further, you can write to them and set forth your witness, reassuring them of your prayers and friendship.

9. If you are meeting in your home, establish __________ __________.

For example, if you give them 10 minutes to speak without interruption, they must give you equal time without interruption.

10. Give a concise ____________ ____________.

Emphasize your salvation by grace through faith in Christ alone, the assurance and security of your salvation, with your good works simply a natural response to God's saving grace.

11. Keep the contact __________.

Take the initiative in communicating with the Jehovah's Witness so that you can continue the witness.

12. Demonstrate __________ and ____________ for the person.

Never be abrupt or ridicule beliefs Jehovah's Witnesses hold dear. To do so is to lose them. Jesus loved them so much that He died to save them.

13. Be ready for an opening to share the FAITH __________ __________________.

The Scriptures in the FAITH gospel presentation clearly present the truth about entering a relationship with God through Jesus Christ. Use what you have learned in FAITH to offer the Jehovah's Witness true freedom, unlimited grace, and eternal life in Christ.

Visitation Time

Do It

1. Pray for God to lead your Team to a divine appointment. If someone is not home, go next door. It just may be God's divine appointment.
2. Use the time in the car to review, allowing Learners to ask questions. This week they have heard the full gospel presentation. Begin preparing them to share the outline in a few weeks. How do they feel about that?
3. Choose one letter in the FAITH Visit Outline and ask Learners how that concept applied to them when they came to Christ.
4. After each visit allow Learners to debrief it. Facilitate the debriefing by asking specific questions.

Celebration Time

Share It

1. Share a divine appointment.
2. Not every Opinion Poll results in a profession of faith, but celebrate all attempts made. Highlight decisions made, prospects discovered, and other outcomes that would encourage and motivate other Teams.
3. Rejoice with other reports.
4. Complete Evaluation Cards.
5. Complete Participation Cards.
6. Update visitation forms with the results of visits.

NOTES

Home Study Assignments

Home Study Assignments reinforce this session by helping you apply what you have learned.

Your Discipleship Journey

Journaling activities in Your Discipleship Journey are an important part of your development as a Great Commission Christian through FAITH training.

1. Match the following Scriptures with Jesus' teachings about hell.

____ 1. Matthew 25:41	a. Hell is a place of torment.
____ 2. Mark 9:43	b. The fire never goes out in hell.
____ 3. Luke 12:5	c. A great chasm is fixed between heaven and hell.
____ 4. Luke 16:26	d. God has the power to judge sin and consign people to hell.
____ 5. Luke 16:28	e. Hell is a place of eternal fire.

2. Jehovah's Witnesses teach that when people die, they cease to be. This teaching is called annihilationism. Summarize the ways the following Scriptures refute this false teaching.

Matthew 25:46: ____

____

John 3:36: ____

____

2 Thessalonians 1:8-9: ____

____

3. Jehovah's Witnesses are very sincere in their beliefs, but sincerity is not sufficient for salvation. Before the apostle Paul met Christ, he sincerely believed that he was correct in regard to salvation. Read Philippians 3:4-6 and list the things Paul sincerely trusted to give him salvation.

____

4. Read Philippians 3:8-9. Record the one experience Paul was now relying on for his salvation.

____

5. What is your attitude toward followers of cults? Is it one of disdain, anger, and contempt or one of compassion and love? Discover in Acts 20:17-27; 26; and Romans 9:1-5 the apostle Paul's heart for those who were pursuing a false way of salvation. Be open to the Spirit's leading in your life to seek those who have been blinded to the truth. Record your thoughts and prayers.

____

____

Growing as a Life Witness

Growing as a Life Witness reminds you of your responsibility to witness and minister to others during the week.

1. Talk or meet with your accountability partner and share ways you have cultivated a lost person or have witnessed or ministered on occasions other than FAITH visits.
2. Discuss ways you can apply the session 5 content. Share any conclusions you wrote in activity 5 of Your Discipleship Journey.
3. Pray for lost persons by name and for each other.

Prayer Concerns	Answers to Prayer

Your Weekly Sunday School Leadership Meeting

A FAITH participant is an important member of Sunday School. Encourage Team members who are elected Sunday School workers to attend this weekly meeting. Use this section to record ways your FAITH Team influences the work of your Sunday School class or department. Use the information to report during weekly Sunday School leadership meetings. Identify actions that need to be taken through Sunday School as a result of prayer concerns, needs identified, visits made by the Team, and decisions made by the persons visited. Also identify ways you can disciple others in your Sunday School class or department and in your church.

1. If you do not have a weekly meeting, meet with your class or department. Consider inviting the Sunday School leadership team from your class or

department to your home after church on a Sunday evening. Excitedly share with the leadership team the results of weekly FAITH visits. Ask for additional names of persons you will need to make a ministry or evangelistic visit. Close with prayer. Consider conducting these meetings regularly until a weekly team prayer meeting is begun.
2. Discuss ways Sunday's Bible-study lesson can involve members and guests in transformational Bible study and discipleship.
3. Make assignments for follow-up calls to prospects and new members, communicating excitement about their participation in Sunday School. Share and receive information about absentees. Make assignments to follow up.
4. Share highlights that reflect the Holy Spirit's leadership and presence in FAITH visits thus far. Include actual visit results, an extraordinary sense of God's presence during visits, divine appointments, and so forth.
5. Pray for FAITH Teams, the pastor and church staff, and Sunday School department directors and teachers.

Discipling Your Team Members

This weekly feature suggests actions the Team Leader can take to support Team members, prepare for Team Time, and improve visits. This work is part of the Team Leader's Home Study Assignments. Add any actions suggested by your church's FAITH strategy.

Support Team Members

- ❑ Pray for and personally follow up on any Learner who may need personal encouragement.
- ❑ Contact Team members during the week to remind them that you are praying for them and to discuss their participation in FAITH. Seek to encourage Learners.
- ❑ Remember, Learners have overviewed the entire gospel presentation in session 5 and may have questions about their role in making a visit. Respond to specific needs and concerns.
- ❑ Think of appropriate ways to involve an Assistant Team Leader, if assigned to your Team.

Prepare to Lead Team Time

- ❑ Preview Leading Team Time for session 6.
- ❑ In a review of session 5 be prepared to overview the entire gospel presentation.

Prepare to Lead Visits

- ❑ Review the FAITH Visit Outline.
- ❑ Think about: Do you need to begin gently pushing some Learners out of their comfort zones during evangelistic visits? Some may be hesitant to participate fully without some encouragement.
- ❑ Be prepared to model a visit in which a Team member is asked to lead in

a visit up to asking the Key Question. Think about who might be ready for this opportunity or to share an evangelistic or Sunday School testimony.
- ❑ Pray for sensitivity as you involve different members in visits and pick up your part of the presentation appropriately and naturally.
- ❑ Prepare to lead your Team during Celebration Time.

Link with Sunday School
- ❑ Participate in your weekly Sunday School leadership meeting. Share pertinent information in this meeting, using Your Weekly Sunday School Leadership Meeting (pp. 97–98) and FAITH-visit results.
- ❑ Take every opportunity in Sunday School to teach the deity of Jesus Christ.

For Further Growth
For Further Growth may include additional reading or activities that will enhance your growth as a disciple and a discipler of others. These assignments are intended to be long-term projects and do not have to be completed during this semester of study.

1. Study in detail the ways the apostle Paul responded to those who were hostile to the truth. The Book of Acts records many of these encounters.
2. Study one or more of the following resources on Jehovah's Witnesses.
    - Belief bulletins and *Closer Look* brochures, available at no cost in limited quantities by writing to LifeWay Church Resources Customer Service, MSN 113; 127 Ninth Avenue, North; Nashville, TN 37234-0113; by calling toll free (800) 458-2772; by faxing (615) 251-5933; by ordering online at *www.lifeway.com*; or by emailing *customerservice@lifeway.com*.
    - *Jehovah's Witnesses: Interfaith Witness Associate's Manual* (Interfaith Evangelism Department, The North American Mission Board of the Southern Baptist Convention, 1995).
    - *Jehovah's Witnesses Answered Verse by Verse* by David A. Reed (Baker, 1986).
    - *Jehovah of the Watchtower* by Walter Martin and Norman Klann (Bethany House, 1974).
3. Read the FAITH Tips on pages 100–102.

---

[1] "They Shall Know a Prophet Was Among Them," *Watchtower*, 1 April 1972, 197.
[2] *Reasoning from the Scriptures* (Brooklyn, NY: Watchtower Bible and Tract Society of Pennsylvania, 1985), 193.
[3] *Jehovah's Witnesses: Interfaith Witness Associate's Manual* (Alpharetta, GA: The North American Mission Board of the Southern Baptist Convention, 1995), 14.
[4] *Happiness: How to Find It* (Brooklyn, NY: Watchtower Bible and Tract Society of Pennsylvania, 1980), 38–39.
[5] *Reasoning from the Scriptures*, 218.
[6] *You Can Live Forever in Paradise on Earth* (Brooklyn, NY: Watchtower Bible and Tract Society of Pennsylvania, 1982), 155.
[7] Ibid., 31.

Answers to matching activity on page 96: 1. e, 2. b, 3. d, 4. c, 5. a

FAITH TIP

Assumptions for Witnessing to Jehovah's Witnesses

1. *Jehovah's Witnesses are sincere in their beliefs.*

Jehovah's Witnesses are convinced that your only hope of escaping annihilation is to embrace their teaching and practices. They are also convinced that unless they are expending their utmost efforts in proselytizing others, Jehovah will destroy them. But sincerity does not in itself commend a person to God. A person may be sincerely wrong.

2. *Jehovah's Witnesses submit to the authority of the Watchtower and their elders.*

Jehovah's Witnesses must accept the pronouncements of the Watchtower, even in their personal and family matters. To do otherwise is to face disfellowshipping and shunning, loss of contact with friends or family, and certain annihilation in eternity. Thus, they are driven, even if subconsciously, by fear. Isolated from normal contact with non-Jehovah's Witnesses, they become codependent on the organization, and leaving becomes a terrifying prospect. Such psychological manipulation by intimidation makes them virtual slaves to the will of the organization, even if they may seem willingly bound.

3. *Jehovah's Witnesses are legalists.*

The New World Translation renders the Greek word for *grace* as *undeserved kindness*. For Jehovah's Witnesses, though, only the instant of salvation is grace. From that instant on, they must work to maintain approval within the Watchtower Society or lose all hope.

4. *Jehovah's Witnesses are well prepared for an encounter.*

Jehovah's Witnesses attend five meetings weekly, in addition to spending hours each week making house-to-house visits and return visits for Bible studies. Much of their time is spent memorizing their presentations, role-playing various encounters, and refuting possible arguments. If you decide to talk with a Jehovah's Witness, be aware that the Witness is well prepared. Even if you have a great deal of witnessing experience, you may be unprepared to engage a Jehovah's Witness without special preparation.

5. *Jehovah's Witnesses are generally ignorant of their organization's history.*

Jehovah's Witnesses may be unaware of the Watchtower Society's failed prophecies and the various scandals associated with it. The Society has carefully hidden from its followers evidence of its checkered past.

6. *Jehovah's Witnesses always visit in pairs or teams.*

Pairs or team are utilized so that honest inquiry by one Witness can be squelched by another. If one exhibits doubts or considers a Christian's witness, the other is there to extract him from the situation and to report him to the elders. The elders will question him and put him on probation or even disfellowship him if he does not recant.

FAITH TIP

The Test of Spiritual Genuineness

What is the test of spiritual genuineness? Is it sincerity? Some of the deadliest events in history have been characterized by sincerity, including the Holocaust of World War II. Sincerity of purpose did not make it acceptable to murder six million Jews.

Is a desired outcome the test? The end does not always justify the means. No doubt, some people who have had strange, ecstatic experiences in the holy-laughter movement have determined to become more loving, kind, and caring toward others. That does not prove that their experiences came from God.

Is it pragmatics? Many people in our society think that if something works, it must be all right. If that were the case, we would approve the hocus-pocus of New Age "medicine" or embrace a thousand gurus of false religion, even the control tactics of assorted cult leaders, because of their followers' claims.

Christians must not give primary attention to sincerity, desired outcome, or pragmatics. Christians must ask, Does it square with the Bible? "Beloved, believe not every spirit, but try the spirits, whether they are from God, because many false prophets are gone out into the world" (1 John 4:1). What is the test? It is the test of sound doctrine, revealed in the accurately interpreted Word of God.

SESSION 6

The Church of Christ, Scientist

TAL DAVIS

In this session you will—

CHECK IT by engaging in Team Time activities;

KNOW IT by reviewing content from session 5;

HEAR IT by examining the beliefs of Christian Scientists and by learning ways to witness to them;

SAY IT by practicing the ***Presentation*** portion of the FAITH Visit Outline;

STUDY IT by overviewing Home Study Assignments;

DO IT by leading your Team in making visits;

SHARE IT by celebrating.

NOTES

Leading Team Time

All Team members participate in Team Time. They are primarily responsible for reciting the assigned portion of the FAITH Visit Outline and for discussing other Home Study Assignments.

As you direct this important time of CHECK IT activities with your Team, keep in mind that Learners look to you as a role model, motivator, mentor, and friend. Team Time activities can continue in the car as the Team travels to and from visits.

Lead CHECK IT Activities

✔ *FAITH Visit Outline*

- ❑ Listen while each Learner recites all of ***Preparation***, ***Presentation*** through the Forgiveness statement and verse (Eph. 1:7a), as well as other key words in ***Presentation*** and ***Invitation***.
- ❑ Indicate your approval by signing or initialing Journals. Encourage Learners.

✔ *Other Home Study Assignments*

- ❑ Check to see whether Learners shared their evangelistic testimonies with two different believers. Briefly discuss how these two believers responded to the testimonies.
- ❑ Discuss benefits Learners are discovering from assigned reading material in *Evangelism Through the Sunday School* and in the FAITH Tip "Nurturing a New Christian" in *A Journey in FAITH Journal*.
- ❑ Make sure Learners are writing in Your Journey in Faith (their journaling section).

✔ *Session 5 Debriefing*

- ❑ Learners have heard the entire gospel presentation by viewing the videotape, hearing the presentation during visits, and overviewing it in session 5. Ask Learners to share how comfortable they are becoming with understanding the significance of sharing the complete gospel presentation.
- ❑ Remind Learners that although the gospel presentation is built on the letters in *FAITH*, *A Step of Faith* is used to help lead a person to make a commitment to Christ and enroll in Sunday School. Indicate that each of the following six sessions will focus on a letter of the gospel presentation and on how to use the leaflet in leading a person to make a decision to follow Christ.

✔ *Help for Strengthening a Visit*

- ❑ Encourage Learners to be constantly in prayer for one another and for persons being visited. Emphasize the importance of looking for opportunities to build bridges that allow us to share the gospel while, at the same time, being sensitive to the needs of the person being visited. Call attention to the fact that many times a Team might inadvertently close a door to receptivity to the gospel because they come across as pushy.

- ❑ Remind Team members of the importance of being available to the Holy Spirit and of relying on Him to prepare someone for the gospel. We are to be prepared to share and to know how to compassionately lead someone to make the commitments that will change his or her life forever.

Notes

____

____

____

____

____

____

Actions I Need to Take with Team Members This Week

____

____

____

____

____

____

____

NOTES

NOTES

A Quick Review

Last week you were introduced to Jehovah's Witnesses. Test your learning of Jehovah's Witnesses' history and beliefs by choosing the correct answers to complete the following sentences. Underline one choice in each group.

1. The founder of Jehovah's Witnesses was (Charles Taze Russell, Brigham Young, Oliver Cromwell).
2. Russell was obsessed with disproving the existence of (Jesus Christ, hell, the Christian church).
3. Russell published his opinions about Jesus' second coming in an attempt to prove that Jesus Christ had returned to earth in (1874, 1968, 70).
4. The only interpretations of Scripture allowed by Jehovah's Witnesses are the ones produced by (the Governing Body of the Watchtower, Jehovah's Witness missionaries, the Gideons).
5. The only name of God accepted by Jehovah's Witnesses is (Elohim, Yahweh, Jehovah).
6. Jehovah's Witnesses believe that the Holy Spirit is merely God's (angels, ideas, invisible force) in the world.
7. Jehovah's Witnesses assert that Jesus Christ is not God but (Lucifer, Gabriel, Michael).

Check the suggestions you studied for witnessing to Jehovah's Witnesses.

❑ 1. Bathe your encounter in prayer.
❑ 2. Study only what you believe so that you can refute them.
❑ 3. Don't quote Scripture, because it might offend them.
❑ 4. Be a better Bible student than they are.
❑ 5. Push for an immediate decision; it may be your only chance.
❑ 6. Read their literature with them, pointing out obvious mistakes.
❑ 7. Persuade them to consider only the Bible in examining beliefs.
❑ 8. Control your anger.
❑ 9. Engage them in discussion even if you are not prepared.
❑ 10. If you are meeting in your home, establish ground rules.
❑ 11. Realize that your personal testimony would be a waste of time.
❑ 12. Demonstrate love and respect.
❑ 13. Don't anger them by sharing the FAITH gospel presentation.

The Legacy of Divine Science

NOTES

Joe, Linda, and Tyra visited elderly Mrs. Connor during their weekly FAITH visitation. "Oh, yes, I am definitely a Christian and closely follow Jesus' teachings. In fact, I have been praying for God to remove this mole from my arm."

The Team looked at one another and at the mole, which Linda, a nurse, recognized as possibly a malignant skin cancer. "You really should see a dermatologist and have that checked," she said.

"Oh, I don't think that's necessary, Dear," Mrs. Connor replied. "In my church we believe that God heals through faith and prayer, not medicine."

"What church is that?" asked Linda.

"For 50 years I've been a member of the Church of Christ, Scientist. Are you familiar with it?"

"Is that Christian Science?"

"Why, yes it is," Mrs. Connor affirmed, smiling.

Mrs. Connor is a follower of one of the most enduring of the American-made religions of the 19th century, The Church of Christ, Scientist, better known by its generic name, Christian Science. Christians who encounter members of this unusual metaphysical cult may think that they are Bible-believing Christians like them. That's why Christians need to understand the core beliefs and practices of Christian Science and learn how it radically differs from historic Christianity. By recognizing the nature of Christian Science, you can more effectively share the true gospel of Jesus Christ and lead followers to saving faith in Him.

The Christian Science Church was founded in 1879 by MARY BAKER EDDY (1821–1910) in Boston, Massachusetts. As a girl and young woman, according to Christian Science sources, Mary was frail and sickly and lived a tragic life. She lost her first husband, George Glover, in 1844 when he died during an outbreak of yellow fever. Nine years later, she married Daniel Patterson, who abandoned her in 1873.

In 1866, while living in New Hampshire, Mary claimed to have experienced a miraculous healing following a fall, which led to her discovery of what she called DIVINE SCIENCE. She began teaching and writing about her experience and in 1875, following her divorce from Patterson, moved to Massachusetts, where she established the Christian Science Association. That year she also released her book SCIENCE AND HEALTH WITH KEY TO THE SCRIPTURES. It is still the foundational work for Christian Science philosophy and theology and is regarded by Christian Scientists as a divinely inspired companion to the Bible.

Mary married for the third time to Asa Albert Eddy in 1877, and

NOTES

together they formally established the Church of Christ, Scientist, in Boston, Massachusetts. The Mother Church in Boston remains today the movement's international headquarters. Mary Baker Eddy died in 1910 without selecting a successor as the pastor of the Mother Church. A self-perpetuating board of directors now directs the church's publishing and ministerial concerns.

Christian Science Beliefs

1. The Bible requires a SPIRITUAL ***interpretation.*** Mary Baker Eddy affirmed that the Bible was an inspired book. Nonetheless, she maintained that it is grossly misunderstood. Her main objection was that it was interpreted too literally to have spiritual value. Her perspective was that to gain the deeper truths of Scripture and thus to apply it accurately to people's lives, the Bible requires a metaphysical, or spiritual, interpretation. Thus, Eddy sought to recover from the Bible its "real" meaning, as Christian Scientists continue to do today.

To aid in this endeavor, Eddy wrote her primary text, *Science and Health with Key to the Scriptures*. This book presents her philosophical musings on 14 topics, including prayer, atonement, marriage, truth, and so on. All are addressed from Eddy's metaphysical ideology. *Science and Health with Key to the Scriptures* also contains two chapters of her commentaries on the Books of Genesis and the Apocalypse (Revelation).

Throughout this book and her other works Eddy completely redefined basic biblical concepts to fit her worldview. She wrote, "In Christian Science we learn that the substitution of the spiritual for the material definition of a scriptural word often elucidates the meaning of the inspired writer."[1] Consider the following examples of her novel definitions from the glossary of *Science and Health with Key to the Scriptures*.

- Angels—"God's thoughts passing to man; spiritual institutions, pure and perfect; the inspiration of goodness, purity, and immortality, counteracting all evil, sensuality, and mortality"[2]
- Bride—"Purity and innocence, conceiving man in the idea of God; a sense of Soul, which has spiritual bliss and enjoys but cannot suffer"[3]
- Gethsemane—"Patient woe; the human yielding to the divine; love meeting no response, but still remaining love"[4]
- Holy Ghost—"Divine Science, the development of eternal Life, Truth, and Love"[5]

These and dozens of other Christian Science definitions illustrate the fallacy of Eddy's incredible approach to biblical authority. Subjected to her method, words and names mean, in essence, whatever she wanted them to mean. In every case she overlaid biblical terms with a mystical or spiritual idea that has virtually nothing in common with the actual meaning of the term in the Bible.

Most Christians would agree that Eddy's method violates the single most important principle of biblical interpretation. That principle states that any text of the Bible must be read and understood in its literal sense. A faithful student of Scripture seeks to discover, as much as possible, the exact meaning of the biblical writer when he wrote it. Only by determining the exact meaning of the text can we determine its most accurate application for our lives. This process is not easy, so most evangelical theological seminaries still require ministerial students to study the biblical languages of Hebrew and Greek so that they can accurately handle the Word of truth (see 2 Tim. 2:15).

2. *God is* Mind *or* Spirit.

Biblical Christianity teaches that God is the infinite yet personal Creator who exists in three persons: Father, Son, and Holy Spirit (the holy Trinity). Mary Baker Eddy rejected the historic concepts of the Trinity, maintaining that "the theory of three persons in one God (that is, a personal Trinity or Tri-Unity) suggests polytheism, rather than the one ever present I AM."[6]

Christian Scientists prefer to describe God in impersonal terms like *Mind, Spirit, Soul, Principle, Life,* and *Truth.*[7] Thus, Christian Science has a radically different understanding of the nature of God and our relationship with Him than historic Christianity does.

3. *Only the divine is* Real.

Christian Scientists maintain that only that which reflects God's nature is real. Therefore, because, as they see it, God is essentially only Mind or Spirit, then the material world does not really exist. As Eddy stated, "Spirit is immortal Truth; matter is mortal error. Spirit is the real and eternal; matter is the unreal and temporal."[8] Understanding Christian Scientists' metaphysical worldview is critical for comprehending the totality of their belief system. Their worldview colors every aspect of their beliefs about God, humanity, Jesus Christ, salvation, sin, death, and physical healing.

4. *Humanity's problem is* IGNORANCE *of our spiritual nature.*

Christian Scientists believe that not only God but also each human is mind or spirit only: "Spirit is God, and man is the image and likeness. Therefore man is not material; he is spiritual."[9] Christian Science, in essence, denies that human beings are really physical beings who sin or get sick. Because, they say, we are spiritual like God, all that really exists

NOTES

NOTES

of our personalities is what is like Him. Thus, physical and negative forces in the universe are only an illusion. As Eddy said, "The only reality of sin, sickness, or death is the awful fact that unrealities seem real to human, erring belief. … They are not true, because they are not of God."[10] The problem, then, is not sinful rebellion against God but ignorance of what we are.

5. *Salvation and healing are realizing human* divinity

Christian Scientists assert that all matter, sin, sickness, evil, and even death are illusions and do not exist. Their ultimate goal is to realize their divinity and convince themselves that it is true. Therefore, salvation is not redemption from real sin but eliminating negative and false thoughts from the mind. When this is accomplished, those negative forces will disappear, including sickness, pain, and death. For Christian Scientists, Jesus Christ was the ultimate example of one who reflected God's spiritual and immaterial nature.

Thus, Christian Scientists are advised not to seek standard medical treatment for physical ailments. Christian Science professionals, called practitioners, come to the aid of church members in times of physical and/or spiritual trouble, not to give tangible treatment but to encourage and pray with members until they regain their spiritual vitality and with it their heath. Many states require medical-insurance companies to cover the fees of Christian Science practitioners for members of that church.

6. *Death is the ultimate* deception.

Christian Scientists, like all people, must face the fact of death. However, for them, death is also unreality, the ultimate deception. What we call death is for Christian Scientists merely a transition from the illusion of the material to the truth of the immortal spirit. Judgment, heaven, and hell are concepts that don't really concern them. They are mere states of mind that result when people believe life's illusions.

Witnessing to Christian Scientists

Christian Science is an unbiblical and unchristian belief system. Its adherents, however, may sincerely believe that they are following the true teachings of Jesus and the Bible. Christians who wish to witness to followers of Christian Science must be able to present a biblical worldview and to support Christian beliefs from a biblical perspective.

1. Explain that the BIBLE ***is the only authoritative guide for faith.***

Explain to the Christian Scientist that anyone's spiritual teachings and writings, including those of Mary Baker Eddy, must conform to those derived from the Bible, using sound principles of interpretation (see 2 Tim. 3:15-17; 2 Pet. 1:19-21).

2. Present a biblical picture of God.

The Bible does not teach that God is equated with abstract concepts like mind, truth, and love. Some of those, such as love, may be attributes of God's nature but are not synonyms for who He is. Emphasize the Bible's teaching that there is one eternal Creator who is a Trinity (see Matt. 28:19; 1 Cor. 12:4-6; 2 Cor. 13:14). He is personal and created everything in the universe that exists.

3. Point out the error ***of Christian Science's philosophical assumptions.***

Scripture teaches that matter is real and in fact was created by God, who declared it good (see Gen. 1). Jesus Himself was physically incarnated and was physically raised from the dead (see John 1:14; 20:26; 1 Cor. 15:1-8; Col. 2:9).

4. Confirm the reality ***of sin, disease, and death.***

The notion that sin, disease, and death are merely illusions contradicts biblical facts. Sin is a reality, and all people (except Christ) are sinners (see Rom. 3:23). Humanity's sin brought evil, sickness, and death into the world, and these realities made necessary divine redemption (see Gen. 3; Rom. 5:12-21). The Bible certainly commands Christians to pray for the sick, but that does not diminish the reality of physical deterioration and disease. God may heal if it is His will, but nowhere are we commanded to reject legitimate medical treatment (see 1 Cor. 12:9,30; Jas. 5:14-16), nor are we guaranteed to survive. Many Christian Scientists have a difficult time reconciling the realities of pain, disease, and death with the teachings of Christian Science. Often, they suffer in silence rather than admit their doubts or personal pain. Also, many Christian Scientists have needlessly died when standard medical treatments could have saved their lives. This was especially tragic when parents refused to provide medical treatment for their children.

5. Offer true salvation and spiritual healing through a relationship with JESUS Christ.

Use the FAITH gospel presentation to explain to Christian Scientists that true salvation was brought about by the physical death and resurrection of Jesus Christ. They can experience salvation and spiritual

NOTES

healing in a personal relationship with the living Savior, not by embracing their own presumed divinity or by denying sin and death.

6. *Be* PATIENT.

If the person has been a member of the Christian Science Church for a long time, he has adopted its worldview and presuppositions and will mentally filter your statements. Thus, take the time to build a relationship. Be willing not only to speak but also to listen to personal needs and concerns. Gently lead the person to realize and confront the self-contradictory nature of Christian Science as you display the consistent nature of the Christian gospel.

Visitation Time

Do It

1. Learners have completed the letter *F*. Ask whether any of them are ready to lead the visit through ***Preparation*** and the Key Question. If so, instruct them: "After the Key Question is asked and the person responds with a works, unsure, or unclear answer, you can say, 'Would you mind if [name of Team Leader] shares with you how the Bible answers that question?' "
2. Use the time in the car to review, allowing Learners to ask questions.
3. After each visit allow Learners to debrief it. Facilitate the debriefing by asking specific questions.

Celebration Time

Share It

1. Ask a Team member to take the lead in sharing reports.
2. Hear reports and testimonies.
3. Complete Evaluation Cards.
4. Complete Participation Cards.
5. Update Visitation Forms with the results of visits.

Home Study Assignments

Home Study Assignments reinforce this session by helping you apply what you have learned.

Your Discipleship Journey

Journaling activities in Your Discipleship Journey are an important part of your development as a Great Commission Christian through FAITH training.

1. Instead of denying the existence of our physical bodies, how are we to view our bodies as Christians? Match the following Scripture references with the correct teachings.

____ 1. Romans 6:12-13
____ 2. Romans 8:23
____ 3. 1 Corinthians 6:13
____ 4. 1 Corinthians 6:19-20
____ 5. 1 Corinthians 15:44
____ 6. Ephesians 5:29
____ 7. Philippians 1:20
____ 8. Philippians 3:21
____ 9. Colossians 3:5
____ 10. 1 Thessalonians 4:3-5

a. As we have a natural body, we also have a spiritual body.
b. We await the redemption of our bodies.
c. Control your body and be holy.
d. Christ will transform our bodies to be like His glorious body.
e. Have courage so that Christ will be exalted in your body.
f. Your body was not meant for sexual immorality but for God.
g. Care for your body.
h. Offer your body parts to God as instruments of righteousness.
i. Your body is a temple of the Holy Spirit. Honor God with your body.
j. Put to death your earthly nature.

2. Christian Science teaches that sin is an illusion, but the Bible teaches that sin is real. Read Psalm 51 and record the source of sin and its effect on David.

Source: ______________________________

Effect: ______________________________

3. In contrast to the Christian Science teaching that humans are divine, the Bible teaches otherwise. Record what the following Scriptures say about our origin and nature.

Psalm 100:3: ______________________________

Genesis 2:7: ____

____

Romans 3:23: ____

____

Psalms 51:5: ____

____

Genesis 6:5: ____

____

Growing as a Life Witness

Growing as a Life Witness reminds you of your responsibility to witness and minister to others during the week.

1. Talk or meet with your accountability partner and share ways you have cultivated a lost person or have witnessed or ministered on occasions other than FAITH visits.
2. Discuss ways you can apply the session 6 content.
3. Pray for lost persons by name and for each other.

Prayer Concerns	Answers to Prayer
______________	______________
______________	______________
______________	______________
______________	______________
______________	______________

Your Weekly Sunday School Leadership Meeting

A FAITH participant is an important member of Sunday School. Encourage Team members who are elected Sunday School workers to attend this weekly meeting. Use this section to record ways your FAITH Team influences the work of your Sunday School class or department. Use the information to report during weekly Sunday School leadership meetings. Identify actions that need to be taken through Sunday School as a result of prayer concerns, needs identified, visits made by the Team, and decisions made by the persons visited. Also identify ways you can disciple others in your Sunday School class or department and in your church.

1. Highlight FAITH needs/reports that affect your class/department or age group. Among persons contacted through FAITH this week, who is likely to attend on Sunday? Ask specific class members to take specific actions to make guests feel welcome. For some ministry visits, is follow-up needed by the class/department?

___

2. Share relevant information about persons who will be the focus of future FAITH assignments so that visits can be especially personal and meaningful. Are some people the focus of continuing cultivation by your FAITH Team? Are additional prospect-discovery activities needed?

___

3. Participate in evaluating last week's Bible-study session and discuss ways Sunday's lesson can involve members and guests in transformational Bible study and discipleship.

___

4. Record prayer requests for your teacher and department director.

___

5. Forgiveness is a significant theme in the gospel and in the FAITH gospel presentation. Is your class/department characterized by a forgiving, loving spirit? List and discuss ways to further cultivate an atmosphere of acceptance and reconciliation.

___

Discipling Your Team Members

This weekly feature suggests actions the Team Leader can take to support Team members, prepare for Team Time, and improve visits. This work is part of the Team Leader's Home Study Assignments. Add any actions suggested by your church's FAITH strategy.

Support Team Members

❑ Contact Team members during the week. Remind them that you are praying for them. Discuss prayer concerns and answers to prayer.

- ❑ This week Learners are memorizing the FAITH presentation through FORGIVENESS. Encourage them to meditate on the significance of forgiveness in their personal lives.
- ❑ Learners have a significant amount of reading this week. Encourage them in this. It is important that they grasp the basic concepts in the reading material.
- ❑ Pray for specific needs and concerns shared by Team members.

Prepare to Lead Team Time

- ❑ Review Team members' Home Study Assignments.
- ❑ Preview Leading Team Time for session 7.

Prepare to Lead Visits

- ❑ Review the FAITH Visit Outline.
- ❑ Be prepared to explain the significance of God's forgiveness.

Link with Sunday School

- ❑ Participate in your weekly Sunday School leadership meeting. Share pertinent information in this meeting, using Your Weekly Sunday School Leadership Meeting (pp. 114–15) and FAITH-visit results.
- ❑ When appropriate, take opportunities during Sunday School lessons to teach the biblical doctrines of sin, humanity, and salvation.

For Further Growth

For Further Growth may include additional reading or activities that will enhance your growth as a disciple and a discipler of others. These assignments are intended to be long-term projects and do not have to be completed during this semester of study.

1. Show compassion to the sick through visitation. Use prayer and Scripture reading to comfort and console those who are suffering because of illness.
2. As you read the Bible, ask the Holy Spirit to teach you so that you can understand the proper meaning of Scripture and to reveal ways Christ can be glorified in your body.
3. Participate in a group study of *Fit 4: A LifeWay Christian Wellness Plan* (LifeWay, 2000).

---

[1]Mary Baker Eddy, *Science and Health with Key to the Scriptures* (Boston: The First Church of Christ, Scientist, 1994), 579.
[2]Ibid., 581.
[3]Ibid., 582.
[4]Ibid., 586.
[5]Ibid., 588.
[6]Ibid., 256.
[7]Ibid., 465.
[8]Ibid., 468.
[9]Ibid., 468.
[10]Ibid., 472.

Answers to matching activity on page 113: 1. h, 2. b, 3. f, 4. i, 5. a, 6. g, 7. e, 8. d, 9. j, 10. c

SESSION 7

The Unity School of Christianity

TAL DAVIS

In this session you will—

CHECK IT by engaging in Team Time activities;

KNOW IT by reviewing content from session 6;

HEAR IT by examining the beliefs of Unity followers and by learning ways to witness to them;

SEE IT by viewing a video segment;

STUDY IT by overviewing Home Study Assignments;

DO IT by leading your Team in making visits;

SHARE IT by celebrating.

NOTES

Leading Team Time

All Team members participate in Team Time. They are primarily responsible for reciting the assigned portion of the FAITH Visit Outline and for discussing other Home Study Assignments.

As you direct this important time of CHECK IT activities with your Team, keep in mind that Learners look to you as a role model, motivator, mentor, and friend. Team Time activities can continue in the car as the Team travels to and from visits.

Lead CHECK IT Activities

✔ *FAITH Visit Outline*

❑ Listen while each Learner recites all of ***Preparation;*** all of *F* and *A*, FORGIVENESS and AVAILABLE; the key words for *I*, *T*, and *H* in ***Presentation;*** and the key outline words in ***Invitation.***

❑ Indicate your approval by signing or initialing Journals. Encourage Learners.

❑ Give Learners an opportunity to practice reciting the portion of the FAITH Visit Outline they have learned to this point.

✔ *Other Home Study Assignments*

❑ Check to see whether Learners listed two or three persons who might have a particular interest in knowing that God's forgiveness is available for them. Discuss how your FAITH Team can impact their lives with the gospel and with ministry. Also discuss the assigned reading material. Encourage Learners to continue writing in Your Journey in Faith (their journaling section).

✔ *Session 6 Debriefing*

❑ Learners are beginning to learn the gospel presentation. God's forgiveness becomes the foundation on which the rest of the gospel is shared. It is vital to understand that God's forgiveness is based on the free gift of grace that God gives because of Jesus' sacrificial death. As part of the gospel presentation, each letter is accompanied by at least one verse.

✔ *Help for Strengthening a Visit*

❑ Many people will not be aware of the free gift of forgiveness that God offers. Some are living with guilt and remorse because of sin in their lives. Others are insensitive to the fact that they are sinners who reject God's love and rebel against Him. The message of forgiveness may be an unfamiliar one to them. Emphasize the importance of showing compassion and understanding with each person being visited. It helps to remember that your Team is not going to be judgmental but to share that real hope exists because God provides forgiveness through faith in Jesus.

- ❑ Have Learners had opportunities to practice parts of the gospel presentation in home visits? When they visit a Sunday School class member or fellow Christian, sometimes practice is a good option.
- ❑ Have Learners seen someone come to know Christ in a home visit?

Notes

____

____

____

____

____

____

____

Actions I Need to Take with Team Members This Week

____

____

____

____

____

____

____

____

____

NOTES

NOTES

A Quick Review

Last week you studied the beliefs of Christian Science. The left column lists statements Christian Scientists believe. Match them with the possible responses a FAITH Team member could make.

___ 1. Mary Baker Eddy has given me the guide to truth.
___ 2. Sin is merely an illusion.
___ 3. God is Mind, Truth, and Love.
___ 4. Angels are God's thoughts passing to humans.
___ 5. The Holy Ghost is the development of eternal life, truth, and love.
___ 6. To correctly understand the Bible, you must not interpret it literally but metaphysically.
___ 7. Only that which reflects God's nature is real.
___ 8. Don't seek medical treatment. Just realize your divinity.
___ 9. Heaven is not an actual place. Death is a transition from the illusion of life to the truth of the immortal spirit.

a. Sin is a reality. All humans are sinners.
b. Everyone must face death. Heaven is a real place that awaits those who put their faith in Jesus Christ.
c. The Holy Spirit is the third person of the Godhead.
d. The Bible is the only authoritative guide for truth and faith.
e. Some of these terms describe God's nature but are not synonyms for who He is.
f. All matter is real. God created matter.
g. The Bible is the inerrant, inspired Word of God, and its meaning is clear and understandable.
h. Sickness is real. We are never commanded in the Bible to reject medical treatment.
i. God created angels for His worship and service. They are real beings who are separate from God.

Mind over Matter

Bowing his head to pray, the pastor said: "You are a person of worth. You are a divine being. You have the power to live and grow in all that life affirms. May you be blessed in all you do. In Christ's name. Amen."

Jack had come to the morning worship service of his friend Dave's church, Unity Life. Jack was a strong Baptist but was interested in other faiths. He had asked Dave where he went to church, having assumed that he was a Christian. Now he was not so sure. The service was unusual, with lots of positive affirmation but little biblical content, and the gospel, as Jack understood it, was not presented.

Later, Dave explained: "We believe in the God within us. Because we all have the spark of divinity, our goal is to enhance it so that we can become all we can in this life and in future lives."

"What about saving people from their sin?" Jack asked. "You know, showing them how to go to heaven when they die."

"Oh, we don't go for that hellfire stuff. We believe that each person can find their own way to God."

"But what about Jesus? Don't you think people must believe in Him?"

"We have the potential to find the Christ Principle in ourselves, just as Jesus did," Dave confidently stated. "He showed us the way."

Jack's visit to Dave's church left him with a lot of questions. So he did some research and found some surprising facts about his friend's faith, the Unity School of Christianity, also known as New Thought.

The Unity School of Christianity traces its beginnings to the late 19th century and the life experiences of a Midwestern-American couple, ____________ and ___________ ________________. In 1886 they attended a lecture on philosophy by E. B. Weeks, a man who had been trained in Christian Science doctrine. Myrtle was convinced that the metaphysical worldview (mind/spirit over matter) Weeks espoused was correct. She began to study for herself and coined a phrase, "I am a child of God and do not inherit ________________."

Charles eventually accepted Myrtle's teaching and claimed that in 1889 he was healed of a lifelong paralysis of his leg. The couple then decided to go into a full-time teaching ministry, spreading their philosophy they called _________ ________________. In 1891 they began publishing a magazine titled *Unity*, which continues to this day as the primary organ for dispensing New Thought doctrine. Today Unity claims that its teachings are biblical but admits that they are based on the metaphysical interpretations of Charles and Myrtle Fillmore.

In 1920 the Fillmores purchased a tract of land in Lee's Summit, Missouri, near Kansas City for establishing Unity Farm. Today on that same 1,300 acres is located ____________ ______________, the movement's international headquarters and publishing house.

Myrtle Fillmore died in 1931 and Charles in 1948 after they had established Unity as a worldwide movement distributing millions of pieces of literature and consisting of more than _______ ministries in _______ countries. The influence of the Unity School of Christianity extends beyond the bounds of its churches and ministries. Through thousands of pieces of Unity literature, radio and television broadcasts, and popular books written by Unity and New Thought adherents, the ideas of Unity have been embraced by many North Americans. Some evangelical Christians, unaware of their unbiblical nature, read ________ magazine, study ____ _______ _______ devotional guide, faithfully listen to "______ _________ _____ _________" radio broadcasts, or make prayer requests to the _________ ________ prayer ministry.

NOTES

NOTES

Unity Beliefs

1. The Bible must be interpreted ____________________.

Like Christian Science, Unity claims that the Bible is its source of authority but only as interpreted metaphysically. Like Mary Baker Eddy, the Fillmores sought to discover the true spiritual meanings of common biblical terms. In their case, New Thought became the normative principle by which to read the Bible.

Unity adherents also honor other spiritual writings and holy books. Some maintain that certain modern writers are divinely inspired, even though their teachings are inconsistent with the Bible. The works of popular American writer Marianne Williamson, for example, are often used in Unity churches for study and edification. Her best-known book, *A Return to Love*, was based on the earlier works of Helen Shucman, who claimed that her volume *A Course in Miracles* was transmitted or verbally channeled to her by Jesus Christ.

2. God is ________________ ____________.

The concept of God in Unity/New Thought is similar in some ways to that of Christian Science. Using impersonal and personal terms, Unity describes God as Divine Mind, Source, or Creator of All. Thus, God is an impersonal, abstract concept that works through people, not a personal being.

The Trinity is also described in both personal and impersonal terms. Unity followers may refer to the Father, Son, and Holy Spirit. However, rather than reflecting the historic concept of one God in three persons, they redefine the names metaphysically. The Father is Principle, or Mind. The Son is Principle Revealed, or Idea. The Holy Spirit is an Executive Agent who carries out plans, or simply the Expression of God.

Unity's concept of God radically differs from the historic Christian perspective that God is the infinite Creator of all that exists. Christians believe that He eternally exists in three persons: Father, Son, and Holy Spirit (see Matt. 28:19; 1 Cor. 12:4-6; 2 Cor. 13:14). The use of impersonal terms obscures the personal nature of God and our ability to know Him.

3. Jesus Christ is the ____________________.

Like other metaphysical cults, Unity/New Thought makes a distinction between the human Jesus and His innate divinity, which they refer to as the Christ Principle, Christ Presence, or Christ Consciousness. Jesus is regarded as different from other people only in that He fully opened Himself to the realization of His Christ Consciousness and thus attained the highest level of atonement, or at-one-ment, with the Divine Mind.

Jesus' birth and death are not regarded so much as historical events but as representations or symbols of spiritual experiences. For example, the virgin birth symbolizes the spiritual birth of the Christ Consciousness in the purified soul of Jesus or anyone else. The blood of Jesus Christ is seen as a metaphor for God's spiritual energy, which purifies the body and conscience. Jesus' death on the cross is thus regarded only in metaphysical terms, symbolizing the eradication of false patterns of thought and atonement (at-one-ment with the pure Mind). Jesus' actual death on the cross is downplayed, as is His physical resurrection.

Again, Unity's view of Jesus differs considerably from that of biblical Christianity. The Bible clearly teaches that God was uniquely in Christ and that there is no distinction between Jesus the man and a Christ Principle. He was both fully man and fully God (God the Son), who existed from all eternity (see John 1:1; Col. 1:15-17; 2:9). He was physically born of a virgin, lived a sinless life, died as a sacrificial atonement on the cross, and physically rose again from the dead (see Luke 24:36-43; John 2:18-22; 1 Cor. 15:1-8).

4. Salvation is realizing your ________________.

The primary goal of Unity adherents is to attain, to the highest extent possible, the realization of their own Christ Consciousness or Christ Principle. This process is undertaken by a lifetime of gradual self-improvement through study of Unity/New Thought concepts and self-affirming prayer.

For a Unity follower, prayer is not the first-person, heart-to-heart conversation of one person to God, as Christians understand it and as Jesus taught it (see Matt. 6:9-13). Rather, it is the utterance of positive affirmations of truth about yourself and the verbal denial of negative thoughts and energy.

Unity Village conducts a 24-hour prayer ministry called Silent Unity. People may call and send requests to a specially dedicated prayer room. Oddly, however, no verbal prayers are uttered. Volunteers sit quietly and meditate but do not actually speak to anyone on the inquirer's behalf. Unity practitioners believe that these methods allow the Mind (the Christ Consciousness within) increasingly to control the totality of the person's thoughts, emotions, behaviors, and physical body. They see this as the route to salvation, which they would identify with health, prosperity, and emotional well-being.

Observers of this aspect of Unity/New Thought doctrine recognize the influence of Eastern philosophy, especially Hinduism. This metaphysical concept of reality resembles the Hindu doctrine of Maya, which is the illusion of all reality, including death and matter.

Christians would respond that the Unity/New Thought concept of salvation ignores several important aspects of the human condition. For example, the notion that we have an innate divine nature contradicts biblical teachings that we are sinners and are separated from God (see

NOTES

NOTES

Rom. 6:23). Thus, whatever spark of divinity that may have once existed in humankind has been extinguished, and we are in need of total regeneration by grace (see Eph. 2:8-9). That has been accomplished by Jesus Christ, the only man who truly had a divine nature, through His death and resurrection.

Our problem is not, as Unity sees it, one of ignorance; rather, it is one of moral guilt or sin. Only Christ's atonement was capable of resolving that problem.

5. Life after death is possible through _________________.

The Fillmores also adopted the doctrine of reincarnation from Hinduism. In that faith, all living beings supposedly experience repeated life-force incarnations, the form of which is determined by the law of Karma. Good Karma ensures a step up; bad Karma, a step down. For followers of Unity, then, heaven and hell are only present states of mind, not actual places or destinies for people after death. At death, which in Unity is euphemistically referred to as a transition or transformation, a person enters a period of soul rest. Eventually, the person is reincarnated in a new bodily form to attain new life experiences and to continue the ascension to higher realms of eternal existence.

The Bible does not support the concept of reincarnation but teaches that we die once and then await the resurrection of the body and the final judgment (see Heb. 9:27).

Witnessing to Unity Followers

Jack's study of his friend's beliefs led him to a sad conclusion: that despite his sincerity and commitment, Dave did not have a saving knowledge of the true Christ. He learned several principles to share Christ effectively and sincerely with Dave and others in Unity/New Thought.

1. Clearly understand historic Christian _______________.

Be sure you have a solid understanding of key doctrinal areas like the nature of God (the Trinity), the nature and work of Jesus Christ, and the biblical way of salvation. Unity followers often use common Christian terms but assign totally different meanings to those words.

2. Help the Unity follower recognize the reality of __________ and ______________.

The follower of Unity believes that his only real problem is lacking a thorough recognition of his divine nature, not that he is a sinner who needs forgiveness. Use the FAITH gospel presentation to show him that sin is real and that he cannot save himself.

3. *Introduce the Unity adherent to the person of ____________ ____________.*

Carefully present the biblical teachings on Christ's life, death and resurrection. Show the person that Jesus was not someone who discovered His Christ Consciousness but that He is the eternal Lord who alone offers the solution for sin. Help him see that real atonement was made by Jesus' death on the cross, where He paid the penalty for our sin. Use the FAITH gospel presentation to show that the person must confess his sin, repent, and receive Jesus as personal Savior and Lord.

4. *Demonstrate your personal relationship with God by ________________ with the Unity follower.*

Praying directly to God will show that you have a personal relationship with Him. To the Unity adherent, prayer is only affirmation. Show that it is communication to God, whom we address as Father.

NOTES

Visitation Time

Do It

1. Pray for sensitivity to the situations the Team will encounter in these visits. Always be open to enrolling someone in Sunday School.
2. During the INTRODUCTION listen for opportunities for you, your Sunday School class, or your church to minister. Be ready to develop a friendship and to offer to meet a need.
3. All Team members should know the FAITH presentation through A is for AVAILABLE. While visiting, invite Team members to support you up to the letter A.

Celebration Time

Share It

1. Ask a Team member to take the lead in sharing the report.
2. Hear reports and testimonies.
3. Complete Evaluation Cards.
4. Complete Participation Cards.
5. Update visitation forms with the results of visits.

Home Study Assignments

Home Study Assignments reinforce this session by helping you apply what you have learned.

Your Discipleship Journey

Journaling activities in Your Discipleship Journey are an important part of your development as a Great Commission Christian through FAITH training.

1. Unity denies the Christian view that Jesus was fully God and fully human. Read the following verses and indicate whether each speaks to Jesus' divinity (*D*) or His humanity (*H*).

____	1. Matthew 4:2	____	9. John 4:6
____	2. Matthew 8:24	____	10. John 8:40
____	3. Matthew 26:38	____	11. John 14:30
____	4. Mark 2:8	____	12. Romans 1:3
____	5. Luke 1:31	____	13. Romans 1:4
____	6. Luke 1:35	____	14. 2 Corinthians 5:21
____	7. Luke 2:52	____	15. Colossians 1:15-17
____	8. Luke 24:39	____	16. 1 Timothy 2:5

2. Unity denies the sinful nature of humanity. How do the following Scriptures describe humankind's fundamental problem?

Psalm 14:1-3: ____

____

____

Jeremiah 17:9: ____

____

____

Romans 3:23: ____

____

____

Romans 5:12: ____

____

____

Romans 7:17-18: ____

____

____

1 John 1:8: ____

____

____

Growing as a Life Witness

Growing as a Life Witness reminds you of your responsibility to witness and minister to others during the week.

1. Talk or meet with your accountability partner and share ways you have cultivated a lost person or have witnessed or ministered on occasions other than FAITH visits.
2. Discuss ways you can apply the session 7 content.
3. Pray for lost persons by name and for each other.

Prayer Concerns	Answers to Prayer
____________________	____________________
____________________	____________________
____________________	____________________
____________________	____________________
____________________	____________________

Your Weekly Sunday School Leadership Meeting

A FAITH participant is an important member of Sunday School. Encourage Team members who are elected Sunday School workers to attend this weekly meeting. Use this section to record ways your FAITH Team influences the work of your Sunday School class or department. Use the information to report during weekly Sunday School leadership meetings. Identify actions that need to be taken through Sunday School as a result of prayer concerns, needs identified, visits made by the Team, and decisions made by the persons visited. Also identify ways you can disciple others in your Sunday School class or department and in your church.

1. Highlight needs that surfaced in FAITH visits and discuss ways these reports affect the ministry of your class/department or age group. Especially discuss ways to keep assimilation of newcomers a priority for the group.

____

____

____

2. How does preparation for Sunday need to consider the varying needs of families/individuals represented by selected FAITH visits?

____

____

____

3. Participate in evaluating last Sunday's Bible-study session. Discuss ways Sunday's lesson can involve members and guests in transformational Bible study and discipleship.

____

____

____

4. Record prayer requests for your teacher and department director.

____

____

____

Discipling Your Team Members

This weekly feature suggests actions the Team Leader can take to support Team members, prepare for Team Time, and improve visits. This work is part of the Team Leader's Home Study Assignments. Add any actions suggested by your church's FAITH strategy.

Support Team Members

- ❑ Contact Team members during the week. Remind them that you are praying for them. Discuss prayer concerns and answers to prayer.
- ❑ Record specific needs and concerns of Team members.

____

____

Prepare to Lead Team Time

- ❑ Review Team members' Home Study Assignments.
- ❑ Preview Leading Team Time for session 8.

Prepare to Lead Visits

- ❑ Review the FAITH Visit Outline.
- ❑ Be prepared to explain the significance of God's forgiveness being available for all but not automatic.

Link with Sunday School

- ❑ Participate in your weekly Sunday School leadership meeting. Share pertinent information in this meeting, using Your Weekly Sunday School Leadership Meeting (pp. 127–28) and FAITH-visit results.
- ❑ Unity beliefs like inner divinity and reincarnation are prevalent in popular culture. Be alert to expressions of these ideas in Sunday School discussions and be ready to counter them with biblical truth.

For Further Growth

For Further Growth may include additional reading or activities that will enhance your growth as a disciple and a discipler of others. These assignments are intended to be long-term projects and do not have to be completed during this semester of study.

1. Participate in a group study of *My Identity in Christ* by C. Gene Wilkes (LifeWay, 1999).
2. Read the FAITH Tip on page 130.

Answers to activity on page 126: 1. H, 2. H, 3. H, 4. D, 5. H, 6. D, 7. H, 8. H, 9. H, 10. D, 11. D, 12. H, 13. D, 14. D, 15. D, 16. D

FAITH TIP

Rightly Dividing the Word

Evangelical Christians reject the loose handling of the Bible by the Unity School of Christianity, Christian Science, and other cults. The Bible must be interpreted according to sound principles of interpretation. Harold Freeman, a professor of preaching at Southwestern Baptist Theological Seminary, teaches his students that before they deliver a message from God's Word, they must make sure they have correctly analyzed each passage, using the following principles of interpretation.

1. A *passage must be interpreted in light of the author's words as understood in the time they were written.*
Carefully study the definitions of biblical terms. Use reliable Bible translations that are faithful to the original meanings of the biblical languages.

2. A *passage must be interpreted in light of its type of literature.*
Not all books of the Bible are the same type of literature. Some are historical, like 1 and 2 Kings and Acts; some are poetic, like Psalms; some are letters, like Paul's epistles; and some are apocalyptic, like Revelation. The kind of literature often affects how the book was intended to be understood.

3. A *passage must be interpreted in light of its historical background.*
The books of the Bible were not written in historical or cultural vacuums. The events of their time and their position in the history of revelation often shed light on the author's specific meanings.

4. A *passage must be interpreted in light of its context.*
Isolated Bible passages can be quoted to justify almost anything. To be interpreted correctly, each passage must be considered in relationship to the other passages surrounding it and in relationship to the totality of the book in which it appears.

5. A *passage must be interpreted in light of Jesus Christ.*
Jesus is the Lord of Scripture and its central character. Thus, no valid understanding of the Bible is possible without considering His ultimate revelation of God's nature.

6. A *passage must be interpreted in light of the Holy Spirit's illumination of its meaning.*
Just as the Holy Spirit inspired the biblical authors to write God's Word, He also helps us comprehend its meaning and apply it to our lives.

SESSION 8

The Unitarian-Universalist Association of Churches

CKY CARRIGAN

In this session you will—

Check It by engaging in Team Time activities;

Know It by reviewing content from session 7;

Hear It by examining the beliefs of Unitarian-Universalists and by learning ways to witness to them;

Say It by practicing the ***Invitation*** portion of the FAITH Visit Outline;

Study It by overviewing Home Study Assignments;

Do It by leading your Team in making visits;

Share It by celebrating.

NOTES

Leading Team Time

All Team members participate in Team Time. They are primarily responsible for reciting the assigned portion of the FAITH Visit Outline and for discussing other Home Study Assignments.

As you direct this important time of CHECK IT activities with your Team, keep in mind that Learners look to you as a role model, motivator, mentor, and friend. Team Time activities can continue in the car as the Team travels to and from visits.

Lead CHECK IT Activities

✔ *FAITH Visit Outline*

- ❑ Listen while each Learner recites all of ***Preparation***; all of the outline points for the letters *F* (FORGIVENESS), *A* (AVAILABLE), and *I* (IMPOSSIBLE); key words for the letters *T* (TURN) and *H* (HEAVEN); and key words for the ***Invitation***.
- ❑ Indicate your approval by signing or initialing Journals. Encourage Learners.
- ❑ Provide an opportunity for Learners to practice reciting the portions of the FAITH Visit Outline they have learned to this point.

✔ *Session 7 Debriefing/Other Home Study Assignments*

- ❑ God's forgiveness is available for everyone. Even the most hardened criminal or the most unloving person is the target of God's love and forgiveness. John 3:16 reminds us of the scope of God's love and forgiveness ("God so loved the world … that whoever"). This same verse introduces us to the fact that God's forgiveness is not automatic ("whoever believes in Him"). This passage also focuses on the consequences of not accepting God's forgiveness ("perish"). It is important to remember that many persons you visit will not understand that God's forgiveness is available to them, but it is not automatic.

✔ *Help for Strengthening a Visit*

- ❑ Many persons you seek to visit will indicate that they do not have much time for a lengthy visit. Some persons may not allow your Team to enter the house because of time or personal constraints. Your primary jobs are to seek to build relationships with people and to introduce them to the idea of enrolling in your Sunday School class or department. Indeed, you look for opportunities to ask the Key Question, hear responses, and share the FAITH gospel presentation. But also look for opportunities to build bridges with the person through Sunday School enrollment. God may be using you to plant a seed. He may also be using you and your Team members to nurture relationships on His behalf and to prepare the harvest. Be sensitive to opportunities God is providing for you in the midst of visits.

Notes

Actions I Need to Take with Team Members This Week

NOTES

NOTES

A Quick Review

Last week you examined the beliefs of New Thought and the Unity School of Christianity. Review by answering the following questions T for *true* or F for *false*. If the statement is false, write in the blank the word or words that would make the statement true.

___ 1. New Thought believes that God is an impersonal, abstract concept that works through people.

____

___ 2. Like Christian Scientists, Unity adherents insist on interpreting the Bible literally.

____

___ 3. Unity's concept of the Trinity is the same as the historic Christian teaching.

____

___ 4. Unity teaches that Jesus Christ is distinct from the Christ Principle or Christ Consciousness.

____

___ 5. Unity teaches that Jesus' birth and death are not significant as historical facts but merely as symbols of spiritual experience.

____

___ 6. The primary goal of a follower of Unity is to receive salvation and sanctification by grace.

____

___ 7. Unity teaches that prayer is the utterance of positive affirmations of truth about yourself and the verbal denial of negative thoughts and energy.

____

___ 8. Unity teaches that at death, a person enters God's presence.

____

___ 9. Unity sees humanity's primary spiritual problem as sin.

____

Check the biblical teachings that would be the most helpful in effectively reaching a person involved in Unity/New Thought.

❑ 1. The deity of Christ
❑ 2. The Ten Commandments
❑ 3. The nature of God
❑ 4. The biblical way of salvation
❑ 5. Christ's intent for marriage
❑ 6. Christian stewardship
❑ 7. The proper view of humankind

The Religion of Tolerance

NOTES

"I believe that all religions have some truth in them," the woman said. "The important thing is that we try to live good lives and work for justice and peace for all people." Steve had just shared the FAITH gospel presentation with Janice, a middle-aged college professor who had recently moved to town. She had listened politely but was now responding to what Steve had said. She continued, "And no, I don't believe that Jesus was divine, nor am I really sure what God is like."

"Do you believe the Bible?" Steve asked.

"It has some good ideas, but it is a human book that is full of errors. Also, I think it is sexist."

Steve was stunned. "But I thought you said you are a member of a church."

"Every week I attend the Unitarian-Universalist Fellowship on campus. Dr. Mary Smith is our pastor. Are you familiar with our church?" she asked.

"Not really," Steve said.

Unitarian-Universalism is another growing cult whose followers desperately need a life-changing relationship with Jesus Christ. Individual members of the Unitarian-Universalist Association of Churches are a loose confederation of self-described heretics.[1] They are a very liberal religion that champions the cause of extreme religious ________________. As a matter of fact, they are so liberal that only 9.5 percent of Unitarian-Universalists describe themselves as Christians.[2] Members of Unitarian-Universalist Association churches describe their theological perspectives in various ways. A recent internal Unitarian-Universalist Association survey of more than eight thousand members showed that around 46 percent consider their theological perspective to be humanism, while 19 percent are earth-centered. Mere theism describes 13 percent of them, and 6 percent of them prefer mysticism. Nearly 4 percent of Unitarian-Universalist Association members claim Buddhism, and about 1 percent claim Judaism as their theological perspective. About 13 percent consider their theological perspective to be outside the scope of all these categories.[3]

The total membership of the Unitarian-Universalist Association has increased by about ________________ since 1982.[4] The vast majority of its present membership of 213,000 does not have a Unitarian-Universalist Association background.[5] This increase in nonbiological growth can be attributed to three primary causes.

1. Baby Boomers were looking for ____________ ________________ for their children outside a particular theological context.
2. Women were looking for a church that promotes women's _________. About half of Unitarian-Universalist Association clergy are women.

NOTES

3. Gays, lesbians, bisexuals, and transgender people are generally attracted to the Unitarian-Universalist Association because it is inclusive on issues of ______________ ______________________.[6] The Unitarian-Universalist Association performs same-sex marriages.

Unitarian-Universalist Beliefs

The vast diversity among Unitarian-Universalist Association churches, both within each congregation and between congregations, makes it virtually impossible to summarize Unitarian-Universalist doctrines. However, a look at the Unitarian-Universalist Association Covenant provides a general understanding of Unitarian-Universalist beliefs. In addition, humanism and neopaganism represent two strains of religious thought embraced by many Unitarian-Universalist members.

The Unitarian-Universalist Association ______________________

All Unitarian-Universalist Association churches have adopted seven key principles that express a broad consensus of beliefs about religion in general. The member congregations covenant with one another to affirm and promote the following values and goals.

1. The inherent __worth__ and __dignity__ of every person
2. __________, __________, and ______________ in human relations
3. ______________________ of one another and encouragement to ______________ ______________
4. A free and responsible search for __truth__ and __meaning__
5. The right of ______________________ and the use of the ______________ process in congregations and in society at large
6. The goal of world community with __peace__, __liberty__, and __justice__ for all
7. Respect for the interdependent __web__ of all existence[7]

The Unitarian-Universalist Association believes that it is a living religious tradition that draws from many sources, including the following.

1. The direct experience of transcendent mystery and wonder
2. The words and deeds of prophetic women and men
3. Wisdom from the world's religions
4. Jewish and Christian teachings
5. Humanist teachings
6. Spiritual teachings of earth-centered traditions[8]

The Role of Secular ______________________

About two-thirds of Unitarian-Universalist Association members are either secular humanists or neopagans (earth/nature-centered religion).

Secular humanism is "any set of beliefs that promotes human values without specific allusion to religious doctrines."[9] Humanism traces its roots to China and classical Greece and Rome. Its growth was propelled by the Enlightenment and the scientific revolution of the modern world. All secular humanists are _atheists_, but all atheists are not necessarily secular humanists. Worldviews that merely reject God's existence are not necessarily the same as the humanist worldview. To be a humanist, a person must be committed to the positive belief in the possibilities of __________ __________ and to the values central to it.[10] For example, a nihilistic atheist is not a humanist, because he is not optimistic about humanity's future. Some famous humanists include John Dewey, an American philosopher and education reformer; Isaac Asimov, a science-fiction writer and religion critic; Joseph Fletcher, the father of situation ethics; Betty Friedan, the founder of the National Organization for Women; and B. F. Skinner, the founder of behavioral psychology.

Humanism is opposed to the ______________ and does not believe in supernatural acts. It regards the universe as __________ and __________.[11] It affirms the atheistic evolution of all things, including humanity. Humanism also rejects any supernatural grounds for an ethical system[12] and rejects any possibility of life after death.[13]

Humanists consider human beings a highly evolved animal that is the measure of all things. Humanity's basic problems are superstition and ignorance, and the chief solutions for their problems are reason and technology. Religion is seen as superstition mixed with moral teachings, and Jesus Christ, if He existed at all, was merely a moral teacher.[14]

In contrast, genuine Christianity affirms the existence of a personal, moral God. It affirms God's supernatural acts in the creation of the universe and in other historic events like His incarnation in Christ and Christ's bodily resurrection. People were created in God's image but are now fallen, incapable of solving their chief problem—sin. The answer to human problems is faith alone in Christ Jesus alone because of grace alone from God. The ethical system of genuine Christianity is based on biblical revelation from a moral God. Genuine Christianity also affirms life after death and believes that Jesus Christ is the eternal Son of God, God incarnate, and unique Savior and Lord.

The Influence of ________________

Nearly one in five Unitarian-Universalists describes herself as an advocate of an earth-centered or nature-based religion. Other common terms for this kind of religion are paganism, the new paganism, or neopaganism. Witchcraft is also associated with paganism. Paganism is so prominent in the Unitarian-Universalist Association that an official organization of pagans is affiliated with the association. The Covenant of Unitarian-Universalist Pagans exists to promote pagan and earth-centered spirituality in the Unitarian-Universalist Association.[15]

NOTES

NOTES

Neopaganism and witchcraft are very diverse religious movements with a variety of fluid beliefs and practices, so the following descriptions may not precisely fit all persons who consider themselves to be earth-centered or nature-based. Also, witches and neopagans are not precisely the same groups, but as a general rule, they both worship the ________ ________ ________ in some form.

The Great Mother Goddess is often seen in three aspects as Maiden (Kore); Mother (Diana); and Crone, or Old Woman (Hecate). For some, the Great Mother Goddess also has a consort called the Horned God (Pan). In the Middle Ages, Christians identified Pan as the devil himself, but neopagans and witches strongly deny that they worship the devil of Christianity. Some also recognize an entire pantheon of deities who may manifest themselves at certain seasonal festivals.[16]

Magic, usually spelled ________ in this context, is a common practice among neopagans and witches. Magick is "the art of causing change through the use of the cosmic power that is believed to underlay [sic] the universe."[17] Magick can be used to change matters of the mundane world, like health, work conditions, or romance, as well as more important things.

The pagan community generally sees itself as devoted to good rather than evil. It generally values ________ and natural things and affiliates with ecological causes, natural foods and remedies, and animal protection. Extreme feminism, homosexuality, and goddess worship are also prominent themes in witchcraft and neopaganism.[18]

Christians believe that only God is worthy of worship (see Ex. 20:2-3; Deut. 6:13; Mark 12:30). The Bible condemns witchcraft and magic (see Lev. 19:26,31; Deut. 18:10-11; 2 Chron. 33:6), the worship of other gods or goddesses (see Ex. 20:3; 1 Kings 11:4-5), and the worship of nature (see Rom. 1:21-25). The Bible also affirms the reality of Satan and his evil influence (see Zech. 3:2; Matt. 4:1-11; Luke 6:45).[19]

Witnessing to Unitarian-Universalists

1. Discover exactly what the Unitarian-Universalist Believes.

Be patient and take time to find out exactly what individual Unitarian-Universalists believe before charting a particular course of evangelistic action. They may be atheistic or theistic. They may have a Christian or Jewish background. They might be Wiccan or Buddhist. You cannot challenge a set of beliefs unknown to you, and it is very difficult to advance someone's thinking if you do not know where to begin.

2. Be especially gentle, humble, **and** non judgemental.

A confrontational approach will almost certainly be met with a great deal of resistance. Unitarian-Universalists highly value religious diversity. Carefully listen to their beliefs, look for common ground, and gently suggest the Christian alternative. Make sure to communicate clearly that they are free to reject your worldview. You may want to soften your discussion by sprinkling your conversation with phrases like "It seems to me," "Perhaps," or "Have you ever considered?" This approach does not compromise your conviction but subtly communicates that you value them as persons, their opinions, and their search for truth.

3. Be prepared to use reason.

Unitarian-Universalists are generally well educated or at least well read. They value reason. They will not be easily moved from their positions merely on the basis of your appeal to an unsubstantiated faith. Emphasize the reasonable aspects of Christian truths. Demonstrate that Christianity is a reasonable faith, in fact, the most reasonable faith. Emphasize the host of rational and empirical evidence that supports the claims of Christianity.

4. Be conscious of issues of equality.

Be careful not to create unnecessary stumbling blocks. Unitarian-Universalists highly value racial and gender equality. Any subtle signs of racial or gender superiority will be met with extreme resistance. Emphasize the biblical model of racial and gender equality in God's universal family (see Gal. 3:28).

5. Be sensitive to enviornmental **issues.**

Be careful not to offend unnecessarily the environmental sensibilities of Unitarian-Universalists. They are generally very environmentally conscious and nature friendly. Emphasize the biblical model of responsibly caring for God's creation (see Gen. 1:28).

6. Present arguments for God's existance.

Secular humanists are basically atheists who deny the existence of a personal, living God. Therefore, arguments for God's existence prepare the Unitarian-Universalist's heart for evangelism. It is very difficult to apply John 3:16 to the life of someone who rejects the very existence of a God who loves the world so much that He sacrificed His only begotten Son for their sin.

Several compelling arguments can be made for God's existence. The cosmological argument establishes evidence for God's existence on the basis of the presence of the universe. Because there is a universe, then there must have been a universe maker, God. The teleological argument

NOTES

NOTES

presents evidence for God on the basis of the design of the universe. Because the universe appears to have been designed with order and purpose, then there must have been a universe designer, God.

7. *Emphasize the danger of* idolatry.

Most Unitarian-Universalist Association pagans will probably not be convinced of their errors by an appeal to Scripture, but some of them have a Christian background and may be positively influenced by the Bible's prohibition against their beliefs and practices. Other approaches, however, might initially be more helpful for witnessing to witches and neopagans associated with the Unitarian-Universalist Association. Witches and pagans do not actually acknowledge the existence of Satan, but because they are essentially idolaters, Satan is still their master. Pagans may not admit it, but they live in a state of fear. Whatever magickal forces are available to them to manipulate their world are also available to others. Satan is a tempter, accuser, devourer, and deceiver. He will exact his wages from all idolaters sooner or later, and when he does, the Christian alternative will be the only safe place of refuge from Satan's oppression.

Therefore, witnessing to witches and neopagans should be seen as seed sowing in soil that may not presently be fertile but may become fertile at some point in the future. Everything pagans are searching for can be found only in Christ. Sincerely love your pagan friends. Tactfully show them that the only way to an abundant life is through Christ. Then wait for Satan to let them down. He will. When he does, be there to reinforce the love and truth of Christ as you share the FAITH gospel presentation.

8. *Persistently point the way to* God.

You have seen that Unitarian-Universalists are a very diverse lot. They are searching for meaning and value in life outside the scope of Christianity altogether. They reject Christianity primarily on the basis of its strict moral code and its supernatural orientation. They are not very tolerant of biblical, evangelistic Christianity, so do not expect an open invitation to your message.

By any standard, Unitarian-Universalists are a hard people to win to Jesus, but with God all things are possible (see Matt. 19:26). Therefore, pray very hard, prepare very hard, persuade very hard, and persevere to the end with your Unitarian-Universalist friends. Never give up. Someday they may become disillusioned with their Christless program. Someday they may realize that there can be no effective moral code without a supreme code giver. Someday they may recognize the futility and meaninglessness of a Godless world. On that someday you can be there and be ready to lead them to God, using the FAITH gospel presentation.

Visitation Time

Do It

1. Be a good listener. You earn the right to share the good news by listening to the stories of the persons you visit. They may share with you some things that make you uncomfortable or may raise some questions you would rather not address—but listen. It is not necessary to be able to answer all of their questions, but it is necessary to care.
2. Are Team members becoming increasingly comfortable with making adjustments as the visit merits? Although your Team should plan in advance what is to happen and what responsibilities the various Team members will assume, the best visit is one in which visitors adjust to the needs of the situation.
3. Team Leader, as you make changes in the FAITH Visit Outline, be sure to explain why. Affirm your Team Learners as they show increasing confidence and ease in sharing their testimonies and in using the FAITH Visit Outline.
4. At the Team Leader's cue, Learners should be able to share FORGIVENESS and AVAILABLE.

Celebration Time

Share It

1. Ask a Team Learner to take the lead in sharing your Team's report.
2. Hear reports and testimonies.
3. Complete Evaluation Cards.
4. Complete Participation Cards.
5. Update visitation forms with the results of visits.

NOTES

Home Study Assignments

Home Study Assignments reinforce this session by helping you apply what you have learned.

Your Discipleship Journey

Journaling activities in Your Discipleship Journey are an important part of your development as a Great Commission Christian through FAITH training.

1. Unitarian-Universalists value tolerance for a variety of religious beliefs. How tolerant is the Bible in regard to false teaching? Read and summarize the following passages.

   Galatians 1:6-8: ______________________________

   ____

   2 Peter 2:15-19: ______________________________

   ____

   ____

   2 John 7-11: ______________________________

   ____

   ____

2. With a proper understanding of the Christian view of environmental stewardship, you may be able to use your concern for the environment to establish a dialogue with a Unitarian-Universalist. Read the following Scriptures. Then rewrite the incorrectly worded statements to correctly summarize the scriptural teachings about the environment.

   Genesis 1:26: People are to worship the fish, birds, and animals.

   ____

   Genesis 1:27: God created man and woman to be essentially the same as the other animals.

   ____

Genesis 1:28: People exist to serve the fish, birds, and animals.

____

Genesis 1:29-30: God warned us not to use His creation for our food supply.

____

Psalm 104:5-30: Nature functions without God's involvement.

____

Psalm 147:15-18: Nature is out of control.

____

3. Paul's sermon in Acts 17:22-31 includes references to secular Greek poets, popular religions, and contemporary philosophy. Record references from this passage that speak to the following beliefs of Unitarian-Universalists.

   A desire to be religious and to find the truth: ______________

   A belief in human potential and achievement: ______________

   Neopaganistic worship of earth deities and nature: ______________

Growing as a Life Witness

Growing as a Life Witness reminds you of your responsibility to witness and minister to others during the week.

1. Talk or meet with your accountability partner and share ways you have cultivated a lost person or have witnessed or ministered on occasions other than FAITH visits.
2. Discuss ways you can apply the session 8 content.
3. Pray for lost persons by name and for each other.

Prayer Concerns	Answers to Prayer
______________	______________
______________	______________
______________	______________
______________	______________

Your Weekly Sunday School Leadership Meeting

A FAITH participant is an important member of Sunday School. Encourage Team members who are elected Sunday School workers to attend this weekly meeting. Use this section to record ways your FAITH Team influences the work of your Sunday School class or department. Use the information to report during weekly Sunday School leadership meetings. Identify actions that need to be taken through Sunday School as a result of prayer concerns, needs identified, visits made by the Team, and decisions made by the persons visited. Also identify ways you can disciple others in your Sunday School class or department and in your church.

1. Highlight FAITH needs/reports that affect your class/department or age group.

____

____

2. In what ways does the reality that people are lost without Christ permeate your class/department? For example, is a clear explanation of the gospel periodically given in class? Is the teacher consistently ready to give an invitation during class if the session and the Holy Spirit so lead? Is the class a praying and caring body that reaches out to the lost?

____

____

____

3. Participate in evaluating last week's session and discuss ways Sunday's Bible-study lesson can involve members and guests in transformational Bible study and discipleship.

____

____

____

4. Pray for teacher(s) and department director(s).

____

____

Discipling Your Team Members

This weekly feature suggests actions the Team Leader can take to support Team members, prepare for Team Time, and improve visits. This work is part of the Team Leader's Home Study Assignments. Add any actions suggested by your church's FAITH strategy.

Support Team Members

- ❑ Contact Team members during the week. Remind them that you are praying for them. Discuss prayer concerns and answers to prayer.
- ❑ Record specific needs and concerns of Team members.

____

____

Prepare to Lead Team Time

- ❑ Review Team members' Home Study Assignments.
- ❑ Preview Leading Team Time for session 9.

Prepare to Lead Visits

- ❑ Review the FAITH Visit Outline.
- ❑ Be prepared to explain the significance of God's forgiveness being available for all but not automatic.

Link with Sunday School

- ❑ Participate in your weekly Sunday School leadership meeting. Share pertinent information in this meeting, using Your Weekly Sunday School Leadership Meeting (p. 144) and FAITH-visit results.
- ❑ Encourage Sunday School teachers to periodically call on Team members to share reports from their FAITH experiences. Encourage your Team members to give periodic updates in your class.
- ❑ Look for ways Sunday School lessons can refute Unitarian-Universalist beliefs that have become part of our culture, such as religious tolerance, humanism, and nature worship.

For Further Growth

For Further Growth may include additional reading or activities that will enhance your growth as a disciple and a discipler of others. These assignments are intended to be long-term projects and do not have to be completed during this semester of study.

1. Participate in a group study *of How Now Shall We Live?* by Chuck Colson and Nancy Pearcey (LifeWay, 2000).
2. Read a book that presents a Christian challenge to atheism, such as *Mere Christianity* by C. S. Lewis (Broadman & Holman, 2000), *Reasonable Faith: Christian Truth and Apologetics* by William Lane Craig (Crossway, 1994),

Scaling the Secular City: A Defense of Christianity by J. P. Moreland (Baker, 1987), *Christian Apologetics* by Norman L. Geisler (Baker, 1988), or *Handbook of Christian Apologetics: Hundreds of Answers to Crucial Questions* by Peter Kreeft and Ronald K. Tacelli (Intervarsity, 1994).

3. Get involved in your community to foster the Christian view of environmental stewardship.
4. Begin a friendship with an unchurched secular person and discover ways to minister and witness to him or her.
5. Read the FAITH Tip on page 147.

---

[1]Mark W. Harris, "Unitarian-Universalist Origins: Our Historic Faith," <*http://www.uua.org/info/origins.html*> (20 July 2000).

[2]<*http://www.uua.org/promise/results.html*>, "The 1997 Unitarian-Universalist Needs and Aspirations Survey" (20 July 2000).

[3]Ibid.

[4]Beth Krodel, "Members like little dogma," *Detroit Free Press*, <*http://www.freep.com/news/religion/nuni3.htm*> (22 January 2000).

[5]Ibid.

[6]Ibid.

[7]<*http://www.uua.org/principles.html*>, "Unitarian-Universalist Association Principles and Purposes" (20 July 2000).

[8]Ibid.

[9]*Random House Webster's Dictionary and Thesaurus, College Edition*, 1992, s.v. "secular humanism."

[10]*Humanist Manifesto I & II*, <*http://www.infidels.org/org/aha/documents/manifesto1.html*> and <*http://www.infidels.org/org/aha/documents/manifesto2.html*> (15 February 2000).

[11]Ibid.

[12]Ibid.

[13]Ibid.

[14]Adapted from Douglas R. Groothius, *Unmasking the New Age* (Downers Grove: InterVarsity, 1986), 167.

[15]<*http://www.cuups.org/html/vision.html*>, "Covenant of Unitarian-Universalist Pagans" (20 July 2000).

[16]J. Gordon Melton, *Encyclopedic Handbook of Cults in America, Revised and Updated Edition* (New York: Garland, 1992), 326.

[17]Ibid.

[18]Ibid.

[19]Rick Branch, "WatchMan Fellowship Profile—Witchcraft/Wicca," *The Watchman Expositor*, <*http://watchman.org/witchpro.htm*> (20 July 2000).

FAITH TIP

Are All Religions Right?

"All religions are basically the same. They just have minor differences." "We should never tell someone their faith is wrong. It all depends on how they were reared." "I don't think doctrine matters. What counts is that we all get along." "Jesus was a great man, just like Buddha, Muhammad, Confucius, or Socrates."

Sound familiar? These are common objections you might hear while sharing Christ with people in modern North America. Most people today feel that it is intolerant or improper to criticize or question someone else's religious beliefs. But is it true that all religions are true and the same? Was Jesus just one of many great religious teachers? Is there no such thing as absolute truth?

As Christians we must answer that there is a difference. That difference is Jesus Christ Himself. We must reply, without apology, that Jesus is unique. Here are several ways the Bible teaches that no other man in all history was like Him.

1. *No other religious leader is eternal as Jesus is.*

John 1 explains that "the Word [Jesus] was with God, and the Word was God" (v. 1). We are told that "all things came into being through Him, and apart from Him nothing came into being that has come into being" (v. 3). Jesus Christ was and always has been God (see Col. 1:15-17). No other man who has ever lived can claim that eternal origin.

2. *No other religious leader entered the world as Jesus did.*

Of all the great leaders of history and religions, only Jesus was born to a virgin and was conceived by the Holy Spirit (see Matt. 1:18-23; Luke 1:34-38).

3. *No other religious leader lived a sinless life as Jesus did.*

Although most other religious leaders taught high moral principles, none of them could claim to be sinless. Only Jesus was without the taint of sin and was totally pure (see 2 Cor. 5:21; Heb. 4:15).

4. *No other religious leader died for our sins as Jesus did.*

Jesus' death on the cross was an atonement for humankind's sin (see Rom. 8:3; Gal. 1:4). Although He was without sin, He willingly gave Himself to save us from our sin (see John 10:18; 15:13).

5. *No other religious leader rose from the dead as Jesus did.*

Other leaders may have founded religions and proclaimed remarkable messages, but only Jesus demonstrated the truth of His message by coming back from the dead. Christ's resurrection defined the truthfulness of who Jesus was, is, and always will be. No other faith or philosophy can point to such an event as the final proof of its reality (see 1 Cor. 15:1-8).

FAITH AT WORK

I had been diligently praying for my mother to accept Christ for about 15 years. Many of my friends and prayer partners had also been praying. Then in September 1999 I was diagnosed with a brain tumor. At first we were very anxious, spending long, sleepless nights asking questions and praying. But then we saw God working in many ways in many lives, and we began to take courage.

My wife, Cindy, contacted our church and asked if a FAITH Team would come to our house on the Tuesday night before my Wednesday-morning surgery. My mother and her husband, Elmer, were staying with us for the surgery. When I told her that a few church members were going to come by to pray with us, I expected her to go upstairs to her room. But she didn't. When the doorbell rang that evening, it was not one but four FAITH Teams. After introductions Glenn, a FAITH Team Leader, asked Cindy and me to sit in chairs while the FAITH Teams encircled us. Then each person began to pray, one after another. My mother and Elmer were sitting at our kitchen table watching, listening, and praying. It was one of the most moving experiences of God I have ever been a part of. The Holy Spirit's presence was so evident that it seemed that we could reach out and touch Him. The outpouring of prayer and support overwhelmed my family, giving us great confidence and encouragement.

Then the true miracle occurred. Glenn explained the purpose of FAITH Teams. Because they had not made evangelistic visits that night, Glenn asked if a Team Learner could practice the presentation with my mother. Truly God was moving in a mighty way. I rejoiced and prayed with expectation as the FAITH Team Learner presented the plan of salvation to my mother. But after the presentation she still didn't seem to understand.

While recovering at home after my surgery, I was talking with my mother about the night the FAITH Teams came to pray. She said: "I know you have been worried for a long time about my going to heaven, so I want you to know that on that Tuesday night, Elmer and I got out of bed and asked the Lord to come into our hearts. I think you will see a difference in my life."

I was overcome with joy. My prayers had been answered. It had taken almost everything, but it was worth it. I now know I will see my mom in heaven someday. I will be eternally grateful for the members of those FAITH Teams who gave up their Tuesday night to come to my house. None of them knew me; I was one of six thousand church members. They came for a ministry visit but were used by God to help answer years of prayer by presenting the gospel to my mother and leading her to eternal life. Thank you, FAITH Teams.

Dan Tanner
Metropolitan Baptist Church
Houston, Texas

SESSION 9

The Unification Church

TAL DAVIS

In this session you will—

CHECK IT by engaging in Team Time activities;

KNOW IT by reviewing content from session 8;

HEAR IT by examining the beliefs of Unification Church followers and by learning ways to witness to them;

SEE IT by viewing a video segment;

STUDY IT by overviewing Home Study Assignments;

DO IT by leading your Team in making visits;

SHARE IT by celebrating.

NOTES

Leading Team Time

All Team members participate in Team Time. They are primarily responsible for reciting the assigned portion of the FAITH Visit Outline and for discussing other Home Study Assignments.

As you direct this important time of CHECK IT activities with your Team, keep in mind that Learners look to you as a role model, motivator, mentor, and friend. Team Time activities can continue in the car as the Team travels to and from visits.

Lead CHECK IT Activities

✔ *FAITH Visit Outline*

- ❑ Listen while each Learner recites the FAITH Visit Outline: all of ***Preparation*** and all of ***Presentation***, adding *T* is for TURN to the gospel presentation, plus the key words for ***Invitation***. Be aware of time limits if two Learners are sharing; someone may need to recite in the car going to and from visits.
- ❑ Initial each Learner's work in his or her Journal.
- ❑ Practice other parts of the outline as time allows.

✔ *Other Home Study Assignments*

- ❑ Emphasize the importance of involving the Sunday School class in FAITH, whether by prayer support, in training, or in follow-up. Explain that in this session Sunday School will be the focus of building bridges to people.
- ❑ Ask: Do class/department members who are not participating in FAITH still see themselves as a part of this ministry? In what ways? Are you sharing prayer needs and results of visits with fellow class members? Are they praying for you and for people you and your Team will visit? Are your class, department, and church growing spiritually and numerically?
- ❑ Home Study Assignments and memorization are reaching their maximum. Make a special effort during the week to personally encourage Learners, especially those who may have fallen behind in memory work or home study.

✔ *Session 8 Debriefing*

- ❑ Some important theological truths are communicated in this part of the gospel presentation. Are Learners at ease and confident in sharing about both God's love and His justice? About their own sinfulness?
- ❑ Ask Learners to recall from their personal experience—
  - their need to be saved;
  - their inability to save themselves;

- God's saving initiative in their lives (their life-changing experience). Doing so will help them continue to identify with the people they visit. All of us are sinners in need of God's grace. Some of us have been fortunate enough to receive and accept it, while others still need to know about God's forgiveness. Letting them know is a big part of what FAITH is all about.

❑ If your group needs it, overview ways to respond to a works answer to the Key Question.

✔ *Help for Strengthening a Visit*

❑ Have most Team members seen someone accept Christ during a home visit by this time? If so, remind Team members of how such a visit should motivate them to continue in their efforts. If not, remind Team members that God is still working, even if they have not seen specific desired results.

❑ Call on the Assistant Team Leader, if your Team has one, to encourage other Team members; he or she may have had experiences in earlier FAITH training that can motivate others.

❑ As important as practice is, it is not the same as sharing the gospel in a home visit. Acknowledge that even as you encourage your Team to practice with one another and with other believers, as the opportunity allows.

Notes

____

____

____

____

Actions I Need to Take with Team Members This Week

____

____

____

____

NOTES

NOTES

A Quick Review

Last week you explored beliefs of the Unitarian-Universalist Association of Churches. Mark the following statements T for *true* or F for *false*.

___ 1. All secular humanists are atheists, but all atheists are not necessarily secular humanists.
___ 2. To be a humanist, a person must be committed to the positive belief in the possibilities of human progress.
___ 3. Humanism places great emphasis on the supernatural.
___ 4. Humanism rejects any possibility of life after death.
___ 5. Secular humanists promote the existence of a personal, living God.
___6. Earth-centered or nature-based religion includes paganism, neopaganism, and witchcraft.
___ 7. Magick is a common practice among neopagans and witches.
___ 8. Neopagans generally admit that they worship the devil of Christianity.

Check the correct guidelines for witnessing to Unitarian-Universalists.

❑ 1. Appeal to your own experience, because Unitarian-Universalists heavily rely on experience.
❑ 2. Discover exactly what the Unitarian-Universalist believes.
❑ 3. Be especially gentle, humble, and nonjudgmental.
❑ 4. Be prepared to use reason.
❑ 5. Be vague in your use of Scripture so that you don't offend them.
❑ 6. Be conscious of issues of equality.
❑ 7. Be sensitive to environmental issues.
❑ 8. Summarize what Unitarian-Universalists are supposed to believe.
❑ 9. Present arguments for God's existence.
❑ 10. Emphasize the danger of idolatry.
❑ 11. Persistently point the way to God.

Claims of a New Messiah

"720,000 to Take Part in Mass Wedding." This headline stunned the world in 1995, when it was announced that Reverend Sun Myung Moon, the founder of the South Korean-based Unification Church, would officiate in the largest mass wedding ceremony in history. Using satellite technology, Moon accomplished the feat by simultaneously blessing 360,000 couples in 545 different venues in more than one hundred countries. Most couples paid several thousand dollars each to receive the blessing from the man they refer to as the True Father and the Lord of the Second Advent.

Most North Americans are vaguely familiar with Moon and his church, the Unification Church. Who is this man who marries thousands of people at one time and claims to be the Lord of the Completed Testament age? Where did he come from? Who are his followers? What are his goals and doctrines? Most importantly, is his movement an authentic Christian church? If not, then how do we share the true Christ with men and women who have committed their lives to Moon as their messiah?

On January 6, 1920, in a northern Korean village, a baby boy was born named Yong Myung Moon. Yong was the second oldest of eight children in a family that converted to Christianity in 1930. His family joined a Presbyterian church, and young Yong felt a special, intense desire to draw close to God.

On Easter in 1936, 16-year-old Yong, as he now claims, saw a vision of Jesus Christ, who appeared to him from the spirit world. Moon says Jesus revealed to him his life's mission and true identity. Moon changed his name to ______ ________ ________ (Sun Shining Moon) and claims to have begun receiving divine revelations. Some years later, Moon codified these messages into his primary text, THE DIVINE PRINCIPLES, which remains the basis of Unification Church theology.

Moon also recounts that during that period of his life he was spiritually tested, particularly during the Japanese military occupation of Korea. In 1939 he was sent to Japan to study. However, due to his unusual religious ideas and involvement in anti-Japanese resistance movements, Moon was arrested, imprisoned, and tortured.

After World War II ended, Moon returned to his homeland and boldly began preaching his new doctrines. In 1946 he was imprisoned again, this time by the Korean government, which charged him with sexual immorality. Soon he was expelled from the Korean Presbyterian Church for his moral failures and alleged occult activity.

In 1948 the North Korean communists arrested Moon for a third time, along with many other religious leaders. He was liberated in 1950 by advancing Allied forces early in the Korean War. He then moved south to Seoul, where he established his ministry's headquarters.

The following year Moon was divorced by his first wife, who charged him with cruelty. Later that same year a prominent Korean, Hwo Won En, converted to Moon's doctrine and began working with him to write *The Divine Principle*, which was completed in 1952.

On May 1, 1954, The Holy Spirit Association for the Unification of World Christianity was formally established by Moon, with Hwo Won En as the first president. On April 11, 1960, Moon married Hak Ja Han, an event the Church refers to as the ____________ of the _______. That event established what they call the ________ _________.

The Unification Church movement gained momentum in Korea, Japan, and several other Asian countries in the 1960s. It came to the

NOTES

NOTES

United States in 1970, when Moon purchased several estates and businesses in New York. During the 1970s he toured the country, preaching to large crowds.

In 1982 Moon was charged with and convicted of tax evasion and spent 18 months in federal prison. He now resides in a palatial estate in Westchester County, New York, with his wife, grown children, and many grandchildren. In 1988 one of his sons died in a car crash at age 17.

In 1997 Nansook Hong, the wife of Moon's oldest son, divorced her husband and cut all ties with the Unification Church. A year later she wrote a scathing exposé of Moon and his family titled *In the Shadow of the Moons*. Her book chronicles the extravagant lifestyle of the Moons and her mental and physical abuse by her husband and in-laws.

In 1999 another of Moon's sons, Younjin Phillip Moon, committed suicide in Reno, Nevada, at age 21.

In North America there have never been more than about 10,000 members of the Unification Church. Nonetheless, the Church exerts a level of public influence of greater proportion than its numbers would seem to indicate. This is made possible primarily by the vast financial resources of the Church, garnered by members who spend hours daily raising funds in America and by the cheap labor of workers in church-owned businesses in Asia. Also, Moon has received millions of dollars of support from several sympathetic Japanese industrialists.

In the United States the Church owns one popular daily newspaper, *The Washington Times*, and a college in Connecticut, the University of Bridgeport. The church also sponsors dozens of front organizations that seek to further its spiritual and political goals. These organizations include the Collegiate Association for the Research of Principles, the Professors' World Peace Academy, the National Council for the Church and Social Action, and the Women's Federation for World Peace.

Unification Church Beliefs

1. Moon's writings are Authoratative.

The belief system of the Unification Church is a complicated mixture of Eastern philosophy, Christian and biblical terminology, and the bizarre notions of Reverend Moon as detailed in the Church's official writings. These documents include *The Divine Principle* and *Master Speaks*, a collection of Moon's sermons. Other recent messages by Moon are also regarded as authoritative. The Bible is referenced only to justify certain Unification Church doctrines, using distorted methods of interpretation.

Christians deny that Reverend Moon's revelations and writings are in any way authoritative, because they contradict clear biblical teachings. Only the Bible is authoritative, because it relates the life and teachings of the true Messiah, Jesus Christ. Only God's Word is a trustworthy guide for life and doctrine (see 2 Tim. 3:16-17). In addition, Reverend Moon's sordid personal life history and moral behavior mitigate against any serious consideration of his grandiose claims for himself.

NOTES

2. *Moon teaches a new philosophy of* HISTORY.

The Unification Church teaches that all world history, beginning in the garden of Eden, is to be understood in terms of a cosmic dualism. This dualism, which exists in both the physical and spiritual realms of the universe, means that all of creation is based on a positive/negative polarization. This concept is very similar to the Yin-Yang dualism taught in the Eastern philosophy of Taoism. This dualism, called the give-and-take action of creation, basically includes universal opposites such as active-passive, direct-indirect, objective-subjective, and masculine-feminine. God is described as Universal Prime Energy, which energizes this constant give-and-take interaction. This interaction is realized practically in what the Unification Church refers to as the Fourfold Foundation of human history: God-Man-Woman-Children. According to this concept, all creation had its origin in God, who then made a division in His creation by creating Adam and Eve. His intention was that from this division a sexual union would produce a divine bloodline of pure, perfect children and a perfect human race.

However, using a wildly metaphorical interpretation of Genesis, the Unification Church teaches that before Adam and Eve could produce their perfect offspring, the serpent deceived Eve. The serpent, in the Unification Church's understanding, symbolizes an evil spirit (Satan), who sexually seduced Eve and thus corrupted the bloodline of the human race (the Fall). Eve's illicit relationship produced an evil blood-line through Cain. Later, she had Abel with Adam, who represents a godly line. Thus, the world throughout history has been a struggle of good (God) and evil (Satan). This struggle in the past century has been manifested in the final world conflict of democracy versus communism.

The Bible does not support a dualist philosophy of history. God and Satan are not equal opposites (see 1 John 4:4). Satan functions only by God's permission (see Job 1:8-12). God has already defeated Satan through the death and resurrection of His Son, Jesus Christ (see 1 Cor. 15:55-57; Col. 2:15; 1 John 3:8), and promises ultimate victory over evil at the end of time (see 1 Cor. 15:24-28; Rev. 20:10).

Satan DEFEATED

Furthermore, Christians cannot agree with Moon's metaphorical interpretation of the events in Genesis. Accurate biblical interpretation requires that the type of biblical literature, the context of the passage, the meanings of the words, and the totality of biblical revelation be considered. None of these elements support a metaphorical reading of the Genesis account.

NOTES

3. *Jesus is the Lord who* failed **.**

According to Unification Church doctrine, because of the corruption of the human race, it was necessary for God to send a redeemer to make restitution. Jesus was sent to pay indemnity for humankind's sin, thereby redeeming humanity from spiritual death. Jesus was also sent to restore the pure bloodline of the race.

The Unification Church claims that Jesus accomplished only the first phase of this mission in that He suffered rejection and pain for spiritual salvation but failed to accomplish the second phase of redemption. Because Jesus was crucified before He could marry and produce children, the Unification Church teaches that He failed to purify the bloodline. Therefore, another redeemer was needed to finish the divine mission.

In contrast, Christians know that Jesus, the unique, incarnate Son of God, accomplished His mission in its totality. His death, along with His resurrection from the dead, provided full atonement for humankind. He therefore provides salvation from the effects of sin and death in both the spiritual and physical realms (see 1 Cor. 15:1-28; Col. 1:19-22).

4. *Moon is the Lord of the* Second Advent **.**

The Unification Church, according to its novel understandings of Bible prophecy, maintains that the second redeemer must have been born in the Far East around 1920. Like Jesus, he would necessarily suffer greatly for humankind (pay indemnity). However, unlike Jesus, he would not die violently but would live a long life, marry a perfect mate, and with her produce a cadre of perfect children. They would then build the Perfect or True Family that would restore fallen humanity to its original, intended four-position foundation of God-Man-Woman-Children.

Unification followers for years were reluctant to say directly that Moon was that second redeemer. Nonetheless, all of the Unification Church's literature and Reverend Moon's sermons certainly pointed in his direction. In the early 1990s it was widely reported that Moon was becoming more blatant in his public claims to be the Lord of the Second Advent.

For Christians, Moon's claims to messiahship are nothing short of blasphemous. Jesus alone can support His claims to deity and messiahship by His sinless life, death, and resurrection (see John 1:1-18; 8:56-59; Phil. 2:6-11; Col. 1:13-22; Heb. 1:3; 13:8).

5. *Moon has ushered in the* Completed Testament ***age.***

In 1999 Moon announced that the Unification Church by revelation had received copies of communications in the spirit world between Satan and God. According to the messages, Satan has formally apologized to God for corrupting the human race and has repented of his obstinate disobedience.

This cosmic reconciliation can also be attributed to the redeeming work of Moon in this world. Thus, Moon declares that we are now in the Completed Testament age of world history. Good (democracy) is now finally triumphing over evil (communism). A period of peace and tranquility will soon emerge in the world, led by Moon's True Family of purified human beings.

The Bible teaches that full peace and tranquility will come only at the return of Christ Himself. Scripture promises that Jesus will come again to end the world as we now know it, will judge all people, and will create a new heaven and a new earth (see Matt. 24:14-51; Mark 13; Luke 21:5-16; Acts 1:11; 1 Thess. 5:1-11).

6. *Salvation is joining the* TRUE FAMILY.
According to Unification Church doctrine, all people may receive the benefits of Moon's messiahship by being grafted into his True Family. This divine adoption process is primarily accomplished by joining Moon's church, pledging total obedience to him, and entering a marriage relationship blessed by Moon to a mate personally selected by him.

Through the years Moon has conducted numerous mass weddings like the one mentioned earlier. In most cases the brides and grooms are not even acquainted with each other before Moon pairs them for marriage. After the wedding the couples are required to refrain from consummating their relationship for at least 40 days and may not even be permitted to live together until they fully prove their commitment to Moon and the Church.

Moon's system of physical salvation by joining his True Family is totally unbiblical. The Bible teaches that complete salvation is available by grace to any person who repents of sin and, by faith, turns to Jesus Christ as personal Savior and Lord (see Rom. 10:9-10; Eph. 2:8-10).

Witnessing to Unification Church Members

Most American Christians are not as likely to encounter members of the Unification Church today as they might have a decade or more ago. The reason is that the Unification Church is no longer as aggressive in its recruitment of new members. Also, rarely do you see Unification Church members selling flowers or other items on street corners or in airports as they commonly did in the 1970s and 1980s.

Nonetheless, though the Church's public profile has diminished, Christians may still encounter its members in various locations. For example, many major universities have offices of the Collegiate

NOTES

NOTES

Association for the Research of Principles near their campuses, which are staffed by Unification Church missionaries. We still need to be prepared to respond to the Unification Church's message with the truth of Christ and to share His true gospel with them.

1. *Treat Unification Church members with* RESPECT.
Do not argue or demean them. Do not refer to them or their church as Moonies or as a cult. Unification followers regard those designations as offensive and may cut off all communication.

2. *Present the claims of* BIBLICAL TRUTH.
Remember that Unification Church members do not believe that they need to become Christians or accept Christ in order to be saved. In fact, they consider historical Christianity incomplete, distorted, and in need of total reform. For them, Sun Myung Moon and his church hold the totality of all religious truth. They see it as their duty and destiny to unite all world religions and governments under the banner of the Unification Church and Moon. Explain why you cannot accept Moon or his church as authentic, being careful not to belittle Moon or demean his work. Explain why you cannot reconcile Moon's doctrine with biblical teaching, which is the authority for your faith and practice.

3. *Focus on the person and work of* JESUS CHRIST.
Explain why you believe that Jesus is the unique Son of God, who accomplished all that is necessary for salvation. Make it clear that you do not believe there is a need for, or a possibility of, a second Messiah. Share your personal testimony of your faith in Jesus and, if permitted, the FAITH gospel presentation.

4. *Prevent* CONVERSION *to the Unification Church.*
Be aware that convincing Unification Church members to exit the group and accept Christ is very difficult. In most cases, they have invested years in the church, have established family roots, and probably depend on the Unification Church for their livelihood. Therefore, the most effective time to reach someone is before she joins the Unification Church. If you can provide accurate information on the Church to persons who are investigating its beliefs, you may be able to prevent their conversion to Moon and lead them to faith in the true Messiah, Jesus Christ, by sharing the FAITH gospel presentation.

5. *Be alert to signs that the person wishes to* EXIT *the cult.*
Although exiting the Unification Church is difficult, be alert to signs that the person wishes to do so. Many people who join the Unification Church and other totalistic cults eventually become disillusioned, leave

the movement brokenhearted, and become bitter toward all religious beliefs. As a Christian, be prepared to demonstrate Christ's love, to share the true gospel through the FAITH gospel presentation, and to provide the support they need to readjust to life outside the cult.

Visitation Time

Do It

1. As you drive to your visit, discuss ways you are learning to reach out to persons you meet in everyday life. Suggest ways your Team's Sunday School class can begin to reach new persons for Christ.
2. In this session your Team Learners studied turning from the world to Christ. Discuss reasons people have difficulty doing this. Emphasize the need to consider the way a Christian witness is perceived by non-Christians.
3. As the Team returns to the church from its visits, the Team Leader should guide in an evaluation of what happened and what follow-through should be made by the Team and/or class/department. Discuss how the report should be presented during Celebration Time; be careful not to tell personal or sensitive details that surfaced during visits.
4. At the Team Leader's cue, Learners should be able to share IMPOSSIBLE.

Celebration Time

Share It

1. Highlight the results of ministry visits as you debrief with your Team. Indicate the different types of Sunday School ministry visits and why certain topics were discussed in the different types of visits. What would Team members suggest as actions for follow-up?
2. Hear reports and testimonies.
3. Complete Evaluation Cards.
4. Complete Participation Cards.
5. Update visitation forms with the results of visits.

NOTES

Home Study Assignments

Home Study Assignments reinforce this session by helping you apply what you have learned.

Your Discipleship Journey

Journaling activities in Your Discipleship Journey are an important part of your development as a Great Commission Christian through FAITH training.

1. Read and meditate on Philippians 2:5-11. Write characteristics our true Savior has that false messiahs do not have.

____

____

____

____

2. In Matthew 7:15-18 Jesus told us that we can recognize false prophets by their fruit. Based on your study so far, what is some identifying fruit of a false prophet or a false messiah?

____

____

____

____

3. Unification Church followers believe that Jesus failed in His redemptive mission. Match the following Scriptures with their teachings about the complete work of Christ for our salvation.

____ 1. John 1:1-2	a. God reconciled all things through Jesus' death.
____ 2. John 3:36	b. Christ died for our sins, was buried, and was raised from the dead.
____ 3. Acts 4:12	c. Jesus is eternally God.
____ 4. Romans 3:24-25	d. Jesus is our hope of glory.
____ 5. 1 Corinthians 15:3-4	e. Salvation is found only in Jesus.
____ 6. Colossians 1:20	f. Jesus gives eternal life.
____ 7. Colossians 1:27	g. Jesus brought redemption and atonement.

4. John 17 records a prayer that Jesus prayed for us. According to verses 14-17, what has God given us for our protection and growth?

____

How are you being sanctified by the Word of truth? ______________

____

Growing as a Life Witness

Growing as a Life Witness reminds you of your responsibility to witness and minister to others during the week.

1. Talk or meet with your accountability partner and share ways you have cultivated a lost person or have witnessed or ministered on occasions other than FAITH visits.
2. Discuss ways you can apply the session 9 content.
3. Pray for lost persons by name and for each other.

Prayer Concerns	Answers to Prayer
____________________	____________________
____________________	____________________
____________________	____________________
____________________	____________________

Your Weekly Sunday School Leadership Meeting

A FAITH participant is an important member of Sunday School. Encourage Team members who are elected Sunday School workers to attend this weekly meeting. Use this section to record ways your FAITH Team influences the work of your Sunday School class or department. Use the information to report during weekly Sunday School leadership meetings. Identify actions that need to be taken through Sunday School as a result of prayer concerns, needs identified, visits made by the Team, and decisions made by the persons visited. Also identify ways you can disciple others in your Sunday School class or department and in your church.

1. Highlight FAITH needs/reports that affect your class/department or age group.

____

____

2. The most significant result of being saved is a restored personal relationship with God now and for all eternity. What are ways the department/class can impact persons with the truth that, for believers, heaven is HERE?

____

____

That heaven is also HEREAFTER?

____

____

3. How will the class begin to follow up on persons who received ministry visits?

____

____

On someone who accepted Christ in an evangelistic visit?

____

____

4. What areas of your Sunday School need to be started or strengthened, based on input from ministry and Opinion Poll visits?

____

5. Pray now for your teacher(s) and department director(s).

Discipling Your Team Members

This weekly feature suggests actions the Team Leader can take to support Team members, prepare for Team Time, and improve visits. This work is part of the Team Leader's Home Study Assignments. Add any actions suggested by your church's FAITH strategy.

Support Team Members

- ❑ Pray for and personally follow up on any Learner who may need personal encouragement.
- ❑ Contact Team members during the week to remind them that you are praying for them and to discuss their participation in FAITH.

❑ Learners are memorizing the gospel presentation through *T* is for TURN. As you discuss this content with Team members, remind them that this is the heart of the gospel.

Prepare to Lead Team Time

❑ Preview Leading Team Time for session 10.

❑ Review the FAITH Visit Outline.

Prepare to Lead Visits

❑ Be prepared to explain the benefits and procedures of making Sunday School ministry visits.

❑ Be prepared to model a visit in which Team members are asked to lead in a visit up to the point of *T* is for TURN.

❑ Be prepared to lead your Team to participate during Celebration Time.

Link with Sunday School

❑ Participate in your weekly Sunday School leadership meeting. Share pertinent information in this meeting, using Your Weekly Sunday School Leadership Meeting (pp. 161–62) and FAITH-visit results.

❑ Be alert to false conceptions of Jesus and salvation that arise in Sunday School, especially among seekers or new members, and be prepared to bring out biblical truths that instruct and correct.

For Further Growth

For Further Growth may include additional reading or activities that will enhance your growth as a disciple and a discipler of others. These assignments are intended to be long-term projects and do not have to be completed during this semester of study.

1. Many Christians have family members who are involved in cults. Consider starting a church ministry to support these families.
2. Many college students are introduced to cults while on campus. Consider helping your youth minister begin to equip high-school students for this future challenge.
3. Read *The Baptist Faith and Message* statement of faith, available as a tract by writing to LifeWay Church Resources Customer Service, MSN 113; 127 Ninth Avenue, North; Nashville, TN 37234-0113; by calling toll free (800) 458-2772; by faxing (615) 251-5933; by ordering online at *www.lifeway.com;* or by emailing *customerservice@lifeway.com.*
4. Read the FAITH Tip on page 164.

Answers to matching activity on page 160: 1. c, 2. f, 3. e, 4. g, 5. b, 6. a, 7. d

FAITH TIP

Discerning the Real Jesus

Most religions have some place in their system for Jesus. For example, Jehovah's Witnesses claim to believe in Jesus, but they deny His deity. Mormons say that Jesus was the Son of God, meaning the literal offspring of the Heavenly Father, a God with a physical body of flesh and bone. Muslims regard Jesus as one of their great prophets but less than Muhammad. Many New Agers regard Jesus as a guru. Even most atheists consider Jesus a great moral teacher.

The issue, however, is how the Bible defines who Jesus is. Anyone who omits, denies, distorts, or redefines any of the following facts is advocating "a different gospel" (see 2 Cor. 11:4; Gal. 1:6).

1. The real Jesus is the preexistent, eternal, one-and-only Son of God, the second person of the holy Trinity.

Jesus (the Word) had no temporal beginning but is equal with the Father and the Holy Spirit in the Godhead (see John 1:1-2; 8:56-59; Col. 1:17; Rev. 3:14).

2. The real Jesus was involved with the Father in the creation of the universe.

See John 1:3; Colossians 1:16.

3. The real Jesus came into the world as a human and was born to a virgin.

Jesus is fully man and fully God incarnate (in human flesh) (see Matt. 1:18-25; Luke 1—2:20; John 1:10-11; Phil. 2:6-11; Col. 1:15; 2:9; Heb. 1:1-3).

4. The real Jesus lived a sinless life on earth and therefore was uniquely qualified to die an atoning death for our sins.

See Romans 3:24-26; 2 Corinthians 5:21; Hebrews 5:8-9; 9:26-28.

5. The real Jesus bodily rose from the dead to claim victory over sin and death.

See Matthew 28; Mark 16; Luke 24; John 2:19-20; 20—21; Acts 1:3; Romans 1:4; 6:4-5; 1 Corinthians 15:1-20.

6. The real Jesus ascended to heaven and now reigns at the right hand of the Father.

In heaven Jesus awaits His return to judge the world and usher in the eternal kingdom of God (see Matt. 24:1-27; Mark 13; Luke 21:5-36; 1 Thess. 5:1-11; Rev. 20—22).

SESSION 10

The Oneness Pentecostal Movement

TAL DAVIS

In this session you will—

CHECK IT by engaging in Team Time activities;

KNOW IT by reviewing content from session 9;

HEAR IT by examining the beliefs of Oneness Pentecostals and by learning ways to witness to them;

STUDY IT by overviewing Home Study Assignments;

DO IT by leading your Team in making visits;

SHARE IT by celebrating.

NOTES

Leading Team Time

All Team members participate in Team Time. They are primarily responsible for reciting the assigned portion of the FAITH Visit Outline and for discussing other Home Study Assignments.

As you direct this important time of CHECK IT activities with your Team, keep in mind that Learners look to you as a role model, motivator, mentor, and friend. Team Time activities can continue in the car as the Team travels to and from visits.

Lead CHECK IT Activities

✔ *FAITH Visit Outline*

❑ Listen while each Learner recites all of the ***Preparation*** and ***Presentation*** content and key words for ***Invitation***.

❑ Give opportunities for Learners to practice reciting the portions of the FAITH Visit Outline they have learned to this point.

✔ *Other Home Study Assignments*

❑ This may be a good time to discuss the benefits of keeping a weekly journal as part of FAITH training. Discuss some of the truths or understandings gained through the weekly Bible studies. Dialogue about how the reflective questions have influenced Learners' training experience.

✔ *Session 9 Debriefing*

❑ *T* is for TURN. This is the point in the gospel presentation when a person makes a significant choice—whether to receive salvation. To be forgiven, a person must turn from his sin and turn to Christ. He must trust Christ and Christ only. The imagery of turning is reinforced with the simple question, If you were driving down the road and someone asked you to turn, what would he or she be asking you to do? (Change direction) Most people can easily understand the idea of changing from one direction to another. The Bible uses the word *repent* to depict the same thing. The Bible is clear about the need for a person to repent of sin and to live for Christ (change direction) by committing to and trusting Him. Team members will need to remember the significance of the concepts behind the letter *T* to help explain and emphasize the how of the gospel.

✔ *Help for Strengthening a Visit*

❑ The illustration of changing directions in a car is the only dialogue that is planned as part of the actual gospel presentation. It is important to ask the person to share his or her answer to the question. The response is predictable, but by asking the question, you call the person's attention to the gospel and increase his or her participation in the discussion. You might be talking with a child, a younger youth, or someone who obviously does not drive. If so, adapt the question to something like "If you were riding down the road and you asked the driver to turn, what would you be wanting the driver to do?" Usually, it will be significant to use the word *repent* only after the question has helped you explain what the word means. Using the turning analogy to emphasize faith in Christ also helps clarify the meaning of *repent*. For many unsaved or unchurched people, *repent* is associated with religious or churchy terms; without a relevant, contemporary explanation, this word might lose much of its significance.

- ❑ Remind Team members to listen during each visit for ministry opportunities, as well as for things a person might say to help you identify with his or her spiritual journey.
- ❑ Discuss how, as a Team Leader, you communicate follow-up information to the appropriate age group/class/department when you encounter family members of different ages in a home visit.

Notes

____

____

____

____

____

Actions I Need to Take with Team Members This Week

____

____

____

____

____

NOTES

NOTES

A Quick Review

Last week you learned about the teachings of Sun Myung Moon and the Unification Church. Read the statements below. In each group of choices, underline the answer that best describes Moon's teaching.

1. The Unification Church teaches that all world history is to be understood in terms of a cosmic (explosion, dualism, force).
2. God is described as (Force, Universal Prime Energy, Cosmic Force Field), which energizes a constant give-and-take interaction.
3. Eve's illicit relationship with (Satan, Adam, Noah) produced an evil bloodline through Cain.
4. The Unification Church believes that Jesus failed to redeem humanity because He never (sinned, married and produced children, taught His disciples thoroughly).
5. According to Moon, (Satan, Moon himself, Hitler) has formally apologized to God and repented of his disobedience.
6. Cosmic reconciliation is being realized through Moon's work in the world, bringing about a new age of world history called the (Second Advent, Marriage of the Lamb, Completed Testament).
7. Moon's followers acknowledge him as the (Heavenly Father, Lord of the Second Advent, Divine Ruler).
8. All people may receive the benefits of Moon's messiahship by being grafted into his (college system, Unified Vine, True Family).

Indicate whether the following principles for witnessing to Unification Church members are true (*T*) or false (*F*).

___ 1. Call the Unification Church follower a no-good Moonie.
___ 2. Ask followers if they have any flowers for sale.
___ 3. Treat Unification Church members with respect.
___ 4. Present the claims of biblical truth.
___ 5. Be willing to compromise on the biblical way of salvation.
___ 6. State that cosmic dualism is compatible with Christianity.
___ 7. Focus on the person and work of Jesus Christ.
___ 8. Admit that belief in a second Messiah might offer certain benefits.
___ 9. Prevent conversion to the Unification Church.
___ 10. Be alert to signs that the person wishes to exit the cult.

Worshiping Jesus Only

NOTES

Reverend Cook was ecstatic. At last his church had found a buyer. For more than one year the people of Eastside Church had wanted to sell their downtown property and relocate on the outskirts of town. At last they had found an interested young congregation that was ready to pay and eager to occupy the facilities as soon as possible. Reverend Cook immediately called his relocation-committee chairman. "Bob, the Pentecostal church down on Logan Street has outgrown its building and wants to buy ours. Isn't that terrific?"

The voice on the other end of the line was silent for a moment. Then Bob slowly asked, "What kind of Pentecostal church is that?"

"What kind?" Reverend Cook answered. "What difference does that make? They are all about the same, aren't they? Oh, I know we disagree on some areas of theology but not enough to matter."

"Pastor, do you remember last year when that consultant on interfaith evangelism spoke? He said that some Pentecostal groups are rapidly growing cultists."

"That's right." Reverend Cook thought for a moment. "Which one did he warn about specifically?"

"I think it was the United Pentecostal Church," Bob answered.

"Uh-oh." Reverend Cook's balloon suddenly burst.

One of the most significant developments in world Christianity in the 20th century was the birth and global expansion of the modern Pentecostal movement. Since it burst on the scene in several revivals in the early 1900s, Pentecostalism has spread across the world with its dramatic practices of speaking in tongues, faith healing, and other charismatic phenomena. It has spawned dozens of new denominations and has even made its way into some mainline denominations.

Most Pentecostal leaders and churches clearly affirm the historic biblical doctrines of the Trinity; Christ's incarnation, deity, and sacrificial atonement; and the personality and deity of the Holy Spirit. Most also espouse the biblical gospel of salvation by grace through faith in Jesus as Savior and Lord. Thus, although Baptists and other mainline evangelicals may differ with Pentecostals on some issues of theology, they certainly regard most Pentecostals as brothers and sisters in Christ and fellow laborers in the work of reaching the world for Him.

Unfortunately, not all streams of the early Pentecostal movement flowed into the waters of orthodox Christianity. One early Pentecostal who veered from the course was a Canadian Assemblies of God preacher named _____ ____________. In 1913 he began to persuade many that the traditional Trinitarian concept of God is flawed. Along with other Assemblies of God ministers Frank Elwart and John Scheppe, McAlister taught that _________ _______ is God to be worshiped. Based on their

NOTES

rigid interpretation of Acts 2:38, they also said that water baptism is not to be pronounced in the traditional Trinitarian formula of Father, Son, and Holy Spirit but addressed only in Jesus' name to be effective. These unorthodox tenets forced the then still young Assemblies of God denomination to expel more than 160 ministers from their fellowship who had accepted McAlister's positions. To their credit, the Assemblies of God adopted a strong Trinitarian-based statement of beliefs in 1916.

Out of that schism several Jesus Only or ____________________ ____________________ groups were formed. Today the largest such organization in North America is the United Pentecostal Church International, headquartered in Hazelwood, Missouri. That body alone claims more than a half million members in the United States and Canada and twice that many in dozens of other countries. Other Oneness bodies include Overcoming Holy Church of God; Assemblies of the Lord Jesus, Incorporated; Bible Way Church of Our Lord Jesus Christ World Wide, Incorporated; Church of Our Lord Jesus of the Apostolic Faith; Pentecostal Assemblies of the World; and Pentecostal Church of Apostolic Faith. As many as ________ __________ North Americans may be associated with Oneness Pentecostal churches.

These movements pose a major challenge to historic Christianity. As you will see, not only do they radically distort and redefine essential Christian doctrines, but they also aggressively seek to proselytize Christians in Bible-believing churches to accept their unbiblical teachings and to join their churches.

Oneness Pentecostal Beliefs

1. Oneness Pentecostals subtract from and add to the ____________.

Evangelical Christians agree with Oneness Pentecostals on one major point: the inspiration and authority of the Bible. Most Oneness teachers claim that their doctrines are derived solely from scriptural study. Many would also claim that some orthodox Christian beliefs are not biblical and should be rejected. For example, they would argue that the historic doctrine of the Trinity is not found in Scripture but was contrived at the Council of Nicea in A.D. 325. Actually, Oneness Pentecostals heavily rely on the supposedly Spirit-anointed teachings of some of their leaders for theological direction and biblical interpretations.

Evangelical Christians, however, maintain that the Bible alone is the final authority in all matters of faith and practice. Biblical scholars follow strict principles of interpretation to derive sound doctrinal tenets. They do not always agree on every item of theology. Nonetheless, they agree to an amazing degree on most basic issues.

2. Oneness Pentecostals reject the Christian doctrine of the ______________.

The doctrine of God is certainly the most important deviation from historic Christianity by Oneness adherents. As stated before, Oneness leaders teach that the traditional Trinitarian concept of the Godhead is wrong. Simply put, the Trinitarian view is that there is only one God, who exists in three separate and eternal persons: the Father, the Son, and the Holy Spirit. The Oneness view is that the Godhead consists of only one person. That one person existed in heaven as the Father but came to earth completely in the man Jesus Christ. For Oneness Pentecostals, Jesus is all there is of God to know. Everything must be done in Jesus' name. That is why Oneness Pentecostals are often referred to as the Jesus Only people.

According to the Oneness perspective, Jesus Christ, while on earth, had two natures that simultaneously existed in one person: the nature of God and the nature of man. This idea may sound like the historic concept of the incarnation, but it goes beyond it by asserting that all of the Godhead was in the divine nature of Jesus. Thus, when Jesus prayed, He was not praying to the Father, who was still in heaven, but His own human nature was praying to His own divine nature.

Oneness teachers also speak often about the Holy Spirit. Again, however, it is not in the traditional Trinitarian sense. For them, the Holy Spirit is not a separate person from the Father or the Son but rather is something of a synonym for them. Thus, the Holy Spirit, when mentioned, is only another term for the one God (Jesus) and the manifestation of His power.

Oneness Pentecostal leaders heavily rely on several biblical passages to establish their positions, while ignoring many others that contradict them. One that is often quoted is Acts 2:38: "Then Peter said unto them, Repent, and be baptized every one of you in the name of Jesus Christ for the remission of sins, and ye shall receive the gift of the Holy Ghost" (KJV).

Another prooftext is Colossians 2:9: "In him dwelleth all the fulness of the Godhead bodily" (KJV). Oneness Pentecostals argue that if the Father, the Son, and the Holy Spirit were separate, then the fullness of the Godhead could not exist in Jesus, as this verse seems to say.

One familiar passage often quoted by Oneness leaders is Matthew 28:19: "Go ye therefore, and teach all nations, baptizing them in the name of the Father, and of the Son, and of the Holy Ghost" (KJV). Oneness teachers point to the fact that Jesus commanded His disciples to baptize new disciples in the name [singular] of the Father, the Son, and the Holy Spirit. They maintain that Matthew's use of a singular designation means that the three are all just one person, not three.

Evangelical Christians disagree with Oneness Pentecostals' use of these verses as prooftexts. The Oneness concept of God resembles the

NOTES

NOTES

ancient heresy of modalism. That position, rejected by churches in the fourth century, stated that God exists eternally as only one person. However, He has manifested Himself in time as three separate and consecutive modes: first in heaven as the Father, second on earth as Christ, and finally in the world as the Holy Spirit.

Although it is true that the Bible teaches that there is only one God, it depicts Him as existing eternally in three separate and eternal persons. Granted, the concept of the holy Trinity is not an easy one to understand, but it is the clear teaching of the total body of Scripture and has been the bedrock of historic Christianity since the New Testament era. Many Bible verses reflect that doctrine, including 1 Corinthians 8:6; 12:4-6; 2 Corinthians 1:21-22; and 1 Peter 1:2.

Christians also take issue with Oneness Pentecostals' doctrine of Christ. Christians affirm without hesitancy Christ's deity. However, the Oneness teaching that Jesus contains the totality of the Godhead is a misreading of Matthew 28:19 and Colossians 2:9. The use of the singular designation ("the name") in Matthew 28:19 actually confirms Trinitarian theology, communicating that the authority and characteristics of the one God are incorporated in the three persons of the Godhead. The Colossians passage states that Jesus totally and uniquely embodied the divine nature, not that the totality of the Godhead is only in Jesus. This interpretation is supported by the fact that the Bible says Jesus often prayed to the Father (see John 11:41-42; 12:27-28; 17:1-26) and was loved by the Father (see Matt. 3:17; 17:5; John 3:35).

3. *Oneness Pentecostals have four requirements for ____________________.*

Most Oneness Pentecostal churches obviously differ from historic Christianity in their beliefs about God and Christ. They also deviate in their understanding of the nature of the gospel. Most of their leaders teach that in order to receive and maintain salvation from sin and to be assured of going to heaven at death, each person must obey the following fourfold system of righteousness.

1. A person must believe in Jesus Christ but specifically the Jesus Only of the Oneness doctrine of God. The Jesus of Trinitarian faith is regarded as inferior and incapable of bringing salvation because, as they see it, He is not fully God.
2. Oneness teachers argue that repentance and water baptism by immersion are necessary for salvation and must be pronounced in the name of Jesus to be legitimate. Therefore, they do not baptize in the traditional Trinitarian-pronouncement formula of Matthew 28:19 but only in Jesus' name, as they say is required by Acts 2:38. Jesus' command in Matthew 28:19 is not perceived as a baptismal formula.
3. Pentecostal and Charismatic groups generally believe that speaking in tongues is a miraculous spiritual gift that can be manifested by

Christians today. Most teach that it is an outward sign of a special, postconversion filling, or baptism, of the Holy Spirit. For Oneness Pentecostals, however, speaking in tongues is regarded as the third essential element in the salvation process. Most Oneness teachers argue that it is an outward and necessary evidence of the salvation experience. In this view, a person who has never spoken in tongues cannot be sure he is truly saved. This teaching is a radical departure from historic Christianity. Even most Pentecostals affirm that salvation is a matter only of grace through faith in Christ.

4. Most Oneness movements demand an extremely legalistic code of personal holiness and conduct for their members. Only by living what they regard as a holy life can a person maintain any assurance of salvation. Certain external evidence demonstrates a person's level of holiness and desire for sinless perfection. Many Oneness churches, for example, require strict dress codes and styles of personal decorum. Most will not allow women to cut their hair or to wear short dresses. Makeup and jewelry are rejected as vainglory. Men must also adhere to strict codes, such as wearing only white dress shirts with dark slacks, being clean shaven, and keeping short haircuts. Violations of those codes may result in harsh church discipline and exclusion from fellowship. In most Oneness congregations the pastor exercises primary authority in determining the levels of conformity that are expected for church members.

Christians must reject the Oneness Pentecostal concept of salvation for several basic reasons. Its contention that baptism is an essential element for salvation negates the clear teaching of Scripture that salvation is by grace through faith in Christ alone and not by any works of righteousness (see Rom. 4:4-5; Eph. 2:8-9; Titus 3:5). Although baptism is not required for salvation, it is a scriptural ordinance that believers should follow in obedience. Baptists and most other evangelicals agree that the proper mode of baptism is immersion. However, the biblical pronouncement formula is, as Jesus taught, "in the name of the Father, the Son, and the Holy Spirit" (see Matt. 28:19).

Most Pentecostal Christians regard speaking in tongues as a legitimate modern gift and the evidence for the postconversion baptism of the Holy Spirit. Baptists and most other evangelicals would biblically argue that tongues or any other spiritual gift cannot be singled out as a special indicator of a person's spirituality (see 1 Cor. 12—14). Both evangelicals and Pentecostals, however, reject the Oneness teaching that speaking in tongues is an essential element for receiving God's gift of salvation.

They also agree that salvation is not based on or maintained by any legalistic works or codes of righteousness. Good works and holy living should be the natural result of salvation after it has been received (see Eph. 2:10). However, salvation is assured for all who have genuinely repented of their sin and received Jesus Christ as their personal Savior and Lord (see John 1:12; 5:24; 1 John 5:13).

NOTES

NOTES

Witnessing to Oneness Pentecostals

As mentioned earlier, Oneness movements are growing worldwide. Therefore, Christians must be ready to respond and witness to Oneness followers they may encounter.

1. *Beware of unholy* ________________.

Oneness Pentecostal doctrine and practice are outside the parameters of historic Christianity. Thus, there is virtually no common ground for fellowship between evangelicals and other mainline churches with Oneness followers. Most Oneness leaders regard traditional Christian churches as unbiblical, unspiritual, or even demonic.

Nonetheless, in recent years a few Oneness leaders and pastors have gained acceptance in the mainstream of the Pentecostal and Charismatic movements. They have quietly ceased their anti-Trinitarian rhetoric, moderated many of their legalistic expectations, and even joined hands with some traditional evangelicals to "preach Jesus."

Unfortunately, in most cases Oneness Pentecostals have not corrected their cultic doctrines of God, Christ, and salvation and, by their willingness to fellowship with mainstream Christians, may be enticing some unwitting believers into their unbiblical system. Christians must be cautious not to naively enter alliances with movements that espouse false doctrines.

2. *Build a personal and respectful* ________________.

A trustful, caring relationship will be essential for leading Oneness Pentecostals to reject their unscriptural doctrines and to properly understand and accept biblical ones.

3. *Focus on* ______________ ___________.

Stay focused on the essential elements of the Christian faith. Do not get sidetracked defending your denomination.

4. *Help the Oneness Pentecostal reconstruct a biblical* ____________ ______________.

The Oneness Pentecostal movement is an extreme derivation of the modern Pentecostal or Charismatic movement. Unfortunately, it has deviated beyond the bounds of historic Christian orthodoxy. You will need to follow a process of leading Oneness followers to deconstruct their unbiblical beliefs and replace them with biblical teachings. For example, use the biblical arguments and Scripture passages in this session to reveal the true nature of God and Christ. Show the person that salvation is not based on outward manifestations or legalistic actions but on the finished work of Christ on the cross.

5. *Follow the FAITH* ______________
______________________________.

After false understandings have been dispelled, use the Scriptures and points in the FAITH gospel presentation to lead the Oneness follower to faith in the true Christ of Scripture.

Visitation Time

Do It

1. Think about being an ambassador to the persons you visit. Your goal is to share God's message of reconciliation through Jesus Christ. Your enthusiastic attitude reflects your deep conviction about the truth you share. Make sure you fulfill your responsibility as an ambassador by speaking and acting in a way that honors Christ.
2. On the drive, discuss what it means to have heaven here and now.
3. All Team members should know the FAITH presentation through *H* is for HEAVEN. While visiting, invite Team members to support you throughout the presentation. Tell them that next week they will be expected to lead the gospel presentation.

Celebration Time

Share It

1. Ask a Team member to take the lead in sharing reports.
2. Hear reports and testimonies.
3. Complete Evaluation Cards.
4. Complete Participation Cards.
5. Update visitation forms with the results of visits.

NOTES

Home Study Assignments

Home Study Assignments reinforce this session by helping you apply what you have learned.

Your Discipleship Journey

Journaling activities in Your Discipleship Journey are an important part of your development as a Great Commission Christian through FAITH training.

1. Oneness Pentecostals deny the biblical doctrine of the Trinity. Match the following Scriptures with the correct teachings about the distinct roles of each person of the Trinity.

____ 1. Matthew 3:16-17
____ 2. John 14:16-17
____ 3. 1 Corinthians 12:4-6
____ 4. 2 Corinthians 13:14
____ 5. Ephesians 1:3-14
____ 6. 1 Peter 1:2
____ 7. 1 Peter 3:18
____ 8. Revelation 1:4-6

a. Christ died for sins once for all to bring us to God. He was made alive by the Spirit.
b. There are many types of gifts, but the same God bestows them on believers.
c. Believers are chosen by the foreknowledge of God and through the sanctifying work of the Spirit for obedience to Christ and salvation through His blood.
d. At Jesus' baptism the Holy Spirit descended, and God spoke from heaven.
e. Paul gives a benediction by invoking the grace of Christ, the love of God, and the fellowship of the Spirit.
f. The Father gives believers the Holy Spirit.
g. Through Christ, God has made known His purpose to bring all things together under Christ. The Spirit guarantees our inheritance.
h. John greets the churches in the name of the eternal Father and the Son, who died for our sins and made us a kingdom and priests to serve His God and Father.

2. One mark of a cult is its emphasis on works to earn salvation. These works often include adherence to outward forms of godliness that are specified by the particular cult. Summarize what the following Scriptures teach about attempts to gain salvation by works.

1 Corinthians 1:26-31: ____

____

Galatians 2:15-16: ______________________________

____

Ephesians 2:8-9: ______________________________

____

Colossians 2:6-12: ______________________________

____

3. The method of salvation is faith in the finished work of Christ. Oneness Pentecostals require baptism for salvation. Read Luke 23:42-43; Romans 10:9-13; 1 Corinthians 1:14-17; and Ephesians 2:8-9 and write a brief rebuttal to this false doctrine.

____

____

____

____

Growing as a Life Witness

Growing as a Life Witness reminds you of your responsibility to witness and minister to others during the week.

1. Talk or meet with your accountability partner and share ways you have cultivated a lost person or have witnessed or ministered on occasions other than FAITH visits.
2. Discuss ways you can apply the session 10 content.
3. Pray for lost persons by name and for each other.

Prayer Concerns	Answers to Prayer
______________	______________
______________	______________
______________	______________
______________	______________
______________	______________

Your Weekly Sunday School Leadership Meeting

A FAITH participant is an important member of Sunday School. Encourage Team members who are elected Sunday School workers to attend this weekly meeting. Use this section to record ways your FAITH Team influences the work of your Sunday School class or department. Use the information to report during weekly Sunday School leadership meetings. Identify actions that need to be taken through Sunday School as a result of prayer concerns, needs identified, visits made by the Team, and decisions made by the persons visited. Also identify ways you can disciple others in your Sunday School class or department and in your church.

1. Highlight FAITH needs/reports affecting your class/department or age group. Receive and provide information about future visitation assignments. Do records reflect the information that is needed for visits and for follow-up?

___

2. Periodically evaluate the growth of your class/department. Are new Christians consistently becoming part of the group? Are these new believers beginning to grow in their faith and to discover their spiritual gifts? Are mature members leaving the class to accept leadership positions? Is the class reaching out beyond itself, so much so that a new unit or more space may be needed? Is the fellowship inclusive and attractive to all people?

___

3. How should preparation for Sunday consider the needs of individuals or families visited through FAITH? Discuss ways Sunday's Bible-study lesson can involve members and guests in transformational Bible study and discipleship.

___

4. Your class/department has committed to support you throughout FAITH training. FAITH assignments are reaching their peak for many Team members, so it is appropriate to ask your leadership team to pray for you and all FAITH participants at this significant time in training.

Discipling Your Team Members

This weekly feature suggests actions the Team Leader can take to support Team members, prepare for Team Time, and improve visits. This work is part of the Team Leader's Home Study Assignments. Add any actions suggested by your church's FAITH strategy.

Support Team Members

- ❑ Contact Team members during the week. Remind them that you are praying for them. Discuss prayer concerns and answers to prayer.
- ❑ This week Learners are memorizing the FAITH presentation through the ***Invitation***. As you discuss this content with Team members, remind them that this is when someone can make a life-changing decision.
- ❑ Learners have a significant amount of reading during home study this week. The information is important to read and understand because it interprets *A Step of Faith*. Encourage Learners to read the FAITH Tips and to be prepared to discuss the significance of this leaflet in preparation for session 11.
- ❑ Record specific needs and concerns shared by Team members.

Prepare to Lead Team Time

- ❑ Review Team members' Home Study Assignments.
- ❑ Preview Leading Team Time for session 11.

Prepare to Lead Visits

- ❑ Review the FAITH Visit Outline.

Link with Sunday School

- ❑ Participate in your weekly Sunday School leadership meeting. Share pertinent information in this meeting, using Your Weekly Sunday School Leadership Meeting (p. 178) and FAITH-visit results.
- ❑ Sunday School lessons may present opportunities to affirm the biblical doctrines of the Trinity, Christ, and salvation. Use these opportunities to warn against a works philosophy of salvation or to correct an inaccurate view of Christ.

For Further Growth

For Further Growth may include additional reading or activities that will enhance your growth as a disciple and a discipler of others. These assignments are intended to be long-term projects and do not have to be completed during this semester of study.

1. Read the Book of Romans, which contains the most comprehensive biblical teaching on salvation. Notice the complete absence of any teaching that adds to or distorts the simple act of faith in Christ as the way to be saved.
2. Commit to pray for people who have been seduced by a cult that their eyes may be opened to the truth.
3. Read the FAITH Tip on page 180.

Answers to matching activity on page 176: 1. d, 2. f, 3. b, 4. e, 5. g, 6. c, 7. a, 8. h

FAITH TIP

Explaining the Trinity

Most Christians take the doctrine of the Trinity for granted, but the Trinity is not a minor issue. It is the most significant concept of the Christian faith. Every basic Christian truth is gleaned from the veracity of this doctrine. Therefore, we must be careful that our explanations to non-Christians are theologically accurate so that we do not inadvertently create barriers.

The word *Trinity* does not appear in the Bible, but we can confidently assert that the concept of the Trinity (or tri-unity) of God is biblical. The Bible teaches that there is only one God (see Ex. 20:1-6; Deut. 6:4; Matt. 6:9). However, the New Testament reveals that He exists in three separate persons. First, the Bible clearly indicates that God is our Heavenly Father. He is the omnipotent being who created the universe from nothing (see Gen. 1:1). God also exists as the one and only begotten Son, Jesus Christ. He also had no beginning and shares all of the attributes of deity with the Father (see John 1:1-18). God also exists in the person of the Holy Spirit. Also called the Spirit of God and the Spirit of Christ, He was present at creation (see Gen. 1:2), was the agent of Jesus' conception (see Matt. 1:18), was present at Jesus' baptism (see Matt. 3:16), and empowers the church to fulfill Christ's Great Commission (see Luke 24:49; John 14:16-18; Acts 1:8; 2). He also inspired the writers of the Bible (see 2 Tim. 3:16) and indwells and empowers believers for Christian growth and service (see John 14:26; Rom. 8:1-2; 1 Cor. 6:19; Gal. 5:22-23). In each case the Father, the Son, and the Holy Spirit are regarded as God and are often inextricably linked in Scripture (see Matt. 28:19; 1 Cor. 12:4-6; 2 Cor. 1:21-22; 13:14; Gal. 4:6; 1 Pet. 1:2).

A number of helpful illustrations have been formulated to help us explain the Trinity. Some theologians compare the Trinity to the three states of matter: solid, liquid, and gas. Others use a relational model: a man can be a father, a son, and a brother. Others use the illustration of a triangle: three sides and angles that together form a single geometric entity. Still others have compared the Trinity to the three aspects of human personality: mind, body, and spirit. Although each illustration may be helpful, we must acknowledge that no human explanation for the Trinity can ever be totally sufficient. God is an infinite and eternal being, so any attempt to explain his nature is limited by our finite human comprehension.

Thus, we must accept the Trinity by faith. We believe it because we believe the Bible. We believe in the one Creator God. We believe that He loves us as our Father, died for us as the Son, and indwells us as the Holy Spirit.

SESSION 11

The Church of Scientology, International

TAL DAVIS

In this session you will—

CHECK IT by engaging in Team Time activities;

KNOW IT by reviewing content from session 10;

HEAR IT by examining the beliefs of Scientologists and by learning ways to witness to them;

SEE IT by viewing a video segment;

STUDY IT by overviewing Home Study Assignments;

DO IT by leading your Team in making visits;

SHARE IT by celebrating.

NOTES

Leading Team Time

All Team members participate in Team Time. They are primarily responsible for reciting the assigned portion of the FAITH Visit Outline and for discussing other Home Study Assignments.

As you direct this important time of CHECK IT activities with your Team, keep in mind that Learners look to you as a role model, motivator, mentor, and friend. Team Time activities can continue in the car as the Team travels to and from visits.

Lead CHECK IT Activities

✔ *FAITH Visit Outline*

❑ Listen while each Learner recites the FAITH Visit Outline beginning with HOW and including all of the ***Invitation***. Indicate any notes for improvement.

❑ Make sure Team members know the correct sequence in using *A Step of Faith* in making a transition from the gospel presentation to leading someone to declare commitments to Christ as Savior and Lord, to enroll in Sunday School, and to publicly acknowledge new faith in Jesus. Since several Home Study Assignments dealt with the use of *A Step of Faith*, you may not need additional review of session 10 assignments.

❑ Make certain Team members are able to lead a person to pray to receive Christ and to pray for Christian growth. Also, be certain Team members are comfortable in leading a person to record commitment(s) they have made and to provide the information the church needs.

✔ *Session 10 Debriefing*

❑ Heaven HERE and Heaven HEREAFTER are fundamental beliefs of the Christian. Do Learners demonstrate a sense of comfort in sharing their joy in Christ and their assurance of eternal life in God's presence?

❑ *H* also stands for HOW. This becomes the hinge on which a Learner is able to clarify for another person how a person can have God's forgiveness, heaven and eternal life, and Jesus as personal Savior and Lord. Make sure the person is becoming increasingly comfortable in using the picture on the cover of *A Step of Faith* to identify with the need for God's forgiveness. You received earlier training to help your Team know what to do if *A Step of Faith* is not available.

✔ *Help for Strengthening a Visit*

- ❑ Remind Team members that they are seeing the Holy Spirit at work as they make themselves available for visitation. Recall examples of ways you have seen the Holy Spirit at work when a person has heard the FAITH gospel presentation.
- ❑ One of the great privileges and responsibilities in FAITH training is to encounter family members of someone you are assigned to visit. Although your Team is focusing on persons from your Sunday School department or class, you quickly learn that there are many opportunities to minister to and share the gospel with persons of other age divisions. Dialogue about ways to meaningfully include preschoolers, children, youth, and adults in a visit who would not be assigned to your department or class.
- ❑ Indicate that next week's practice session is a good way to improve skills and increase confidence. Share schedule adjustments.

Notes

____

____

____

____

____

Actions I Need to Take with Team Members This Week

____

____

____

____

____

____

NOTES

NOTES

A Quick Review

Recall what you learned last week about Oneness Pentecostals by identifying the following statements as true (*T*) or false (*F*).

___ 1. The origin of Oneness Pentecostal beliefs can be traced to R. E. McAlister.
___ 2. One of the largest Oneness Pentecostal organizations in North America is the United Pentecostal Church International.
___ 3. Evangelical Christians and Oneness Pentecostals agree on the biblical view of the Trinity.
___ 4. Evangelical Christians and Oneness Pentecostals agree on the inspiration and authority of the Bible.
___ 5. The Trinitarian view states that there is only one God, who exists in three separate and eternal persons—the Father, the Son, and the Holy Spirit.
___ 6. Oneness Pentecostals believe that the Godhead consists of only two persons—the Son and the Holy Spirit.
___ 7. Oneness Pentecostals baptize converts in the name of the Father, the Son, and the Holy Spirit, just as evangelical Christians do.
___ 8. Although Oneness Pentecostals do not agree with the biblical view of the Trinity, they regard a person's salvation as genuine no matter what he or she believes about the Godhead.
___ 9. Oneness Pentecostals believe that water baptism is required for salvation.
___ 10. Oneness Pentecostals believe that speaking in tongues is essential for salvation.

Check the doctrinal areas in in which Oneness Pentecostals deviate the most from evangelical Christianity.

❑ 1. The Trinity
❑ 2. The inspiration of Scripture
❑ 3. The priesthood of believers
❑ 4. The doctrine of Christ
❑ 5. Angelology
❑ 6. The gifts of the Holy Spirit
❑ 7. The mode of baptism
❑ 8. The role of works in a believer's life
❑ 9. The pervasiveness of sin in the world

The Celebrity Cult

NOTES

Tom Cruise, John Travolta, Anne Archer, Kirstie Alley, Priscilla Presley, Isaac Hayes. If you saw that lineup of stars listed somewhere, you might assume it was for an entertainment awards program, a movie premiere, or a celebrity charity event. Actually, these names are some of the better-known celebrities who have identified themselves with one of the most controversial organizations in the world today, the Church of Scientology, International. These and thousands of other followers of this unusual movement claim that the psychological and spiritual counseling techniques in Scientology changed their lives in positive ways as nothing else had ever done. They testify that Scientology's training freed them from personal problems, guilt, and self-destructive behaviors. Some also claim that Scientology has enhanced their creativity and productivity to achieve greater levels of success in their lives and careers.

Despite these glowing testimonials, Scientology does not enjoy a high public image. Many former adherents and other critics claim that it is nothing more than a vast pseudotherapeutic scheme that dupes people out of their money and, in many cases, harms more than it helps. Also, Scientology has waged a bitter, 25-year battle with the Internal Revenue Service over its religious tax-exempt status, which was restored in 1993.

Scientologists believe that _____ ________ _________________, a late science-fiction writer and psychological theorist, was a genius who discovered the keys to unlocking the secret of human personality and the purpose of life. He is honored by Scientologists with reverence, and his prolific writings are virtually regarded as infallible scriptures.

Born in 1911 in Nebraska, Hubbard claimed that as a child and a young man he traveled the world learning the philosophies, religions, and sciences of many diverse cultures. While earning a living in the 1940s as a pulp science-fiction writer, Hubbard developed a novel theory of human psychology he termed ____________________. In 1950 he published his theory in *Dianetics: The Modern Science of Mental Health*, a controversial book that still appears on some best-seller lists.

Hubbard decided that the best way to spread his ideas was to establish a religion. In 1954 he incorporated the Church of ________________. Hubbard died in 1986, but the Church of Scientology, currently led by David Miscavige, still controls the multimillion-dollar empire Hubbard built from the sales of his books and from the fees charged for his therapeutic methods.

Scientology front organizations include educational groups like Applied Scholastics, the Association for Better Living and Education, and the Way to Happiness Foundation. Therapy programs using Scientology methods include Hubbard Dianetics Centers, Narconon, and Criminon. Business-enhancement seminars are provided by Sterling

NOTES

Management Systems. Many Hollywood celebrities are recruited through Scientology's Celebrity Center training resort in southern California.

Perhaps the most controversial of Scientology's affiliate groups is the Citizens' Commission on Human Rights, created to further its political and social agenda. This agenda includes the abolition of the United States income tax and the Internal Revenue Service, as well as the total discreditation of all traditional psychological and psychiatric therapeutic theories, all of which regard Scientology as scientifically untenable.

Scientology has created a firestorm of controversy worldwide. Several countries have banned the movement or have restricted Scientologists from government service. Regardless of the pros and cons of the social, political, or scientific issues involved, Christians must ask several significant questions about this movement: What does the Church of Scientology teach, and is it compatible with biblical Christianity? Should a Christian participate in Scientology training or therapeutic methods? How can Christians share the good news of Jesus Christ with people involved in the Church of Scientology?

Church of Scientology Beliefs

1. *Humanity's basic problem is ______________.*

L. Ron Hubbard's overarching theory forms the basis of Scientology. He stated that human mental personality is composed of thousands of bits of information collected in the brain since the womb by input through the five senses. These bits establish themselves as permanent images in the mind. Negative bits of information, called engrams, are believed to cause all negative traits in someone's personality. These engrams are located in what Hubbard called the reactive mind, which is irrational, unconscious, and outside a person's control.

2. *Engrams can be eradicated through ______________.*

Hubbard stated that it is possible to gradually remove the effects of engrams and allow a person to attain mental and physical health. Thus, Hubbard designed a therapeutic technique based on his theories, called Dianetics. The therapy, which costs from five hundred to one thousand dollars per session, involves the use of a psychoreactive instrument Hubbard invented called an electropsychometer, or E-meter.

In Hubbard's system a trained therapist, called an auditor, leads a client through a series of sessions by asking specific questions designed to elicit emotional responses. As the questions are issued and the answers received, the client holds in each hand a tubular metal object that resembles an aluminum can. These objects are connected to the E-meter by wires and electrodes.

As the client responds, the auditor closely observes a needle on the E-meter, which moves across a scale in reaction to neuroelectrical stimuli from the clients. It works somewhat on the same principle as a polygraph (lie-detector) machine. Supposedly, these electrical stimuli indicate when a person has mentally uncovered an engram, which can then be expunged from the mind through verbal therapeutic discussions with the auditor. As sessions progress, the client, called a preclear, approaches the goal of freedom from all engrams, a state of mind Hubbard termed clear.

Hubbard's ideas are widely disseminated in the movement's promotional literature and publicly marketed books. However, Scientology teaches other doctrines that are imparted only to committed followers who have advanced along its path to enlightenment. For example, the organization teaches Hubbard's belief that even after a person has attained the state of clear, he will need further auditing to remove the other engrams held over the mind from their lives.

NOTES

3. *A person progresses through* ________________________.

Hubbard taught that human beings are immortal beings consisting of three dimensions: the soul, which is called the thetan; the mind; and the physical body. The thetan and the mind transfer to new bodies as they move down the time track through various physical reincarnations, collecting the baggage of engrams as they go. Only after years of expensive auditing does the person rid himself of the layers of negative energy to become an Operating Thetan.

As someone advances to higher levels of Operating Thetan (paying more and more money as he goes), he learns more of Hubbard's incredible belief system. These secret truths include bizarre tales of ancient alien worlds and humankind's creation. It all sounds very much like something concocted by an imaginative science-fiction writer.

The Church of Scientology's teachings and practices seem strange to most people, especially Christians. Nonetheless, its enthusiastic adherents, such as the celebrities mentioned, claim that it has changed their lives, making them better and more successful people. However, many other former members have testified to their personal abuse and exploitation at the hands of this organization.

Some former Scientology staff members have recounted the extreme methods of accountability and social control exercised over them by the Scientology management. Others have described austere living conditions for church staff, such as requiring several families to share small, church-owned apartments. Still others have spent months at sea working for low wages on a Sea Org (Sea Organization) cruise ship.

Perhaps the most disturbing tactic of Scientology is the way it deals with its critics. The church seems willing to do whatever is necessary, by any means, to silence its opponents, a practice Hubbard called fair game. Its most effective weapon has been using the civil legal system to

NOTES

intimidate those who would expose its esoteric beliefs or publicly criticize its practices. For example, one sociologically oriented countercult organization in the 1980s and '90s often criticized Scientology's pseudoscientific therapeutic principles. It also aided persons wishing to exit the movement. Eventually, the group was driven to bankruptcy defending itself from the church's constant and expensive legal attacks.

Probably the Church of Scientology's most embarrassing moment occurred in 1995, when a staffer at the Church's Sea Org Flag Land Base headquarters in Clearwater, Florida, was stricken ill and died. Other Scientology staffers at the church office building attempted to treat her with Scientology-based methods instead of allowing her to stay in the hospital under the care of the medical staff. The woman, unfortunately, died of a blood clot while being kept at the Scientology building. Her family later filed a wrongful-death suit in Florida court.

This brief explanation of the basics of L. Ron Hubbard's doctrine and the church's practices can lead to only one conclusion: Scientology and Christianity are incompatible. Most of the concepts espoused by Hubbard and Scientology differ from those of the Bible. Scientology's presupposition that humankind's problem rests in the unconscious collection of engrams directly conflicts with the Bible. Scripture teaches that humanity's problem is sin, that is, our tendency toward rebellion against God (see Rom 3:23; 1 John 3:4). This sin results in our alienation from God, who is the source of all meaningful life (see Rom. 6:23; 1 John 5:17).

Scientology's assumption that this problem can be corrected by the process of auditing also conflicts with Christian teaching. Counseling techniques of all kinds may be helpful in dealing with emotional problems. The Bible, however, teaches that true mental and spiritual healing can be realized only by first resolving humankind's sin problem. That can be accomplished only by repenting from sin and putting faith in Jesus Christ alone as Savior and Lord.

In addition, nowhere does the Bible teach concepts of time tracks, past lives, and reincarnation. It teaches that we have one chance in this life, after which comes judgment. Those who have trusted in Christ will inherit eternal life in heaven, and the lost will suffer eternal punishment in hell (see Matt. 25:46; Heb. 9:27).

Witnessing to Scientologists

NOTES

Witnessing to members of the Church of Scientology or those involved in its programs is not a simple process. Remember several specific points as you seek to reach out to them with the gospel.

1. Explain that Scientology and Christianity are ____________________.

Many Scientologists may regard themselves as Christians and may be members of Christian churches. Therefore, they see no contradiction between its practices and the Christian faith. This usually means that the person does not fully understand the teachings of Scientology and/or the basic doctrines of Christianity. In this case establish a friendly relationship with the Scientologist and explain the important differences between the two systems. Carefully detail why they are incompatible and lovingly encourage the person to put his faith in Christ rather than the bizarre notions of L. Ron Hubbard. The FAITH gospel presentation provides a succinct, scriptural explanation of humanity's sin problem and God's solution.

2. Emphasize biblical ______________.

Many Scientologists acknowledge the significant differences between their beliefs and the teachings of the Bible; yet they are unconditionally committed to Hubbard's system. In these cases respectfully present the reasons Christianity is true. Point them to basic apologetic concepts such as the reliability of the Bible; the sinful nature of humanity; the historicity of Jesus' life, death, and resurrection; and the basis for His unique deity and lordship. Sensitively explain why you regard Hubbard's ideas as false.

3. Share your personal ____________________.

Tell your friend that being a Christian does not guarantee that you will not have problems or that you will always be happy. However, Christ is the only one who can cleanse your sin. He gives meaning and purpose that transcend circumstances and emotions. He gives abundant life today and assurance of eternal life when you die. Testify of your personal relationship with Him, His love for all people, and the unchanging truth of His gospel.

If all of the celebrities on earth testified to something that was false, their word would not make it true. Scientology and Christianity cannot both be correct. The issue comes down to one of trust. Do we trust our lives and eternal destinies to a dead L. Ron Hubbard and his strange teachings, or do we trust a living Jesus Christ and the Bible He inspired? Help the Scientologist recognize this crucial choice.

NOTES

Visitation Time

Do It

1. As you visit, view the lost persons you meet with the same sense of urgency you would have for your own family members.
2. On the way to visit, ask Team members what they felt and thought when they looked at the *Step of Faith* picture.
3. Part of your discipling role is to turn over the responsibility to Learners. All Team members should know the FAITH presentation through ***Invitation***. Prepare them to take the lead and present most if not all of the presentation.

Celebration Time

Share It

1. Ask a Team member to take the lead in sharing reports.
2. Hear reports and testimonies.
3. Complete Evaluation Cards.
4. Complete Participation Cards.
5. Update visitation forms with the results of visits.

Home Study Assignments

Home Study Assignments reinforce this session by helping you apply what you have learned.

Your Discipleship Journey

Journaling activities in Your Discipleship Journey are an important part of your development as a Great Commission Christian through FAITH training.

1. Read Ephesians 2:1-10. What has God done to provide the remedy for a depraved mind and sinful nature?

   ____

   ____

2. Read 1 Corinthians 2:11-16. What prerequisite is given for spiritual understanding?

   ____

3. To keep our minds pure, we must practice godly habits. Match the following Scriptures with the practices they encourage.

   ____ 1. Romans 12:1
   ____ 2. Romans 12:2
   ____ 3. 2 Corinthians 10:5
   ____ 4. Ephesians 4:22-24
   ____ 5. Philippians 4:8
   ____ 6. Colossians 3:2

   a. Put off your old self and put on the new self.
   b. Offer your body as a living sacrifice to God.
   c. Set your mind on things above.
   d. Take captive every thought to make it obedient to Christ.
   e. Be transformed by the renewing of your mind.
   f. Think about things that are excellent or praiseworthy.

4. Scientology utilizes the false teaching of reincarnation in claiming to bring its followers to a state of perfection. The Bible teaches resurrection and heaven as the completion of our salvation. What do the following Scriptures teach that the believer receives at the resurrection and in heaven?

   1 Corinthians 15:52-53: ______________________________

   ____

   Philippians 3:20-21: ______________________________

   ____

1 John 3:2: ______________________________

____

Revelation 21:3-5a: ______________________________

____

Revelation 22:3-5: ______________________________

____

Growing as a Life Witness

Growing as a Life Witness reminds you of your responsibility to witness and minister to others during the week.

1. Talk or meet with your accountability partner and share ways you have cultivated a lost person or have witnessed or ministered on occasions other than FAITH visits.
2. Discuss ways you can apply the session 11 content.
3. Pray for lost persons by name and for each other.

Prayer Concerns	Answers to Prayer
____________	____________
____________	____________
____________	____________
____________	____________
____________	____________

Your Weekly Sunday School Leadership Meeting

A FAITH participant is an important member of Sunday School. Encourage Team members who are elected Sunday School workers to attend this weekly meeting. Use this section to record ways your FAITH Team influences the work of your Sunday School class or department. Use the information to report during weekly Sunday School leadership meetings. Identify actions that need to be taken through Sunday School as a result of prayer concerns, needs identified, visits made by the Team, and decisions made by the persons visited. Also identify ways you can disciple others in your Sunday School class or department and in your church.

1. Highlight FAITH visit reports and discuss ways they affect your class/department or age group. Especially highlight results of any evangelistic visits.

____

____

____

2. Indicate any individuals/families who might attend on Sunday as a result of FAITH ministry visits. Will a FAITH Team member meet the guest? How will other class members help newcomers feel at home? If any calls to class members or to prospects need to be made before Sunday, make assignments.

____

____

____

____

3. Participate with others on your leadership team in evaluating the previous session and in discussing ways Sunday's lesson can involve members and guests in transformational Bible study and discipleship.

____

____

____

____

4. Pray for your teacher(s), department director, and others on the leadership team. Intentionally pray for all FAITH Learners, who are at the height of their memory work and leadership in home visits.

____

____

____

Discipling Your Team Members

This weekly feature suggests actions the Team Leader can take to support Team members, prepare for Team Time, and improve visits. This work is part of the Team Leader's Home Study Assignments. Add any actions suggested by your church's FAITH strategy.

Support Team Members

- ❑ Contact Team members during the week. Remind them that you are praying for them. Discuss prayer concerns and answers to prayer.
- ❑ Pray about concerns shared by Team members.

Prepare to Lead Team Time

- ❑ Preview Leading Team Time for session 12.

Prepare to Lead Visits

- ❑ Review the FAITH Visit Outline.
- ❑ Be prepared to explain the benefits of and procedures for making ministry visits.
- ❑ Be prepared to model a visit in which Team member(s) are asked to lead in a visit to the point of the letter *H* (HEAVEN).
- ❑ Be prepared to lead your Team to participate during Celebration Time.

Link with Sunday School

- ❑ Participate in your weekly Sunday School leadership meeting. Share pertinent information in this meeting, using Your Weekly Sunday School Leadership Meeting (pp. 192–93) and FAITH-visit results.
- ❑ Some cults teach that humanity's basic problem is ignorance of its divinity, while Scientology points to the need for psychological healing. Use occasions in Sunday School to teach that the Bible identifies humankind's fundamental problem as sin and clearly presents God's solution.

For Further Growth

For Further Growth may include additional reading or activities that will enhance your growth as a disciple and a discipler of others. These assignments are intended to be long-term projects and do not have to be completed during this semester of study.

1. Read Psalm 119 and notice the power of God's Word for salvation, for living a life that is pleasing to God, and for purifying your mind.
2. Participate in a group study of *MasterLife 2: The Disciple's Personality* by Avery T. Willis Jr. (LifeWay, 1996) to gain a greater understanding of the Christian mind.

Answers to matching activity on page 191: 1. b, 2. e, 3. d, 4. a, 5. f, 6. c

SESSION 12

Practicing FAITH

In this session you will—

CHECK IT by spending the entire time in extended Team Time/ practice activities;

STUDY IT by overviewing Home Study Assignments;

DO IT by making visits in which a Team member may take the lead;

SHARE IT by celebrating.

NOTES

Leading Team Time

All Teams remain together during this session for an extended Team Time. All Team members participate in Team Time. They are primarily responsible for reciting the assigned portion of the FAITH Visit Outline and for discussing other Home Study Assignments.

As you direct this important time of CHECK IT activities with your Team, keep in mind that Learners look to you as a role model, motivator, mentor, and friend. Team Time activities can continue in the car as the Team travels to and from visits.

Lead CHECK IT Activities

✔ *FAITH Visit Outline*

Spend the entire time with your Team members, leading them to practice the entire FAITH Visit Outline. Consider rehearsing appropriate approaches to take in strengthening the skills and confidence of Learners in leading the visit. It may be helpful to suggest that the Team role-play several situations your Team or others have encountered during FAITH training.

FAITH Visit Outline

NOTES

Preparation

INTRODUCTION
INTERESTS
INVOLVEMENT

Church Experience/Background

- Ask about the person's church background.
- Listen for clues about the person's spiritual involvement.

Sunday School Testimony

- Tell general benefits of Sunday School.
- Tell a current personal experience.

Evangelistic Testimony

- Tell a little of your preconversion experience.
- Say: "I had a life-changing experience."
- Tell recent benefits of your conversion.

INQUIRY

Key Question: In your personal opinion, what do you understand it takes for a person to go to heaven?

Possible Answers: Faith, works, unclear, no opinion

Transition Statement: I'd like to share with you how the Bible answers this question, if it is all right. There is a word that can be used to answer this question: FAITH (spell out on fingers).

Presentation

F is for FORGIVENESS

We cannot have eternal life and heaven without God's forgiveness.

"In Him [meaning Jesus] we have redemption through His blood, the forgiveness of sins"—Ephesians 1:7a, NKJV.

A is for AVAILABLE

Forgiveness is available. It is—

AVAILABLE FOR ALL

"For God so loved the world that He gave His only begotten Son, that whoever believes in Him should not perish but have everlasting life" —John 3:16, NKJV.

BUT NOT AUTOMATIC

"Not everyone who says to Me, 'Lord, Lord,' shall enter the kingdom of heaven"—Matthew 7:21a, NKJV.

NOTES

I is for IMPOSSIBLE

It is impossible for God to allow sin into heaven.

GOD IS—

- LOVE
  John 3:16, NKJV
- JUST
  "For judgment is without mercy"—James 2:13a, NKJV.

MAN IS SINFUL

"For all have sinned and fall short of the glory of God"—Romans 3:23, NKJV.

Question: But how can a sinful person enter heaven, where God allows no sin?

T is for TURN

Question: If you were driving down the road and someone asked you to turn, what would he or she be asking you to do? (change direction)

Turn means *repent*.

TURN from something—sin and self

"But unless you repent you will all likewise perish"—Luke 13:3b, NKJV.

TURN to Someone; trust Christ only

(The Bible tells us that) *"Christ died for our sins according to the Scriptures, and that He was buried, and that He rose again the third day according to the Scriptures"—1 Corinthians 15:3b-4, NKJV.*

"If you confess with your mouth the Lord Jesus and believe in your heart that God has raised Him from the dead, you will be saved" —Romans 10:9, NKJV.

H is for HEAVEN

Heaven is eternal life.

HERE

"I have come that they may have life, and that they may have it more abundantly"—John 10:10b, NKJV.

HEREAFTER

"And if I go and prepare a place for you, I will come again and receive you to Myself; that where I am, there you may be also"—John 14:3, NKJV.

HOW

How can a person have God's forgiveness, heaven and eternal life, and Jesus as personal Savior and Lord?

Explain based on leaflet picture, FAITH (Forsaking All, I Trust Him), Romans 10:9.

Invitation

INQUIRE

Understanding what we have shared, would you like to receive this forgiveness by trusting in Christ as your personal Savior and Lord?

INVITE

- Pray to accept Christ.
- Pray for commitment/recommitment.
- Invite to join Sunday School.

INSURE

- Use A *Step of Faith* to insure decision.
- Personal Acceptance
- Sunday School Enrollment
- Public Confession

Visitation Time

Do It

1. Throughout FAITH you have been preparing your Team members to take the lead in a visit. Make sure Team members are informed that they will take the lead in specific visits.
2. As always, be prepared to assist, but do everything you can to encourage Team members to lead the entire visit. Encourage and support them when they make mistakes.

Celebration Time

Share It

1. Ask a Team member to take the lead in sharing reports.
2. Hear reports and testimonies.
3. Complete Evaluation Cards.
4. Complete Participation Cards.
5. Update visitation forms with the results of visits.

NOTES

Home Study Assignments

Home Study Assignments reinforce this session by helping you apply what you have learned.

Your Discipleship Journey

Journaling activities in Your Discipleship Journey are an important part of your development as a Great Commission Christian through FAITH training.

1. Many cults claim to have gifted teachers with special knowledge that leads followers to true spiritual freedom. The Bible describes true teachers who are equipped with God's knowledge and who have been given to the church to equip believers. Identify the qualifications of a true teacher by matching each Scripture with the correct instruction.

____ 1. Ephesians 4:11
____ 2. Ephesians 4:12
____ 3. Ephesians 4:13
____ 4. Ephesians 4:14
____ 5. Ephesians 4:15-16
____ 6. 2 Timothy 2:1-2
____ 7. 2 Timothy 3:14
____ 8. 2 Timothy 3:15-17
____ 9. Titus 1:7-8
____ 10. Titus 1:9

a. Teachers pass on what they have learned.
b. Teachers prepare God's people for service and build up the body of Christ.
c. A godly leader must be blameless, holy, self-controlled, and disciplined.
d. Teaching brings growth in Christ.
e. The Holy Spirit gives the gift of teaching.
f. The goals of teaching are unity in the faith, knowledge of Jesus, and spiritual maturity.
g. A godly leader teaches sound doctrine and refutes those who oppose it.
h. The Scriptures bring wisdom and are useful for teaching and equipping for good works.
i. Teachers arm believers against false teaching and deception.
j. Teachers continue in what they have learned.

2. Read the following Scriptures and summarize what they teach about truth.

Psalm 119:142: ____________________

John 1:14: ____________________

John 4:23-24: ____________________

John 8:32: ____________________

John 14:6: ____________________

John 16:13: ______________________________

John 17:17: ______________________________

Ephesians 4:15: ______________________________

Ephesians 6:14: ______________________________

1 Timothy 2:3-4: ______________________________

2 Timothy 2:15: ______________________________

Growing as a Life Witness

Growing as a Life Witness reminds you of your responsibility to witness and minister to others during the week.

1. Talk or meet with your accountability partner and share ways you have cultivated a lost person or have witnessed or ministered on occasions other than FAITH visits.
2. Pray for lost persons by name and for each other.

Prayer Concerns	Answers to Prayer
______________	______________
______________	______________
______________	______________
______________	______________
______________	______________
______________	______________

Your Weekly Sunday School Leadership Meeting

A FAITH participant is an important member of Sunday School. Encourage Team members who are elected Sunday School workers to attend this weekly meeting. Use this section to record ways your FAITH Team influences the work of your Sunday School class or department. Use the information to report during weekly Sunday School leadership meetings. Identify actions that need to be taken through Sunday School as a result of prayer concerns, needs identified, visits made by the Team, and decisions made by the persons visited. Also identify ways you can disciple others in your Sunday School class or department and in your church.

1. As a result of FAITH visits this week, have any ministry needs surfaced? Any cultivation opportunities? Any need to share information with other departments or age groups for appropriate follow-up? Record actions that need to be taken.

2. When Christians who have previously been reluctant to share their faith become confident and intentional in doing so, 2 Timothy 2:1-2 is made personal. Celebrate as a group if any Learners took the lead in a FAITH visit and had the opportunity to share the FAITH gospel presentation. How did that Learner respond to that opportunity?

3. With others on your leadership team, evaluate last week's session. Discuss ways Sunday's lesson can involve members and guests in transformational Bible study and discipleship.

4. Evaluate the extent to which department/class leaders and members are following up on prospects being contacted through FAITH visits. What actions need to be started or strengthened to better assimilate newcomers into the Sunday School department or class?

5. Pray for your teacher(s) and department director. Also pray for individuals who are considering decisions for Christ. Record names here.

Discipling Your Team Members

This weekly feature suggests actions the Team Leader can take to support Team members, prepare for Team Time, and improve visits. This work is part of the Team Leader's Home Study Assignments. Add any actions suggested by your church's FAITH strategy.

Support Team Members

- ❑ Pray for and personally follow up on any Learner who may need personal encouragement.
- ❑ Contact Team members during the week to remind them that you are praying for them and to discuss their participation in FAITH.
- ❑ Learners are taking the lead in making the visits from this point on. Look for opportunities to encourage each Team member about ways he or she is successfully leading in the visit. Continue to identify ways each Learner can improve.

Prepare to Lead Time Time

- ❑ Preview Leading Team Time for session 13.

Prepare to Participate in Visits

- ❑ Review the FAITH Visit Outline.
- ❑ Identify the Team member who will be responsible for leading specific visits.
- ❑ Be prepared to lead your Team to participate during Celebration Time. Look for ways to encourage Team members to take the lead in reporting during Celebration Time.

Link with Sunday School

- ❑ Participate in your weekly Sunday School leadership meeting. Share pertinent information in this meeting, using Your Weekly Sunday School Leadership Meeting (pp. 201–2) and FAITH-visit results.

Answers to matching activity on page 200: 1. e, 2. b, 3. f, 4. i, 5. d, 6. a, 7. j, 8. h, 9. c, 10. g

FAITH AT WORK

Last Friday a friend, my husband, and I went to see a hockey game. God gave me an opportunity to share the FAITH Visit Outline with two women, and both prayed to receive Christ. What a joy to witness this demonstration of God's faithfulness and love.

People everywhere are waiting to hear the mystery of the gospel. He puts people in my path, and I praise God for giving us the Holy Spirit and for allowing me to be part of His team. The FAITH presentation is so effective, and I thank God for including me in bringing others to Christ through FAITH. What an honor it is to be used by the almighty God.

Ruth Semmler
Metropolitan Baptist Church
Houston, Texas

SESSION 13

The International Churches of Christ

JIMMY FURR

In this session you will—

CHECK IT by engaging in Team Time activities;

KNOW IT by reviewing content from session 11;

HEAR IT by examining the beliefs of the International Churches of Christ and by learning ways to witness to their members;

SEE IT by viewing a video segment;

STUDY IT by overviewing Home Study Assignments;

DO IT by leading your Team in making visits;

SHARE IT by celebrating.

NOTES

Leading Team Time

All Team members participate in Team Time. They are primarily responsible for reciting the assigned portion of the FAITH Visit Outline and for discussing other Home Study Assignments.

As you direct this important time of CHECK IT activities with your Team, keep in mind that Learners look to you as a role model, motivator, mentor, and friend. Team Time activities can continue in the car as the Team travels to and from visits.

Lead CHECK IT Activities

✔ *FAITH Visit Outline*

❑ Listen while each Learner recites the FAITH Visit Outline. Because there is no new memory work, it may be best to ask Learners to recite the segment they have the most difficulty sharing during a visit.

✔ *Session 11 Debriefing*

❑ Because session 12 was a practice session with no new material, debrief session 11. Session 11 focused on the important time when a person is given the opportunity to personally accept God's forgiveness and salvation, so it is important that Team members be well trained. It is even more important that they grow in their sensitivity to the Holy Spirit's prompting during visitation.

❑ Discuss ways Team members are finding *A Step of Faith* helpful in prompting discussion in a visit. If time permits, allow Team members to practice the ***Invitation***, using *A Step of Faith.*

✔ *Help for Strengthening a Visit*

❑ Discuss difficulties the Team has encountered in leading someone to hear and consider the FAITH gospel presentation. Evaluate ways the Team responded to selected experiences and identify appropriate ways to improve responses. Indicate that although most visits go smoothly, next week's session will help all Team members better handle challenges in a visit. Difficulties are things that happen or are said that could keep you from sharing the gospel and leading someone who is ready to respond to make a commitment to Christ. Principles for dealing with difficulties relate primarily to building bridges of relationships with the person, dealing with questions and objections, and working through the obstacles and distractions that take place.

❑ As you talk with Team members during the week, share ways you are seeking to take advantage of your daily-life witnessing opportunities. Also talk with them about opportunities they have to share the gospel during the week with persons they encounter.

Notes

Actions I Need to Take with Team Members This Week

NOTES

NOTES

A Quick Review

In session 11 you were introduced to the Church of Scientology. Check the groups that are front organizations for Scientology.

- ❑ 1. UNICEF
- ❑ 2. ACLU
- ❑ 3. Narconon
- ❑ 4. FAITH
- ❑ 5. Criminon
- ❑ 6. Applied Scholastics
- ❑ 7. Planned Parenthood
- ❑ 8. The Association for Better Living and Education
- ❑ 9. World Hunger Organization
- ❑ 10. Hubbard Dianetics Centers
- ❑ 11. The Way to Happiness Foundation
- ❑ 12. Citizens' Commission on Human Rights

Underline the word or words that best complete each sentence.

1. The founder of the Church of Scientology was (Mary Baker Eddy, L. Ron Hubbard, Sun Myung Moon).
2. Before establishing the Church of Scientology, its founder was (a science-fiction writer, an astronaut, a Baptist minister).
3. Scientology teaches that negative thoughts in the mind, called (habits, sinful thoughts, engrams), cause negative traits in the personality.
4. Scientologists use an (electropsychometer, electrode, encoder) to identify negative information that needs to be removed from a person's reactive mind to allow the person to succeed.
5. When a person reaches the goal of total freedom from all engrams through therapy with an auditor, he is in a state called (E-freedom, clear, perfection).
6. The term Hubbard used to define the soul is (spirit, collective mind, thetan).
7. Scientology teaches that when a person dies, he moves down the time track through (space-time travel, reincarnation, spatial continuums).

The One True Church

Jack sat down at the cafeteria table with his lunch. A small group of other students was at the next table. "Hi," a young woman said to him. "I'm Sherry, and this is Bob and Mitch. What's your name?"

"Jack."

"We're having a Bible study tonight at Bob's apartment near campus," she said. "Do you like to study the Bible?"

"Well, yeah. I usually go to church when I go home," Jack replied a bit sheepishly. They had caught him off guard.

"Do you want to come to our Bible study? It starts with food at 6:30.

Here's the address." She handed him a small leaflet invitation with a map. "See you tonight?" they asked him with big smiles.

"Why not?" Jack responded.

Today on many college campuses and in other places where young adults congregate, a growing movement is befriending Christian students, many of whom are out on their own for the first time and need support. That movement is the International Churches of Christ. On the surface, the International Churches of Christ may seem like any other American religious group. However, like many fringe churches that appear to be orthodox, the teachings and the methods of growth deviate from Christianity in important ways.

Paul Martin, in his book *Cult-Proofing Your Kids*, lists several characteristics of fringe churches:

- Control-oriented ______________________
- Spiritual ______________
- _________________________ of members
- Harsh ____________________ of members
- Painful __________ processes[1]

Most of these characteristics describe the International Churches of Christ. Although this sect follows orthodox Christian teachings about God and Jesus Christ, it demands cultic allegiance to the church and its leaders. For example, this strong disciplinarian group teaches that the International Churches of Christ are the only true church. Salvation comes only through this church and its baptism. Members' salvation also depends on their active recruitment of new disciples. Leaders are not to be questioned, because doing so would amount to questioning God. Consequences must be paid when church teachings are not followed. Many members fear that if they leave the church, they will lose their salvation or at least their friends and fellowship.

The International Churches of Christ began as part of the Crossroads Church of Christ, a mainline Church of Christ in Gainesville, Florida. The first leader of the movement was ____________ ____________, who was the minister of the Crossroads church and also led the campus ministry at the University of Florida. One of Lucas's students was ________ ________________, whom Lucas baptized in 1972. After being discipled by Crossroads ministers and after graduating from the University of Florida, McKean served as a mainline Churches of Christ campus minister at Eastern Illinois University. However, he and an associate, Roger Lamb, were released from their responsibilities because of their aggressive discipling methods.

In 1979 the Lexington, Massachusetts, Church of Christ invited McKean to serve as pulpit and campus minister. There McKean and 29 others committed themselves to restoring biblical Christianity to the world. International Churches of Christ leaders point to that event as the foundation of their restoration movement. Over the next few years

NOTES

NOTES

McKean and his team developed their philosophy of ____________ and designed their strategy for expansion. In 1983 McKean's church began holding services in Boston Opera House and changed the church's name to the Boston Church of Christ. For this reason many people still identify the movement as the Boston Movement.

During this period the Boston Church maintained ties with Chuck Lucas and the Crossroads Church of Christ in Florida. However, in 1985 the Crossroads church dismissed Lucas as minister because of alleged moral indiscretions. Shortly after that, Kip McKean and the Boston Movement broke fellowship with the Crossroads church, which retained its status within the mainline Churches of Christ.

In 1990 McKean moved his headquarters to the Los Angeles area. In 1993 the name was officially changed to the ________________ ________________ ____ ______________. Today the name of a specific congregation is usually derived from the name of the city where the congregation is located. For instance, in Nashville, Tennessee, the church is called the Nashville Church. The International Churches of Christ now have a membership of more than _________ in _____ churches in ______ countries.[2]

Although the International Churches of Christ sprang from mainline Churches of Christ, their primary teachings are far apart. Mainline Churches of Christ trace their roots to Alexander Campbell, who patterned the church after the New Testament church. This Christian denomination uses nonordained (lay) leadership, allows no musical instruments other than voices in worship, and is conservative in theology. Both mainline and International Churches of Christ believe that baptism is necessary for salvation, and both groups claim that the Bible is at the heart of their teaching.

The International Churches of Christ depart from mainline Churches of Christ in a number of ways. The International Churches of Christ do not accept the baptism of a mainline church. Only baptism in an International Church of Christ is legitimate. For the International Churches of Christ, only disciplers are Christians. The recruiting methods of the International Churches of Christ are far more intrusive than those employed by mainline Churches of Christ.

Beliefs of the International Churches of Christ

1. The International Churches of Christ are the one true ______________.

The International Churches of Christ teach that only members of their particular church are saved. All mainline churches are doomed to hell. Because their salvation is tied to the church, International Churches of Christ members are reluctant to leave the group. Therefore, fear is a major barrier to a Christian who tries to reach an International Churches of Christ member. Individuals feel there would be no hope for someone who leaves the one true church that dominates their lives so completely.

The Christian view is that the true church is not identified with one specific organization. In the New Testament the term *church* (Greek, *ecclesia*) refers to people who are God's called-out ones. It does not refer to an organization but to all redeemed people of God (see Rev. 7:9). The true church of Christ is not limited to one time or place but consists of diverse local fellowships of believers who regularly unite for corporate worship, study, discipleship, prayer, ministry, and evangelism.

2. _______________ *in the church is required for salvation.*

Baptism in an International Church of Christ is essential for salvation. No other church's baptism is valid, including that of a mainline Church of Christ. Baptism is considered the moment of salvation. International Churches of Christ, along with other advocates of baptismal regeneration, argue that some Bible verses teach the necessity of water baptism to demonstrate a person's faith and to receive the forgiveness of sins. One such verse is Mark 16:16: " 'He who has believed and has been baptized shall be saved; but he who has disbelieved shall be condemned.' " A careful analysis of this verse reveals that it cannot be used to establish the necessity of baptism. Although the first clause states that those who believe and are baptized are saved, it does not necessarily require that the converse is true. In other words, it does not identify who is lost. The second clause answers that question: those who do not believe. The verse does not say that those who are not baptized are lost but establishes the necessity of belief in Christ to avoid condemnation. To argue that this verse requires baptism for salvation is illogical and goes beyond what the verse actually says.

Another commonly quoted passage is Acts 2:38: "Peter said to them, 'Repent, and each of you be baptized in the name of Jesus for the forgiveness of your sins; and you will receive the gift of the Holy Spirit.' " Again, the text does not specify baptism as the cause of salvation. The phrase "for the forgiveness of your sins" is to be interpreted "on account of the forgiveness of your sins."

The International Churches of Christ's insistence that baptism by immersion is a requirement for salvation is biblically unwarranted. The clear teaching of the Bible is that salvation is entirely the result of grace through faith in Jesus Christ (see Eph. 2:8).

NOTES

NOTES

3. *Making* ________________ *is required for salvation.*

The International Churches of Christ are a shepherding group. This means that members are expected to bring other persons into the fold. Salvation is tied to the amount of discipling, defined as bringing others into the church, an individual does. If discipling is not a part of members' lives, they are not considered saved. In the International Churches of Christ system, salvation is entirely related to fruit—in other words, how many new disciples are recruited. If members do not recruit, they are not saved. Numbers are required of each member each day.

The method of discipling practiced by the International Churches of Christ is hierarchical and pyramidal in structure. An authoritarian relationship exists between the discipler and the disciple. Confessions of sins, submission, obedience, and imitation of the discipler are expected. All decisions are taken to the discipler for approval, including dating, dating partners, the number of times couples may date, and giving tithes to the local congregation.

The chain of command goes from the disciple to Bible-talk leaders to house-church leaders to zone leaders to section leaders and then to lead evangelists. The final group in the hierarchy is the world-sector leaders, who are discipled by Kip McKean. McKean, however, is not discipled by anyone.

Most Christians would argue that the International Churches of Christ's stringent discipleship requirements exceed biblical expectations. The purpose of discipleship, as revealed in Scripture, is healthy spiritual growth for the individual and the body of Christ, which leads to loving fellowship, Christlike ministry, bold evangelism, and the building of Christ's kingdom. The Bible teaches that discipleship is a result of the Holy Spirit's work in the life of a believer (see Gal. 5:22-23; Eph. 4: 11-16), not something the believer does to earn salvation. Salvation is neither received nor maintained by works. Salvation is based entirely on grace through faith in Jesus Christ alone. Good works and righteous living are the result of salvation, not its cause (see Eph. 2:8-10).

4. *The church has absolute* ________________.

With any shepherding group, concerns arise over the basis of authority and the exercise of that authority. The International Churches of Christ seek to dominate the individual's life. School and other secular activities are frowned on. In fact, because so much time is spent with the group, members have little time for anything else. Disciples are often told when to date, whom to date, and how often. Dating outside the group is forbidden. Dating restrictions within the group are also regulated.

Exclusion of involvement with persons outside the church is strictly enforced. Roommates, parents, and friends are neglected. The church fears that contact with these persons might cause a member to ask questions and doubt the church and its authority. Parents, usually considered of the devil, are to be avoided. Many college students are told not to go home for the holidays but to stay at college and spend time with the group.

The church demands not only members' time but also their money. Disciples are expected to tithe. In fact, giving is an essential part of the individual's salvation. As with any works-related salvation system, everything is tied to what members do and how much they do it. If they do not have the money, they are encouraged to borrow it and to do whatever it takes to keep their tithes active. When special offerings are taken, International Churches of Christ members are expected to give. Again, borrowing money is suggested if they do not have the money to give. Disciples are accountable to their disciplers for their giving. If members fail to give, their disciplers confront them and continue to remind them until their tithing is caught up.

Spiritually abusive groups like the International Churches of Christ routinely use guilt, fear, and intimidation as effective means to recruit and control their members.[3] They may manipulate by using love bonding or "bombing" and acceptance as a lead or hook. Phone calls and sudden visits are common tactics. Many use guilt not only to recruit people for the church but also to keep them involved: "I have done all this for you; the least you could do is to attend a meeting."

The International Churches of Christ's authoritarian leadership style is also reflected in its approach to Bible teaching. The meaning of Scripture is twisted, and minute portions of Scripture are used to teach a point. The church does not allow any other interpretations, especially those of an individual member. Total authority is vested in the leader of the Bible study, and the training process is virtually a cloning of the group's leader. In their book *The Boston Movement* cult experts Carol Giambalvo and Herbert L. Rosedale comment, "Any right of personal interpretation is expressly and explicitly forbidden and interpretation is not based on a consensus of members, scholars, or any others than the leaders of this one movement."[4]

A Christian response to the International Churches of Christ's authoritarian stance is to emphasize that the only absolute head of the true church is Jesus Christ (see Eph. 1:22-23; Col. 1:18). As the living body of Christ in the world (see 1 Cor. 12:12-27), the church exists not to control individuals and alienate families but to build the Kingdom and exalt Jesus Christ. The New Testament picture of the church is a fellowship of believers (see 1 Pet. 2:9-10) who are united in love for ministry (see Acts 2:42-47) and mission (see Eph. 4:11-13). The church is also referred to as the family of believers (see Gal. 6:10; Eph. 2:19). As brothers and sisters in Christ, we are to love one another (see 1 John 3:11), not exercise control and tyranny over one another (see 1 John 4:18). In addition, a system that encourages division within families is not biblical, for God ordained the family (see Gen. 2:18-24; Ps. 128:3-6).

NOTES

NOTES

Witnessing to International Churches of Christ Members

1. *Know relevant Christian _______________.*

Understand your faith and have a general knowledge of biblical doctrines, particularly salvation by grace, baptism, eternal security, and the church, as well as biblical support for these beliefs. Appeal to the Bible's teaching, not to your own knowledge or to any leader's authority. As in discussions with any cult or sect member, define your terms biblically and ask the person to define hers so that your communication will be clear.

Also seek to educate children and young people on Bible knowledge and biblical doctrines. Children's and Youth Bible Drills can play a major role in shielding children and youth from the dangers of becoming involved in a group like the International Churches of Christ. When they hide God's Word in their hearts, they build an inner resistance to the tricks of the devil and to the manipulative twisting of Scripture.

2. *Offer ___________________ and _______________.*

Because many people are drawn into the International Churches of Christ due to a need to belong, acts of loving ministry may effectively influence the person. Show that your church is not an elitist group but offers a loving, open environment of grace in which persons can be accepted, ask questions, receive help, and grow in their relationships with God. Be prepared to spend time ministering to and discipling those who wish to exit the sect.

3. *Present the way to be assured of _______________.*

International Churches of Christ use fear and intimidation to maintain their hold on followers. Therefore, members are afraid to exit the movement for fear of losing their salvation. Use the FAITH gospel presentation to make sure the person is saved. Then assure her that her salvation does not depend on remaining in an International Church of Christ. Provide biblical support to emphasize that her salvation is secure (see Rom. 8:16,38-39; 2 Tim. 1:12).

4. *Equip young people to ___________.*

Centralized and authoritarian churches like the International Churches of Christ present many possibilities for abuse and opportunities for distorted biblical interpretations. Psychological and emotional dependency and unhealthy personality alterations are possible. A member's family is often alienated, and extreme separation is encouraged. With this type of siege mentality comes the rejection of Christian influences in the person's life.

Christians must not make the mistake of thinking that the Christian young people they know or come in contact with are not at risk of becoming involved in a sect. Even though they have been reared in the church, all young people and young adults are vulnerable to these types of influences. Our churches need to teach children and youth broad skills for appraising religious groups. We need to teach them skills for critical thinking and analysis and to teach them to recognize the signs of thought-reform movements, such as desiring to control an individual's entire life, exercising unbalanced discipling methods, denying freedom to decide, and prohibiting disagreement.

Keep the lines of communication open with youth and college students. When parents notice changes in grades, relationships with friends, and association with them, they should take action to discover the cause. If necessary, remove minor students from the situation. For college students a family intervention may be necessary to allow time to persuade them to leave the movement.

NOTES

Visitation Time

Do It

1. As you make visits with your Team, look for opportunities to connect lost persons with Sunday School classes that can love and minister to them.
2. This week Learners have learned how to live FAITH in daily life. Share with them how this happens in your life.
3. Learners should have memorized the entire FAITH Visit Outline. Provide opportunities to let them share in FAITH visits.

Celebration Time

Share It

1. Ask a Team member to take the lead in sharing reports.
2. Hear reports and testimonies.
3. Complete Evaluation Cards.
4. Complete Participation Cards.
5. Update visitation forms with the results of visits.

Home Study Assignments

Home Study Assignments reinforce this session by helping you apply what you have learned.

Your Discipleship Journey

Journaling activities in Your Discipleship Journey are an important part of your development as a Great Commission Christian through FAITH training.

1. The International Churches of Christ encourage followers to reject and limit contact with their families. Summarize what the following Scripture passages teach about the place of family in a Christian's life.

   Deuteronomy 6:4-9: ______________________________

   ____

   ____

   Joshua 24:15: ______________________________

   ____

   Proverbs 6:20-23: ______________________________

   ____

   Ephesians 5:22,25: ______________________________

   ____

   Ephesians 6:1-4: ______________________________

   ____

   ____

   Colossians 3:18-20: ______________________________

   ____

2. International Churches of Christ members fear losing their salvation. On the following page, match the Scriptures with the truths they teach about a believer's eternal security.

___ 1. Luke 22:31-32
___ 2. Romans 8:38-39
___ 3. Ephesians 1:4-5
___ 4. Ephesians 1:13-14
___ 5. Philippians 1:6
___ 6. 1 John 1:8-10

a. Conviction and confession of sin bring assurance.
b. God initiates and completes salvation.
c. Nothing separates us from Christ.
d. God chose us to be adopted as His sons.
e. Jesus guarantees that our faith never fails.
f. The Holy Spirit guarantees heaven.

3. Doubt about salvation can be caused by ignorance of God's Word; unconfessed sin; lack of prayer; or habitual, reccurring sin. Are any of these areas affecting your confidence in your salvation or in your spiritual growth? If so, list and confess these to the Lord. Plan changes you need to make.

____

____

Growing as a Life Witness

Growing as a Life Witness reminds you of your responsibility to witness and minister to others during the week.

1. Talk or meet with your accountability partner and share ways you have cultivated a lost person or have witnessed or ministered on occasions other than FAITH visits.
2. Discuss ways you can apply the session 13 content.
3. Pray for lost persons by name and for each other.

Prayer Concerns	Answers to Prayer
____________________	____________________
____________________	____________________
____________________	____________________
____________________	____________________
____________________	____________________

Your Weekly Sunday School Leadership Meeting

A FAITH participant is an important member of Sunday School. Encourage Team members who are elected Sunday School workers to attend this weekly meeting. Use this section to record ways your FAITH Team influences the work of your Sunday School class or department. Use the information to report during weekly Sunday School leadership meetings. Identify actions that need to be taken through Sunday School as a result of prayer concerns, needs identified, visits made by the Team, and decisions made by the persons visited. Also identify ways you can disciple others in your Sunday School class or department and in your church.

1. Highlight FAITH visit results and discuss needs that affect your class/ department or age group. Are prospect-discovery activities continuing to generate good prospect information?

____

2. Participate with others on your leadership team in evaluating last week's session and in discussing ways Sunday's lesson can involve members and guests in transformational Bible study and discipleship.

____

3. How should preparation for Sunday consider the needs of individuals or families visited through FAITH?

____

4. In what ways can the truths you discovered in this session be communicated with the rest of your Sunday School leadership team? With fellow class members?

____

5. Discuss ways to involve members in praying for and celebrating God's leadership in raising up new persons to begin FAITH training.

____

6. Pray for your teacher and other leadership. Request prayer for any persons contacted through Opinion Poll visits.

Discipling Your Team Members

This weekly feature suggests actions the Team Leader can take to support Team members, prepare for Team Time, and improve visits. This work is part of the Team Leader's Home Study Assignments. Add any actions suggested by your church's FAITH strategy.

Support Team Members

❑ Contact Team members during the week. Remind them that you are praying for them. Discuss prayer concerns and answers to prayer.
❑ As you talk with Learners this week, discuss opportunities they have for

witnessing during the week. Encourage them as they seek to witness to persons they encounter.
- ❑ Pray for needs and concerns shared by Team members.

Prepare to Lead Team Time
- ❑ Review Team members' Home Study Assignments.
- ❑ Preview Leading Team Time for session 14.

Prepare to Lead Visits
- ❑ Review the FAITH Visit Outline.

Link with Sunday School
- ❑ Participate in your weekly Sunday School leadership meeting. Share pertinent information in this meeting, using Your Weekly Sunday School Leadership Meeting (pp. 217–18) and FAITH-visit results.
- ❑ Ask Sunday School leaders to think about others who may become involved in FAITH training.
- ❑ International Churches of Christ foster an unhealthy dependence on the fellowship of the sect. Make sure your Sunday School and church offer a sense of acceptance and belonging that is based on the love of Christ.

For Further Growth
For Further Growth may include additional reading or activities that will enhance your growth as a disciple and a discipler of others. These assignments are intended to be long-term projects and do not have to be completed during this semester of study.
1. Read *Saved Without a Doubt* by John MacArthur (Chariot Victor, 1992).
2. Using the Books of Ephesians and 1 Peter, discover your access to spiritual truth, your privileges in possessing spiritual truth, and your responsibilities for handling spiritual truth.
3. Participate in a group study of *Jesus on Leadership* by C. Gene Wilkes (LifeWay, 1996) to understand what it means to be a spiritual leader in the local church.
4. Using the New Testament Epistles, research and discover the qualities of a biblical New Testament church.
5. Read the FAITH Tip on page 220.

---
[1]Paul R. Martin, *Cult-Proofing Your Kids* (Grand Rapids: Zondervan, 1993), 31–32.
[2]"Growth Charts," *International Churches of Christ*, *<http://www.icoc.org/html/whoset.html>* (1 August 2000).
[3]Ronald M. Enroth, *Churches That Abuse* (Grand Rapids: Zondervan, 1992), 103.
[4]Carol Giambalvo and Herbert L. Rosedale, *The Boston Movement* (Bonita Springs, FL: American Family Foundation, 1997), 17.

Answers to matching activity on page 217: 1. e, 2. c, 3. d, 4. f, 5. b, 6. a

FAITH TIP

What Is the True Church?

According to the Church of Jesus Christ of Latter-day Saints, in 1820 young Joseph Smith Jr. was told by Jesus Himself that he should join none of the existing churches, because "they were all wrong ... that all their creeds were an abomination in his sight; that those professors were all corrupt."[1] That statement typifies the views of many sects and cults that all mainline Christian churches are apostate and have lost the essence of true Christianity. Thus, as the Mormons still assert, theirs is the only true church on the face of the earth.

Jehovah's Witnesses believe their leadership organization, the Watchtower Bible and Tract Society, is God's only channel of truth and salvation. Most Jehovah's Witnesses will not enter a Christian church, fearing it is inhabited by demons and, if Armageddon came while they were inside, they would be killed.

Other movements make similar exclusivistic claims., referring to themselves by various terms like the restored church, the remnant church, or the end-times church. Christians may wonder, *What is the true church?* Scripture reveals several key indicators that identify the true church of Jesus Christ.

1. *The true church is the redeemed people of God.*

The true church is not identified with any one specific organization. In the New Testament the term *church* (Greek, *ecclesia*) refers to people who are God's called-out ones. It does not refer to an organization but to all redeemed people of God (see Matt. 16:18).

2. *The true church is local fellowships of believers.*

The true church of Christ is not limited to one time or place but consists of diverse local fellowships of believers who regularly unite for corporate worship, study, discipleship, prayer, ministry, and evangelism.The primary models used in the New Testament are the body of Christ (see 1 Cor. 12:12-27) and the living temple of God (see Eph. 2:19-22).

3. *The only absolute head of the true church is Jesus Christ.*

Local congregations may have pastors, deacons, elders, and higher levels of authority. None can claim exclusive authority over all churches or claim to be more divinely anointed than all others. Any group that claims modern apostolic, prophetic, or messianic leadership or a unique corner on biblical understanding is overstepping the legitimate bounds of biblical authority (see Matt. 16:15-19; 18:15-20; Acts 14:23-27; 16:5; 20:28; Rom. 1:7; 1 Cor. 1:2; 3:16; Eph. 1:22-23; 4:11-13; 1 Tim. 3:1-15; 4:14; 1 Pet. 5:1-4; Rev. 2—3).

---

[1]*The Pearl of Great Price*, "Joseph Smith—History," 2:19–20.

FAITH AT WORK

I grew up in a Christian home. My parents were examples of godliness, so I'm not sure how I messed up so badly. At 18 I threw away college and my family to join a religious cult, trying to fill a void in my life. I was married only one month after high-school graduation and then had two children. At 22 I was a divorced, single mom. I got a job and worked long hours trying to succeed, hoping to find satisfaction at the top or at least in material things. I neglected my two children and lost custody of them. I quickly remarried and had another baby, only to have that husband leave me after only one year. I then turned to alcohol, drugs, and partying all night. I've even spent a few nights in jail. Meanwhile, my father was diagnosed with cancer and was withering away. I was so ashamed of my life that I stayed away when my family needed me most.

When I thought I couldn't mess up my life any worse, I got involved with a guy who was just as much trouble as I was, with a past as ugly as mine. We tried everything to be happy but just dug ourselves into a hole, getting into more trouble. When we got so far down that we could only look up, we decided to try church. After all, church seemed to make my parents happy, even through the rough times. For three months we attended Highview, but we sat in the back and kept to ourselves. Then one Sunday our hearts were convicted, and my husband asked the pastor for help. That Wednesday evening the pastor's FAITH Team visited us, and we discovered how FAITH could make a difference in our lives:

F I needed forgiveness and a lot of it!
A It was available even to me but not automatic.
I It's impossible for God to let sin into heaven, so I wasn't going to get there unless …
T I turned from my sin and trusted Jesus.
H I found out that I could experience heaven here and now on earth and for eternity with Jesus, my Savior. Then I found out how.

So on February 3, 1999, Michael and I accepted Jesus into our lives. My void was filled. On February 14, 1999, we were baptized together. What we have experienced since is unexplainable. We have truly had a life-changing experience. With Jesus in our lives, Michael and I have an incredible relationship. We now know what true friends are. We don't hang out at the bars anymore; we don't even miss them! The Christian life isn't boring as we anticipated. Our Sunday School class has been supportive through all of our life changes. Never has anyone looked down on us for where we have been or what we have done.

Michael and I now have a two-year-old son. Michael adopted my third child, the one whose dad left her. I also regained custody of my two older children, who had been taken from me. I'm now blessed to be a stay-at-home mom, working to make up lost time with my children. Our house is now a happy home. Instead of bad words and arguments, we hear things like "Can I take my purple baby to heaven with me?" My 10-year-old son has accepted Jesus into his life. Our children are telling all of their friends about Jesus and inviting them to church.

I also want to tell everyone I meet and know about God and what He has done in my life and for my family. It is truly a miracle that only He could have done. I hope my former way of life will serve as an example of what not to do. I don't want anyone to endure the loneliness and pain I experienced because I chose to do things my way instead of God's way. Even though I had been active in church as a teen, going on mission trips, singing in the youth choir, and helping in Vacation Bible School, none of those things gained me salvation or true happiness. The difference came when I accepted Jesus into my life. I am now confident that all of the ugly things I did are forgiven. They are forgotten, covered up with Jesus' blood. I am now enjoying heaven here on earth.

And my dad—God gave him a second chance at life. I look at it, though, as a second chance for me to prove to him that I can be the daughter he deserves, the mom and wife he taught me to be—God's way!

DiAnna Breeding
Highview Baptist Church
Louisville, Kentucky

SESSION 14

The Seventh-day Adventist Church

TAL DAVIS

In this session you will—

CHECK IT by engaging in Team Time activities;

KNOW IT by reviewing content from session 13;

HEAR IT by examining the beliefs of Seventh-day Adventists and by learning ways to witness to them;

STUDY IT by overviewing Home Study Assignments;

DO IT by leading your Team in making visits;

SHARE IT by celebrating.

NOTES

Leading Team Time

All Team members participate in Team Time. They are primarily responsible for reciting the assigned portion of the FAITH Visit Outline and for discussing other Home Study Assignments.

As you direct this important time of CHECK IT activities with your Team, keep in mind that Learners look to you as a role model, motivator, mentor, and friend. Team Time activities can continue in the car as the Team travels to and from visits.

Lead CHECK IT Activities

✔ *FAITH Visit Outline*

- ❑ Listen while each Learner recites as much of the FAITH Visit Outline as time allows. Make sure each person has a turn. It may be best to ask Learners to recite the segment they have the most difficulty sharing during a visit.
- ❑ As time permits, allow for additional practice on any part of the visit presentation, sequence, and materials (*My Next Step of Faith—Baptism*, for example).

✔ *Session 13 Debriefing*

- ❑ Review: The FAITH Sunday School Evangelism Strategy is designed to help equip the Sunday School member and leader to share the gospel and minister to prospects and members. A strength of this evangelism training is that participants learn a simple yet direct approach to talking with people about the message of the gospel when visiting with a Team of three. Another wonderful benefit is that someone who learns to share the gospel becomes more aware of witnessing opportunities during encounters throughout the week. Remind Team members that, as they continue training, they will become more aware of opportunities to share both a verbal and a lifestyle witness with people whose lives they intersect.

✔ *Help for Strengthening a Visit*

- ❑ Discuss some of the difficulties Teams have encountered in leading someone to hear and consider the FAITH gospel presentation. Call attention to the fact that this session formally introduces Learners to ways to deal with difficulties and distractions. At the same time, Team Leaders and other participants will learn other ways to help their Teams respond appropriately.
- ❑ As time allows, consider sharing a copy of the Witness Awareness Quotient (from *Building Bridges Through FAITH*) for Team members

to use at their convenience. Or discuss some things you learned as a result. Briefly help Team members see the impact of increasing their awareness of witnessing opportunities. It is one way to focus attention on strengthening both lifestyle and verbal opportunities to witness.

Notes

____

____

____

____

____

____

____

____

Actions I Need to Take with Team Members This Week

____

____

____

____

____

____

____

____

____

NOTES

NOTES

A Quick Review

Last week you studied the International Churches of Christ. Check the tactics the churches use to enlist members and to keep them faithful.

- ❑ 1. Teaching spiritual elitism
- ❑ 2. Communal living
- ❑ 3. Fear
- ❑ 4. Hierarchical discipleship
- ❑ 5. Tolerance of all religions
- ❑ 6. Trust
- ❑ 7. Domination
- ❑ 8. Privacy
- ❑ 9. Salvation by works
- ❑ 10. Intimidation
- ❑ 11. Teaching God's grace
- ❑ 12. Control-oriented leadership
- ❑ 13. Strong family relationships
- ❑ 14. Involvement in politics
- ❑ 15. Love bonding or "bombing"
- ❑ 16. Guilt
- ❑ 17. Excluding involvement with outsiders
- ❑ 18. Discouraging monetary support
- ❑ 19. Psychological dependency

Underline the best word or phrase to complete each sentence.

1. The primary doctrinal error of the International Churches of Christ is their (view of angels, denial of Christ's virgin birth, view of salvation by works).
2. Implied guilt and (Scripture twisting, Bible study, singing) are used to manipulate members in the International Churches of Christ.
3. The moment of salvation happens when a member of an International Church of Christ (tithes, leaves his family, is baptized).
4. Disciples are encouraged to tithe. If they do not have money, they are encouraged to (make a pledge, pray, borrow money).
5. Members are taught that only members of (their particular church, a mainline Church of Christ, a FAITH church) are saved.
6. The International Churches of Christ target (other churches, assisted-living complexes, college campuses) to recruit new members.
7. An effective way to reach an International Church of Christ member is to offer (tea and crumpets, acceptance and ministry, free Bibles).

Keepers of the Sabbath

Steve had just been named the manager of his office unit and wanted to do something special for his new team. "I've got a great idea for team building," he announced at the first staff meeting. How about next Saturday morning we all go and play a round of paintball together?"

"Sounds like fun! Let's go for it!" was the general response. A few minutes after the meeting, however, Ann approached Steve. "I'm sorry, Steve, but I won't be able to attend that day."

"Family conflict?" he inquired.

"Well, sort of. That's when we go to church. We're Seventh-day

Adventists, and we believe that Saturday is the Sabbath," Ann asserted.

Steve, a Baptist, asked, "But don't we worship on the first day of the week because the early Christians did?"

"We disagree," Ann replied. "It's right there in the Ten Commandments: 'Remember the sabbath day, to keep it holy.' You follow the other nine Commandments, don't you?"

"Of course," Steve replied.

"Then why do you think the fourth one isn't valid?" she asked.

"I … I don't know," Steve stammered. "I've never thought about it."

Steve and Ann's conversation illustrates the confusion that sometimes exists between evangelical Christians and Seventh-day Adventists, members of one of the fastest-growing religious organizations in the world today. Most evangelical Christians have only a slight acquaintance with the teachings of the Seventh-day Adventist Church. They are often unprepared to answer Seventh-day Adventists' doctrinal challenges. In this session we will examine Seventh-day Adventists' history and distinctive doctrines, and we will suggest ways evangelicals can respectfully respond to them.

The Seventh-day Adventist Church traces its origin to the visions and oracles of a young woman from Maine named Ellen G White (1827–1915). Claiming a supernatural gift of prophetic utterance, she maintained that God told her that the middle 1800s marked a milestone in history for God's work in the last days. She later claimed that God revealed to her that He was greatly displeased with the Christian church's practice of worshiping on Sunday rather than observing the divinely appointed seventh-day Saturday.

With the help of her husband, James White, Ellen proclaimed her message and became known as the Seventh day Adventist. In 1863 she established the Seventh-day Adventist Church in Battle Creek, Michigan. Ellen G. White died in 1915, but her movement lives on, led by the General Conference of Seventh-day Adventists, which is headquartered in Silver Springs, Maryland. The current General Conference president is Jan Paulsen.

Today the Seventh-day Adventist Church is a diverse worldwide movement with ________________ members (891,000 in North America). Popular national radio and television ministries associated with the church include "The Voice of Prophecy," "Amazing Facts," and "It is Written." Publishing houses include Review and Herald Publishing Association and Pacific Press Publishing Association, which continue to publish White's works, along with other popular books such as *Uncle Arthur's Bedtime Stories* and *The Bible Story* children's series.

Seventh-day Adventist universities and medical institutions have attracted international attention for their research and academic excellence. These include Andrews University, the Kettering College of Medical Arts, and Loma Linda University.

NOTES

NOTES

Seventh-day Adventist Beliefs

Seventh-day Adventists affirm the basic historic doctrines of the Christian faith. According to official Seventh-day Adventist documents, the church teaches the biblical doctrines of the Trinity and affirms Jesus Christ's unique deity, sinless life, death, and bodily resurrection. Thus, Seventh-day Adventists do not fit the profile of most pseudo-Christian cults. Nonetheless, the Seventh-day Adventist Church has several unusual doctrinal distinctives that distinguish it from nearly all other Christian denominations, qualifying the church as a Christian sect.

1. *Seventh-day Adventists are the* ________________ ________________.

The Seventh-day Adventist Church has historically insisted that it is the remnant church of the last days. Seventh-day Adventist ministers teach that they are the only church that correctly and fully observes God's law, particularly in regard to the Sabbath. Seventh-day Adventists therefore regard all other Christian churches as being in a state of apostasy, asserting that after the New Testament era the Sabbath was wrongfully abolished by the paganized Roman Church. Ellen G. White claimed that God Himself confirmed this apostasy to her in visions, which she later codified in her books on world and church history.

Evangelical Christians challenge White's supposed revelations. No single organization or church that is limited to one time and place can make the exclusive claim to be the true or remnant church, as do most cults and sects. The Bible teaches that the church universal consists of all true believers in Christ in all times and places (see Matt. 16:18).

2. *The Sabbath is the seal of the* Beast.

Perhaps the best-known tenet of Seventh-day Adventist teaching is its contention that the biblical Sabbath should be observed from sundown on Friday until sundown on Saturday (the seventh day). They argue that this practice was established by God at creation (see Gen. 2:2-3), was confirmed by God in the Ten Commandments (see Ex. 20:8-11), and was followed by Jesus and the apostles (see Luke 4:16).

Sunday worship is regarded as the foremost sign of the Christian church's general apostasy. White taught that in the last days all Christians will be required by law to worship on Sunday by a world government controlled by a world church. Only true believers will resist this mark of the beast and will face severe persecution.

Most Christians have no biblical objection to Seventh-day Adventists' choice to observe the seventh-day Sabbath. However, they would emphatically disagree with Seventh-day Adventists' assertion that it is biblically mandated for Christians. According to the New

Testament, the early church met on the Lord's Day, or the first day of the week. This was adopted as a way of remembering Christ's resurrection on a weekly basis. Seventh-day Adventists' insistence that keeping the Sabbath demonstrates a superior level of commitment to Christ contradicts the New Testament's emphasis on salvation by grace rather than an adherence to external legalities (see Rom. 14:4-13; 1 Cor. 16:2; Gal. 4:9-11; Col. 2:13-17). Jesus placed the observance of the Sabbath in its proper perspective when He said: " 'The Sabbath was made for man, and not man for the Sabbath. So the Son of Man is Lord even of the Sabbath' " (Mark 2:27-28).

3. *Christ's investigative judgment is weeding out ________ ______________________.*

William Miller was a Baptist minister in New England in the early 19th century who preached, based on his study of the Bible, that Christ would return in 1844. His prediction obviously failed, and Miller recanted of his presumptuousness. Some of his followers, however, believed the date was nonetheless historically significant. Ellen G. White, for one, stated that God Himself revealed to her the true importance of the date. According to her visions, in 1844 Jesus Christ began what she termed the investigative judgment in the heavenly sanctuary. In this judgment the Lord began His last-days examination of His people and churches to discover who was truly worthy of salvation and who would ultimately be raised from the dead at His second coming.

This controversial doctrine has led many Christian observers to charge Seventh-day Adventists with teaching a works- or merit-based concept of salvation. Indeed, Seventh-day Adventist doctrine includes a definite reliance on the observances of specific moral and religious duties to ensure righteous standing with God. These legalisms include strict Sabbath keeping, observance of kosher dietary laws, and other personal ethical considerations such as not wearing jewelry.

Evangelical Christians reject the doctrine of investigative judgment. The Bible clearly indicates that redemption was totally and permanently accomplished by Christ's death on the cross and resurrection. It is received, maintained, and eternally ensured by grace through faith in Christ and His finished work (see Eph. 2:8-9).

Scripture does not indicate a second stage of Jesus' redemptive work in which He examines the worthiness of His followers. Our salvation is completely based on His worthiness and none of our own (see John 5:24; Rom. 5:6-10; 8:1; Col. 1:20-22; Heb. 1:3-4; 1 John 5:11-13).

4. *The life beyond is __________ ______________, ______________________, and __________________.*

Seventh-day Adventists teach that when Christians physically die, their spirits do not go directly into Christ's presence. Rather, they teach that

NOTES

NOTES

when even committed Christians die, they wait in the grave for Christ's return and the general resurrection of the dead. During this period they rest in an unconscious state sometimes called soul sleep. At the end of time, Christ will return, and all worthy believers will then be consciously and bodily raised to meet Him in the air. The wicked lost will not be raised until the end of the one-thousand-year millennium. Then will come the final judgment.

Seventh-day Adventists teach that at the final judgment the redeemed will be those who have believed in Christ, obeyed His commandments, and endured to the end by resisting the mark of the beast (Sunday worship). They will be resurrected at Christ's return and will eventually inherit eternal life in heaven.

The lost will be those who rejected Christ, disobeyed Him, and submitted to the dictates of the antichrist and his apostate church. They will be raised after the millennium, judged by Christ, and then bodily cast into the lake of fire, where they will be totally annihilated out of existence forever. Thus, Seventh-day Adventists deny the doctrine of eternal hell.

Most evangelical Christian denominations, contrary to Seventh-day Adventist beliefs, have historically affirmed the Bible's teachings that born-again Christians at death go immediately to be with the Lord, where they wait in a conscious spiritual state. They will accompany Him at His return, where they will be reunited with their resurrected physical bodies (see John 11:25-26; 2 Cor. 5:8; Phil. 1:23; 1 Thess. 4:13-18; 2 Tim. 1:10).

The Bible also teaches that at the final judgment the redeemed will inherit eternal life in heaven, and the unsaved lost will suffer eternal separation from God in hell (see Matt. 18:8-9; 25:41-46; Mark 9:43-48; John 14:1-3; 2 Thess. 1:9; Rev. 20—22).

Witnessing to Seventh-day Adventists

Several years ago I received a brochure advertising a free conference on biblical prophecy in our community. The attractive brochure caught my interest, but nowhere did it state who was sponsoring the event. Most Christians would probably assume that it was an interdenominational lecture sponsored by an evangelistic group.

I later learned that the meeting was conducted by several local Seventh-day Adventist congregations and that the speaker was a Seventh-day Adventist minister. I wondered then why they failed to identify themselves in their promotional material. I realize now that, due to the unusual nature of Seventh-day Adventist theology, they may have been reluctant to identify themselves, feeling that some people, especially evangelical Christians, might have been frightened away.

It is important to understand that Seventh-day Adventists regard even believers in Christian churches as potential converts to the "remnant church." Although many Seventh-day Adventist ministers focus on evangelizing people to Christ, the group still officially regards only itself as the true church. Therefore, when witnessing to Seventh-day Adventists, you may need to defend your faith. Consider the following points.

1. *Be aware of doctrinal* ____________________.

Granted, Seventh-day Adventists have standard biblical beliefs about essential doctrines on the nature of God and the person of Jesus Christ. However, Seventh-day Adventists deviate from biblical teachings on several critical points. Their teachings on the requirements for salvation, the nature and extent of Christ's atonement on the cross, life after death, and the end times radically differ from traditional Christian biblical understandings. Be knowledgeable of the biblical positions on these doctrines so that you can clearly explain them when you have opportunities.

2. *Determine whether the person is* ____________.

Many Christians may wonder whether Seventh-day Adventists are saved and whether they need to witness to them. The answers to those questions must be addressed individual by individual with Seventh-day Adventists. First evaluate the person's spiritual standing by asking specific questions about his relationship with Christ. What is he trusting for salvation? Is it his Seventh-day Adventist church membership? Is it his seventh-day Sabbath keeping? Is it his observance of Seventh-day Adventist dietary laws? Is it doing good works? If it appears that he relies on any form of external legalism rather than faith in Christ, sensitively explain the biblical way of salvation. Your FAITH gospel presentation provides a clear plan, along with biblical support.

3. *Focus on salvation by* GRACE.

Avoid debating Seventh-day Adventist doctrines, but focus on the basic, essential concept of salvation by grace through faith in Jesus Christ alone. The person may attempt to convince you that you need to adopt Seventh-day Adventist doctrine or may try to cast doubts on your assurance of salvation. In that case tell him that you rely solely on the Bible as the authority for your beliefs. Share biblical texts that support salvation by grace. Share your personal testimony and tell him that you respect his beliefs on the Sabbath but that you can find no biblical mandate requiring all Christians to adhere to them.

NOTES

NOTES

4. Invite the person to accept ___________.

If your Seventh-day Adventist friend is not saved, invite him to accept Jesus Christ as personal Savior and Lord, using the FAITH gospel presentation. If you feel that he already has a genuine relationship with Christ, you may want to engage him in a respectful dialogue about doctrinal issues. Above all, show the love of Christ to your Seventh-day Adventist friend, pray for him, and trust the Holy Spirit to guide you in your discussions.

Visitation Time

Do It

1. All Team members should know the entire FAITH presentation. Are they ready to take the lead in a visit? Are they growing in their faith and in their capacity to share their faith? Are they learning to recognize when the FAITH Visit Outline needs to be adjusted in visits? Are they helping to establish bridges of relationship between the community and your Sunday School? Use your leadership role to challenge them to take the lead in visits and to offer support.
2. Share with Learners the importance of making ministry visits in order to strengthen their Sunday School and to connect members with a loving fellowship. Help them make the transition from asking, "How can I meet my needs?" to asking "How can I meet someone else's need?"
3. How far have Team members come since session 1? Have you taken the time to affirm them for their progress and to thank God for this mentoring experience?

Celebration Time

Share It

1. Ask a Team member to take the lead in sharing reports.
2. Hear reports and testimonies.
3. Complete Evaluation Cards.
4. Complete Participation Cards.
5. Update visitation forms with the results of visits.

Home Study Assignments

Home Study Assignments reinforce this session by helping you apply what you have learned.

Your Discipleship Journey

Journaling activities in Your Discipleship Journey are an important part of your development as a Great Commission Christian through FAITH training.

1. Record what the following Scriptures teach about the afterlife.

   Matthew 25:41-46: ______________________________

   ____

   John 11:25-26: ______________________________

   John 14:1-3: ______________________________

   1 Thessalonians 4:13-18: ______________________________

   ____

   2 Thessalonians 1:8-9: ______________________________

   Revelation 20:4-6: ______________________________

   Revelation 20:12-15: ______________________________

   ____

   Revelation 21:3: ______________________________

   ____

2. Although all Baptist churches meet on Sunday mornings, some now offer services on alternative days. Is this prohibited by the Bible? Explain why you agree or disagree with this practice.

   ____

   ____

   ____

3. Match the following Scriptures with the activities they specify that are appropriate for churches to practice.

____ 1. Colossians 3:16	a. Make requests, prayers, intercession, and thanksgiving for everyone.
____ 2. 1 Timothy 2:1-4	b. Continue in the Scriptures, which teach, rebuke, correct, and train in righteousness.
____ 3. 1 Timothy 4:13	c. Don't quarrel but teach the truth to those who oppose you.
____ 4. 2 Timothy 2:2	d. Practice love and good deeds; meet together; encourage one another.
____ 5. 2 Timothy 2:24-26	e. Publicly read Scripture, preach, and teach.
____ 6. 2 Timothy 3:14-17	f. Preach the Word; be prepared; correct, rebuke, and encourage with patience and careful instruction.
____ 7. 2 Timothy 4:2	g. Teach those who then teach others.
____ 8. Titus 2:1-10	h. Dwell in Christ's word; admonish one another with wisdom; sing with gratitude to God.
____ 9. Hebrews 10:24-25	i. Teach sound doctrine, self-control, submission, purity, trustworthy behavior; be an example; show integrity in your teaching.

Growing as a Life Witness

Growing as a Life Witness reminds you of your responsibility to witness and minister to others during the week.

1. Talk or meet with your accountability partner and share ways you have cultivated a lost person or have witnessed or ministered on occasions other than FAITH visits.
2. Discuss ways you can apply the session 14 content.
3. Pray for lost persons by name and for each other.

Prayer Concerns	Answers to Prayer
____________________	____________________
____________________	____________________
____________________	____________________
____________________	____________________
____________________	____________________
____________________	____________________

Your Weekly Sunday School Leadership Meeting

A FAITH participant is an important member of Sunday School. Encourage Team members who are elected Sunday School workers to attend this weekly meeting. Use this section to record ways your FAITH Team influences the work of your Sunday School class or department. Use the information to report during weekly Sunday School leadership meetings. Identify actions that need to be taken through Sunday School as a result of prayer concerns, needs identified, visits made by the Team, and decisions made by the persons visited. Also identify ways you can disciple others in your Sunday School class or department and in your church.

1. Highlight FAITH-visit results and implications for your class/department or age group. How can ministries of your class/department or Sunday School further extend bridges of relationship?

   ____

   ____

2. Pray for your teacher(s) and department director. Ask God to strengthen and encourage Team Leaders as they continue to train and equip new Learners. Record your requests.

   ____

   ____

3. With others on your leadership team, evaluate last week's session and discuss ways Sunday's lesson can involve members and guests in transformational Bible study and discipleship.

   ____

4. In what ways can the truths you discovered in this session be communicated with your Sunday School leadership team? How has FAITH changed your priorities? Those of your Team members? Those of new believers?

   ____

   ____

Discipling Your Team Members

This weekly feature suggests actions the Team Leader can take to support Team members, prepare for Team Time, and improve visits. This work is part of the

Team Leader's Home Study Assignments. Add any actions suggested by your church's FAITH strategy.

Support Team Members

- ❑ Contact Team members during the week. Remind them that you are praying for them. Discuss prayer concerns and answers to prayer.
- ❑ As you talk with Learners this week, discuss opportunities they have for witnessing during the week. Encourage them as they seek to be witnesses to persons they encounter.
- ❑ Record specific needs and concerns shared by Team members.

Prepare to Lead Team Time

- ❑ Review Team members' Home Study Assignments.
- ❑ Be prepared to remind Team members to draft a "What FAITH Has Meant to Me" testimony, due in session 16.

Prepare to Lead Visits

- ❑ Review the FAITH Visit Outline.

Link with Sunday School

- ❑ Participate in your weekly Sunday School leadership meeting. Share pertinent information in this meeting, using Your Weekly Sunday School Leadership Meeting (p. 235) and FAITH-visit results.
- ❑ Look for ways your Sunday School ministry can reinforce a proper understanding of Sabbath observance through worship, teaching, ministry, encouragement, and discipleship.

For Further Growth

For Further Growth may include additional reading or activities that will enhance your growth as a disciple and a discipler of others. These assignments are intended to be long-term projects and do not have to be completed during this semester of study.

1. Teaching and preaching are significant worship functions that edify and nurture the church. Keep notes of Sunday School teaching and your pastor's messages to help you discern, remember, and trace God's work in your life.
2. Pray that your pastor and Sunday School teachers will be effective in communicating biblical truth.
3. Regularly pray for the expansion of your church's teaching and preaching ministries.
4. Read the FAITH Tip on page 237.

Answers to matching activity on page 234: 1. h, 2. a, 3. e, 4. g, 5. c, 6. b, 7. f, 8.i, 9. d

FAITH TIP

When Should the Sabbath Be Observed?

Seventh-day Adventists and other groups that observe the seventh-day Sabbath, like the Seventh-day Baptist General Conference, maintain that Christians should still observe the Hebrew Sabbath as specified in the Ten Commandments: " 'Remember the Sabbath day, to keep it holy' " (Ex. 20:8).

Many Seventh-day Adventists argue that this Commandment is practically the most important of the 10 and even allege that churches that fail to observe it by worshiping on Sunday are under the mark of the beast referred to in Revelation 13:16-18. They contend that the apostles and the early church kept the Sabbath and never intended for it to change. The change was made, they say, by a later corrupt church that sought accommodation with pagan sun worship on Sunday.

The preponderance of biblical and historical evidence, however, is that as early as the New Testament era, Christian churches observed the first day of the week as the Lord's Day (see Acts 20:7; 1 Cor. 16:2; Rev. 1:10). This shift was not an effort to supplant the Hebrew Sabbath observance but rather another way to reverence and remember Christ's resurrection, which occurred on the first day of the week (see Matt. 28:1; Mark 16:9).

We are also told in Scripture that the disciples and the early church met together on the first day of the week to break bread and fellowship (see John 20:19; Acts 20:7). The allegation that the church began meeting on Sunday to accommodate pagan sun worship is without historical justification.

Also, several New Testament passages indicate that legalistic observation of the Sabbath is unnecessary because salvation is by grace through faith, not through works of righteousness (see Gal. 4:9-11; Col. 2:13-17). The Scriptures imply that those who wish to keep the Sabbath or other legal requirements may freely do so but should not condemn other Christians who regard them as a hindrance (see Rom. 14:4-13). In Mark 2:27-28 Jesus announced that He is Lord of the Sabbath, suggesting that the object of Sabbath observance must take precedence over the details of the observance itself.

Most Christians, therefore, recognize a need for a Sabbath principle, which sets aside one day a week for rest, worship, family, and service to God. Nonetheless, they do not equate the Lord's Day observance with the legalistic observance of the Hebrew Sabbath. As Herschel H. Hobbs wrote, "The Hebrew Sabbath was a recognition; the Lord's Day is a celebration. It is a day when believers worship God not as Creator alone but as Redeemer."[1]

[1]Herschel H. Hobbs, *The Baptist Faith and Message*, rev. ed. (Nashville: Convention, 1996), 81.

FAITH AT WORK

When I was a younger man, I was gifted with athletic abilities and was offered a scholarship at a military institute. As a freshman I played varsity football, basketball, and baseball. I also received some significant awards, which I thought at the time were the greatest things life could give me. Now I know that isn't true.

FAITH training was offered at our church, but after 17 years of school I wasn't about to take it. I figured I had done enough reading and homework. But I started the training and enjoyed all 16 weeks of it, including the reading and the Home Study Assignments. On one visit the Lord gave me the opportunity to lead two persons to Him. God was so gracious that the very next day at work He gave me the opportunity to lead three more persons to His throne. What a wonderful God we have to let me lead three of His children to our Savior. I was so excited that I think it took me about a week to come back to earth. All of the sports awards and the newspaper articles about me didn't come close to what God gave me.

By the way, I am still involved in FAITH training. My message to all participants is to keep the FAITH.

Bob Kinslow
Metropolitan Baptist Church
Houston, Texas

SESSION 15

The Word of Faith Movement

JAMES NEWMAN

In this session you will—

CHECK IT by engaging in Team Time activities;

KNOW IT by reviewing content from session 14;

HEAR IT by examining the beliefs of Word of Faith followers and by learning ways to witness to them;

STUDY IT by overviewing Home Study Assignments;

DO IT by leading your Team in making visits;

SHARE IT by celebrating.

NOTES

Leading Team Time

All Team members participate in Team Time. They are primarily responsible for reciting the assigned portion of the FAITH Visit Outline and for discussing other Home Study Assignments.

As you direct this important time of CHECK IT activities with your Team, keep in mind that Learners look to you as a role model, motivator, mentor, and friend. Team Time activities can continue in the car as the Team travels to and from visits.

Lead CHECK IT Activities

✔ *FAITH Visit Outline*

❑ Listen while each Learner recites as much of the FAITH Visit Outline as time allows. It may be best to ask Learners to recite the segment they seem to have the most difficulty sharing during a visit.

❑ As time permits, allow for any additional practice that is needed on the visit presentation and sequence.

✔ *Session 14 Debriefing*

❑ Briefly talk about distractions Team members have encountered in earlier visits.

❑ While reminding Team members that most visits go smoothly, help them begin to recognize principles and actions for handling difficulties. As you model ways to handle difficult situations during visits, explain what you did and why. Deal appropriately with difficulties that could take place at any time during visits. Difficulties are things that happen or are said during the visit that could keep you from sharing the gospel and leading a person who is ready to respond to make a commitment to Christ. Principles for dealing with difficulties relate primarily to building bridges of relationship with the person, dealing with any questions and objections, and working through the obstacles and distractions that take place.

✔ *Other Home Study Assignments*

❑ Remind the group of the assignment, due next week, to write a testimony describing what FAITH has meant personally.

✔ *Help for Strengthening a Visit*

❑ Remind Team members to listen during each visit for ministry opportunities and for ways to follow up appropriately.

❑ If you have shared the Witness Awareness Quotient with Team members (from *Building Bridges Through FAITH*), reemphasize as follows.

- The greater the Number of Unsaved identified, the greater the potential for sharing a witness. The greater the number of Yes responses, the more someone is taking advantage of witnessing opportunities.
- If No responses are higher than Yes responses, then someone can consciously strengthen awareness of opportunities to share the gospel. If Yes responses are higher, then a witness can comfortably model for others the significance of sharing FAITH during daily-life opportunities.

Notes

____

____

____

____

____

____

Actions I Need to Take with Team Members This Week

____

____

____

____

____

____

____

____

NOTES

NOTES

A Quick Review

Last week you discovered ways Seventh-day Adventist beliefs differ from Christianity. Review by checking the statements that represent Seventh-day Adventist doctrines.

- ❑ 1. The biblical doctrine of the Trinity is affirmed.
- ❑ 2. The unique deity of Christ is affirmed.
- ❑ 3. Seventh-day Adventists are the remnant church of the last days.
- ❑ 4. The correct day for worship is Saturday, the true Sabbath.
- ❑ 5. The day you worship is not important as long as you worship.
- ❑ 6. Worshiping on Sunday is the mark of the beast.
- ❑ 7. Jesus is weeding out false believers until He returns.
- ❑ 8. Salvation is eternally secured by grace through faith in Christ.
- ❑ 9. When Christians die, they enter an unconscious state of soul sleep.
- ❑ 10. When Christians die, they are immediately in Jesus' presence.
- ❑ 11. The unsaved suffer eternal separation from God in hell.
- ❑ 12. There is no hell. Lost people are annihilated.

Indicate whether the following ideas for witnessing to Seventh-day Adventists are true (*T*) or false (*F*).

____ 1. Refuse to talk to anyone who observes the seventh-day Sabbath.
____ 2. Be aware of doctrinal differences.
____ 3. Determine whether the person is saved.
____ 4. Assume that all Seventh-day Adventists are saved.
____ 5. Be willing to admit that Sunday worship is unscriptural.
____ 6. Focus on salvation by grace.
____ 7. Invite the person to accept Christ.
____ 8. Encourage the person to earn salvation through adherence to Seventh-day Adventist dietary laws and Sabbath observance.

Name It and Claim It

Pandas, those big, cuddly-looking black-and-white creatures, are widely thought of as bears. They look like bears in shape and size. However, there is a fundamental distinction. They are not bears at all; they are marsupials. Under that big, bearlike exterior, they are more closely related to opossums than to bears.

The Word of Faith movement is a lot like that. It uses Christian terminology, employs Christian hymns, and occasionally preaches gospel sermons. Yet beneath this veneer of evangelical Christianity lie significant doctrinal problems. Many times Word of Faith teachers embrace elements that misrepresent God, distort faith, redefine humanity, and offer false hope. Strip away the Christian verbiage, and these teachings sound more like the New Age movement, deifying humanity, humanizing God, minimizing sin, and trivializing revelation.

Session 2 defined a cult as a group that deviates from traditional Christian teachings on the nature of God and/or Christ. A sect affirms those Christian doctrines yet exhibits other characteristics of cults. Word of Faith is difficult to categorize because of diverse, often contradictory teachings by different teachers. We have chosen to refer to Word of Faith not as a cult but as a Christian sect because the movement basically presents orthodox views of God and Jesus. However, believers cannot ignore the serious doctrinal difficulties presented by Word of Faith preachers and followers.

Although Word of Faith preachers insist that their message is biblical, it appears to be rooted in the ________ ______________ movement of the 19th century, particularly the teachings of Phineas Parkhurst Quimby (1802–66). Quimby's teachings gave rise to Mary Baker Eddy's Christian Science and Charles and Myrtle Fillmore's Unity School of Christianity. The basic premise of these schools of thought is that humans create their own reality through ______________ ______________. Therefore, we can control our health, wealth, and other matters by exercising faith in our _________.

E. W. Kenyon (1867–1948), a one-time Methodist turned Pentecostal, took Quimby's concepts and dressed them in biblical language. ____________ ____ __________ later adopted Kenyon's teachings, virtually plagiarizing a number of his writings.[1] In 1934 Hagin opened the Rhema Bible Training Center near Tulsa, Oklahoma, which boasted more than 12,000 graduates by 1992.

In the 1960s when young ______________ ______________ worked as a pilot for faith healer Oral Roberts, he was exposed to Hagin, embraced his teachings, and with wife Gloria rapidly moved to the forefront of Word of Faith teaching. The couple founded Kenneth Copeland Ministries in Fort Worth, Texas, in 1968. They have been joined by a growing retinue of other ministries on the positive-confession campaign trail to big followings and big dollars, including Frederick K. C. Price, Robert Tilton, John Avanzini, John Osteen, T. L. Osborne, Marilyn Hickey, Jerry Savelle, Morris Cerullo, Casey Treat, Dwight Thompson, and Oral and Richard Roberts.[2]

Word of Faith Beliefs

Not all Word of Faith advocates agree on all of the following issues. However, they are in basic harmony on the overarching principles, and they lend aid and comfort to one another on most of the rest.

NOTES

NOTES

1. The spoken word has supernatural ____________.

This is the basic premise of the Word of Faith movement. Just as God spoke and the whole of creation came into existence, He has given this same creative potential to His children; they can speak forth their own reality by speaking it in faith. Word of Faith claims that when God spoke, He had faith in the words He spoke and this faith produced the reality. Speaking your desired reality can allegedly dispel sickness, ensure financial prosperity, and even change your surroundings.

2. You must have faith in __________.

Word of Faith followers see faith itself as the power that controls everything—our surroundings, demons, even God, whose faith in the power of His spoken words was necessary to all He did in creation. So great is the dependence on a believer's word of faith that followers are taught not to pray, " 'Thy will be done,' " (Matt. 6:10), as Jesus taught. Doing so, Word of Faith teachers claim, negates a believer's prayer of faith.

There is no biblical justification for the conclusion that divine power resides in faith itself. The world was spoken into existence through the power of God's Word (see Gen. 1), but humans do not have the same creative power. When the Bible admonishes us to have faith (see Matt. 17:20-21), our faith must be placed in God's goodness, wisdom, and power, not in our own expression of faith (see Mark 11:22). The teaching against praying for God's will to be done arrogantly defies the greater wisdom of God and His loving purpose in all our circumstances.

3. God stands ready to meet our ______________.

Despite all the praise music employed, the Word of Faith movement reduces God to little more than a celestial grocery clerk, faithfully filling the shopping lists of those who have captured Him with their spoken faith words. Prominent Word of Faith preachers reduce God to human proportions, giving physical descriptions of Him as a result of visits to heaven they have made or other revelations they have had. One preacher has made much of his alleged visits to heaven, complete with detailed descriptions of God and persons he has conversed with there. Another Word of Faith preacher estimates God's height at six feet, two or three inches and His weight at about two hundred pounds. Another says that God's hand span is nine inches, slightly larger than his own.

Such a being bears no resemblance to the God who reveals Himself in the Bible, whom no one has seen (see John 1:18; 1 John 4:12). The idea that God is waiting to grant the demands of our words of faith is contrary to the biblical picture of His omnipotence, wisdom, and glory (see Ps. 8:1; 1 Cor. 1:18-25; Eph. 1:19-21). God is not the servant; rather, His people serve Him (see Matt. 4:10; Col. 3:24; Rev. 22:3).

4. Human beings are potential __________.

Word of Faith proponents would likely draw back from the suggestion that they teach equality with Jesus Christ, but it is impossible to deny that conclusion when their statements are analyzed. Jesus is seen as a prototype of the believer. He came so that we could live the same empowered life He lived. Word of Faith teachers run amok with Jesus' statement " 'He who believes in Me, the works that I do, he will do also; and greater works than these he will do' " (John 14:12). Kenneth Hagin, for example, has said: "The believer is called Christ. … That's who we are; we're Christ!"[3] Kenneth Copeland once proclaimed: "Am I a god? Man was created in the god class. … We are a class of gods!"[4]

The view that humans possess the same power as Jesus or are a class of gods is unbiblical. Although believers are children of God (see 1 John 3:1), we are not divine beings like Jesus, whom the Bible describes as God's " 'only begotten Son' " (John 3:16). Although we can grow in Christlikeness (see 2 Pet. 3:18), we cannot attain perfection on earth because we will always struggle with the old, sinful nature (see Rom. 7:15-25). In addition, we are not capable of exercising Jesus' power in our own right, only of allowing Him to work through us in His power. The works Jesus referred to in John 14:12 do not result from believers' ability to speak words of divine power as Jesus did but from God's willingness to work through yielded, committed believers (see 1 Cor. 2:4-5; 2 Cor. 4:7; 12:9-10; Eph. 3:20).

5. Humanity's problem is ____________________.

In the Word of Faith view, our problem is not so much sin as ignorance of faith and ignorance of the devil. We sin because of demonic activity rather than because of our willful choices. We need exorcism more than repentance. Likewise, sickness, poverty, and other ills result from the activity of demons or at least from the lack of faith.

For those whose faith needs propping up, the touch of the faith-healing evangelist is enough to make the difference. Sometimes it takes only a token that the evangelist has prayed over—an anointed cloth, a vial of oil, water from the Jordan River brought from one of the evangelists' many trips to the Holy Land, or something else sent in return for an appropriate donation. Television viewers are taken by the sight of Benny Hinn and other Word of Faith preachers laying hands on huge stacks of letters to guarantee answers to the multitude of requests.

In contrast, the Bible teaches that humanity's fundamental problem is sin (see Rom. 3:23), not ignorance, a lack of faith, or attack by demonic powers. When we repent and place our faith in Christ, we are forgiven of our sin and gain access to His power for resisting evil (see Jas. 4:7) and for growing in godly character, love, and faith in the One who has already won the victory over evil (see Rom. 8:37-39).

NOTES

NOTES

6. *Human _____________ is never God's will for believers.*

Word of Faith preachers believe that Christ's sufferings not only secured forgiveness and eternal life but also guaranteed physical healing in this life. Illness, deformity, and material lack can thus be banished by speaking a word of faith, although cancer, heart disease, failing eyesight, and other afflictions visit the movement's leaders in similar proportion to the rest of humanity.

The Bible shows that suffering and illness are facts of life in this fallen world. God does not cause suffering, but He participates in our suffering and can use even difficult circumstances in a believer's life as part of His redemptive, Christ-shaping plan (see Rom. 8:26-39). We are not guaranteed physical healing on this earth, although spiritual healing is always possible through a relationship with God. When physical healing is granted, it is only through God's power (see Jas. 5:13-16).

God also does not guarantee material blessing based on a spoken word of faith. The Bible clearly distinguishes between Kingdom values and materialistic values (see Matt. 6:19-21; Luke 12:15-21).

7. *The Bible must be interpreted in light of new ____________________.*

Word of Faith preachers interpret the Bible according to their theological preconceptions, seeking assurances of physical and material blessing for believers in the pages of Scripture. In addition, they claim to receive new revelations through visions, prophecies by means of tongue speaking, and direct communication from God. Thus, sound doctrine falls before any experience, ecstatic or otherwise. The assumption in the Word of Faith movement is that this latest word from God is somehow more immediate and significant than the Bible, regardless of how trivial or contradictory.

The more bizarre and outrageous the experience, the more eagerly it seems to be embraced and exalted in the Word of Faith community. Followers are convinced that "miracles" or ecstatic phenomena such as uncontrollable laughter, barking, roaring, and babbling are the manifestations of the Holy Spirit, as they have been marketed by Word of Faith preachers.

For believers, the Bible is the eternal, inspired, authoritative, sufficient revelation of God to humanity (see 2 Tim. 3:16-17; 1 Pet. 1:23-25; 2 Pet. 1:20-21). Christians do not accept that the Bible requires or teaches modern-day revelations and experiences that supersede its truth (see Deut. 4:2; Prov. 30:5-6; Rev. 22:18). Human experiences may arise from a number of emotional and psychological sources, not solely from the work of the Holy Spirit. Any experience, therefore, must be tested by the Bible to determine whether it is from God. The Bible offers no precedent for uncontrolled laughing, roaring, barking, or being slain in the Spirit.

Witnessing to Word of Faith Followers

NOTES

1. Identify ____________ the person follows Word of Faith.

Understanding the appeal of Word of Faith teaching can help you identify ways the follower has been misled, as well as needs a legitimate Christian fellowship can meet.

1. Word of Faith offers a _________ _____ to life's problems. The temptation to reduce faith to a recipe is ever-present and always dangerous. Formula faith is contrary to the Bible and is deadly when the recipe doesn't work. Sometimes Word of Faith methods seem to work, especially as presented on television. Some may appear to be healed in response to the preacher, and others may view winning a lottery as an answer to prayer so that they can "sow seeds" with the TV evangelist. But recipe religion has failed for thousands of people, who then write off Christianity as false or believe themselves incapable of sufficient faith to stimulate God to act.
2. Word of Faith appeals to _________. The thought that people can control their destinies by their words has an intoxicating appeal for many. It breeds an arrogance that flourishes under the guise of spirituality, deceiving followers into believing that they can enjoy a superior intimacy with God, far beyond that of a mere Christian.
3. People are impressed by financial and numerical _______________, and Word of Faith is big business. Each year hundreds of millions of dollars flow into the coffers of Word of Faith preachers. Millions more are generated through a tidal wave of books, tapes, and souvenir mementos. The posh, luxurious trappings of its leaders are proof that this belief system works. And many followers are like players at a religious lottery, hoping that their seed-faith gifts will result in material wealth and physical health far beyond their monetary donations.

Perhaps the person was drawn into the Word of Faith movement because of a perceived need that was not being met in church. Your Sunday School testimony can reveal the role of Bible study in anchoring a believer in the truth of God's Word and the importance of other believers in holding one another accountable.

2. Pray in preparation for spiritual _______________.

You are engaged in spiritual warfare. The grip of the enemy is all the more deadly because it masquerades as genuine Christianity. Use prayer to prepare yourself spiritually (see Eph. 6:10-20) and to ask the Holy Spirit to prepare the listener's heart and circumstances.

NOTES

3. *Show unconditional ________.*

Your love must be unconditional and without hypocrisy. The person to whom you witness must be convinced that you can be counted on, regardless. The time may come when disillusionment tests the person's faith, and he will need someone he can count on.

4. *Don't __________.*

Speak the truth in love, but do not be drawn into heated exchange. At that point you lose, and your friend is hardened in his position.

5. *Don't attack their ____________.*

As your relationship develops and your friend begins to question the Word of Faith system, information about leaders may be introduced.

6. *Be ____________.*

Don't try to change the person's mind in a single encounter. Save some discussion for later visits. Don't give up on your friend.

7. *Establish the superiority of biblical truth over ______________________.*

One danger is the movement's emphasis on experience. For its spokespersons it seems that no experience, however bizarre, must stand the test of Scripture. Lead the Word of Faith follower to understand that truth is more reliable than feelings. The test of genuine faith is not success, power, or even alleged miracles. The test is truth, and Scripture is the rule against which we must measure all teaching, including our own. The Bible repeatedly calls the church and the individual believer to sound doctrine and warns against false teaching and false prophets. In Acts 17:11 we are encouraged to examine the Scriptures "to see whether these things were so." And in 1 Thessalonians 5:21 we are called on to "examine everything carefully; hold fast to that which is good." The Bible makes it clear that sound doctrine is vitally important to individual believers and to the body of Christ. Emphasize that truth is not based on random experiences. Truth is not a matter of pragmatics but of integrity.

8. *Get agreement on legitimate principles of biblical ____________________________.*

Show that we may not impose arbitrary opinions on the Bible to force agreement with our opinions.

9. *Define __________.*

For example, ask the person to define *faith*. Establish that genuine, biblical faith is not the ability to maneuver God but a recognition of God's power and wisdom, confidence in His loving purpose in the believer's life, and submissive trust in His will.

10. *Share the FAITH* ___________ _________________.

Sometimes Word of Faith followers may begin to believe that their contributions to a television ministry are tantamount to purchasing their salvation. They may also place their trust in their own faith rather than in the atoning work of Jesus Christ on the cross. Try to determine whether the person is trusting anything for salvation other than Jesus Christ. If so, invite the person to accept the only legitimate object of biblical faith as you share the FAITH gospel presentation.

Visitation Time

Do It

1. As you drive, ask Team members to recall persons who are frequently absent from Sunday School. These persons may be facing crises. Ask Learners to think about what they can do to reinvolve these persons through caring ministry and loving fellowship.
2. Remember that this is the last week to visit before the final review. By now your Learners should be accepting responsibility for the visit. You should participate as a prayer partner on the FAITH Team. Take responsibility to deal with distractions like the baby, dog, phone, and so on. Always be ready to step in if Learners need assistance.
3. As you travel, talk about whom Team members have enlisted to be on their Teams for the next semester of FAITH. If they have not enlisted their Team members, encourage them to do so this week.

Celebration Time

Share It

1. Ask a Team member to take the lead in sharing reports.
2. Hear reports and testimonies.
3. Complete Evaluation Cards.
4. Complete Participation Cards.
5. Update visitation forms with the results of visits.

NOTES

Home Study Assignments

Home Study Assignments reinforce this session by helping you apply what you have learned.

Your Discipleship Journey

Journaling activities in Your Discipleship Journey are an important part of your development as a Great Commission Christian through FAITH training.

1. The Bible teaches that faith is to be placed in God. Write what the following Scriptures say about faith.

   Mark 11:22: ______________________________

   Acts 3:16: ______________________________

   Acts 20:21: ______________________________

   Romans 1:17: ______________________________

   Romans 4:5: ______________________________

   Galatians 5:6: ______________________________

   Ephesians 6:16: ______________________________

   Hebrews 11:1: ______________________________

   Hebrews 11:6: ______________________________

   James 2:17: ______________________________

   James 5:15: ______________________________

2. In our culture many religions claim to be the truth. Christians must be discerning in order to filter through the false doctrines of our day. Match the following Scriptures with the qualities of a discerning Christian.

____ 1. 1 Kings 3:9	a. Searches Scripture for truth
____ 2. Proverbs 2:3-6	b. Examines all things
____ 3. Acts 17:11	c. Desires wisdom
____ 4. 1 Thessalonians 5:21	d. Prays for discernment
____ 5. 2 Timothy 2:15	e. Obeys the Word
____ 6. Hebrews 5:12-14	f. Is a good workman in the Word
____ 7. James 1:22	g. Is a mature believer skilled in the Word

3. Think about the religious media to which you and your family are exposed. Do you consciously exercise a spirit of discernment toward the teachings that enter your home and your mind? ❑ Yes ❑ No What changes would help keep false teachings from influencing you and your family?

____

____

Growing as a Life Witness

Growing as a Life Witness reminds you of your responsibility to witness and minister to others during the week.

1. Talk or meet with your accountability partner and share ways you have cultivated a lost person or have witnessed or ministered on occasions other than FAITH visits.
2. Discuss ways you can apply the session 15 content.
3. Pray for lost persons by name and for each other.

Prayer Concerns	Answers to Prayer
____________________	____________________
____________________	____________________
____________________	____________________
____________________	____________________
____________________	____________________

Your Weekly Sunday School Leadership Meeting

A FAITH participant is an important member of Sunday School. Encourage Team members who are elected Sunday School workers to attend this weekly meeting. Use this section to record ways your FAITH Team influences the work of your Sunday School class or department. Use the information to report during weekly Sunday School leadership meetings. Identify actions that need to be taken through Sunday School as a result of prayer concerns, needs identified, visits made by the Team, and decisions made by the persons visited. Also identify ways you can disciple others in your Sunday School class or department and in your church.

1. Discuss plans for the next semester of FAITH training. Give the dates.

____

2. Update the group on plans to enlist a Team of new Learners from your class/department. Who are potential Learners? Invite current Team members or new Christians to share testimonies and benefits of participating as a Team Learner. Indicate other promotional efforts that are under way.

____

____

____

3. With others on your leadership team, evaluate last week's session and discuss ways Sunday's lesson can involve members and guests in transformational Bible study and discipleship.

____

____

4. Discuss plans to keep evangelism and ministry contacts consistent and strong between semesters.

____

____

____

5. Thank the Sunday School class/department leaders for their support and encouragement throughout this semester.

6. Pray for your teacher and department director. Specifically ask God to bless and multiply your church's ministry through Sunday School.

Discipling Your Team Members

This weekly feature suggests actions the Team Leader can take to support Team members, prepare for Team Time, and improve visits. This work is part of the Team Leader's Home Study Assignments. Add any actions suggested by your church's FAITH strategy.

Support Team Members

❑ Contact Team members during the week. Remind them that you are praying for them. Discuss prayer concerns and answers to prayer.

❑ Record Team members' specific needs and concerns on the following page.

❑ Identify specific ways you can encourage Team members as they prepare for their written and verbal reviews.

Prepare for Session 16

❑ Review Team members' Home Study Assignments.
❑ Preview instructions for session 16.
❑ Be prepared for your final verbal and written reviews.

Prepare to Lead Visits

❑ Review the FAITH Visit Outline.
❑ Make sure a Team member is ready to take the lead during visits.

Link with Sunday School

❑ Participate in your weekly Sunday School leadership meeting. Share pertinent information in this meeting, using Your Weekly Sunday School Leadership Meeting (pp. 251–52) and FAITH-visit results.
❑ Ensure that Sunday School teaching reinforces the integrity of God's Word in contrast to ecstatic, subjective human experience.

For Further Growth

For Further Growth may include additional reading or activities that will enhance your growth as a disciple and a discipler of others. These assignments are intended to be long-term projects and do not have to be completed during this semester of study.

1. Examine your life to identify any influence by the false teachings of the Word of Faith movement in the areas of prayer or finance.
2. For a biblical understanding of the process of prayer, read *Alone with God* by John MacArthur (Chariot Victor, 1995) or participate in a group study of *Disciple's Prayer Life* by T. W. Hunt and Catherine Walker (LifeWay, 1997).
3. In your daily quiet time ask God to develop in you a discerning heart.
4. Read the FAITH Tip on page 254.

---

[1]D. R. McConnell, *A Different Gospel: A Historical and Biblical Analysis of the Modern Faith Movement* (Peabody, MA: Hendrickson, 1988), 57–58.
[2]Richard Abanes, "The Word Faith Movement," in Walter Martin, *The Kingdom of the Cults*, ed. Hank Hanegraaff (Minneapolis: Bethany House, 1997), 495.
[3]Hank Hanegraaff, *Christianity in Crisis* (Eugene, OR: Harvest House, 1993), 108.
[4]"Praise the Lord" radio program, 5 February 1986.

Answers to matching activity on page 250: 1. d, 2. c, 3. a, 4. b, 5. f, 6. g, 7. e

FAITH TIP

Testing Spiritual Experiences

The Bible, God's eternal, unchanging Word, must always be our standard for judging the validity of our experiences. Word of Faith exponents and practitioners of ecstatic excess err when they interpret the Bible through the filter of their experiences. Human experiences vary and may arise from a wide range of emotional and psychological sources, not solely from the work of the Holy Spirit. The Bible, on the other hand, stands firm. It is the unwavering standard by which all else must be measured.

Uncontrolled giggling, roaring, and barking; frenzied running and jerking; and being slain in the Spirit or stuck to the floor with Holy Ghost glue have no precedents in the experiences of the saints in the Bible. Nowhere in the Bible is anyone slain in the Spirit. Neither Jesus nor any of the apostles blew on people to have them collapse in a stupor or waved a handkerchief or a hand to bowl people over. The Bible contains no evidence of mass hypnotic responses.

To defend this modern excess, practitioners offer several biblical instances as "proof." Peter's vision on the rooftop is offered as proof of being slain in the Spirit (see Acts 10:9-10). An honest examination of the passage demonstrates the bias with which Word of Faith teachers twist God's Word. Far from being a humanly induced trance, this event was God's means of widening the door of the gospel to embrace the Gentile world. It is a far cry from the antics of today's self-styled prophets. What we see and hear in their meetings is more like the trance channelers of New Age mysticism or the tricks of a Las Vegas magician. When we turn to the Bible to justify or find proof that our experience is from God, we will almost always find it. It is dangerously misleading to prooftext rather than objectively test the experience by the Bible. The adage is true: A text without a context is a pretext.

In the Bible, people who encountered a divine presence fell on their faces in humble worship to acknowledge their unworthiness; never were they knocked senseless. The suggestion that the infilling of the Holy Spirit results in a state similar to being drunk on alcohol has no basis in truth. The accusation of drunkenness at Pentecost was skeptics' desperate attempt to explain the miracle of spoken languages, whereby everyone present heard in his native tongue the proclamation of the gospel (see Acts 2:1-13).

The Bible does not say, "Be drunk with the Spirit." The command is "Be filled with the Spirit." When we are filled with the Spirit, we manifest the fruit of the Spirit, not the fruit of the vine: "The fruit of the Spirit is love, joy, peace, patience, kindness, goodness, faithfulness, gentleness, self-control" (Gal. 5:22-23).

SESSION 16

Final Review

In this session you will—

CHECK IT by engaging in Team Time activities;

KNOW IT by taking written and verbal reviews to evaluate your learning over the past 16 weeks;

STUDY IT by overviewing Home Study Assignments;

DO IT by leading your Team in making visits;

SHARE IT by celebrating accomplishments this semester or by announcing plans for a FAITH Festival in which the celebration will occur.

NOTES

Leading Team Time

All Team members participate in Team Time. They are primarily responsible for reciting the assigned portion of the FAITH Visit Outline and for discussing other Home Study Assignments.

As you direct this important time of CHECK IT activities with your Team, keep in mind that Learners look to you as a role model, motivator, mentor, and friend. Team Time activities can continue in the car as the Team travels to and from visits.

Lead CHECK IT Activities

✔ *FAITH Visit Outline*

❑ Listen while each Learner recites any designated portion of the FAITH Visit Outline. It may be best to ask Learners to recite the segment they seem to have the most difficulty sharing during a visit.

❑ A brief time to practice the outline can help Team members confidently approach the verbal review.

✔ *Session 15 Debriefing*

❑ Emphasize the importance of each Team member's being available to serve as a Team Leader during future semesters. Review the potential results of choosing not to continue participating in FAITH training.

✔ *FAITH Testimony*

❑ Ask participants to turn in their "What FAITH Has Meant to Me" testimonies. Present them to the FAITH Director.

✔ *Help for Strengthening a Visit*

❑ Discuss some of the things that have been learned by making evangelistic, ministry, and Opinion Poll visits. Make sure Team members know who will be responsible for taking the lead in making the visits after the written and verbal reviews.

Notes

Actions I Need to Take with Team Members This Week

1. Write thank-you notes to Team members. Include congratulations for their completion of this semester of training. Indicate your continued support.

NOTES

NOTES

Written Review

Many years ago Paul issued a chilling warning that could have easily been written to believers today: "The time will come when they will not endure sound doctrine; but wanting to have their ears tickled, they will accumulate for themselves teachers in accordance to their own desires; and will turn away their ears from the truth, and will turn aside to myths" (2 Tim. 4:3-4). This semester you have examined a variety of cults and sects that have turned away from the truth and embraced lies, to the detriment of millions of souls.

Paul's instruction to first-century Christians is also relevant today. We are to hold to God's Word (see 2 Tim. 3:14-16), teach sound doctrine (see Titus 1:9; 2:1), and "preach the word; be ready in season and out of season; reprove, rebuke, exhort, with great patience and instruction" (2 Tim. 4:2). We hope that your study this semester has equipped you further as a growing disciple and as a Great Commission witness by increasing your understanding of sound Christian doctrine and by offering ways to share biblical truth with followers of cults and sects. This course has also given you an opportunity to develop greater compassion for cult and sect followers, who have been misled by evil and deception, so that you will be eager to share Christ's love with them through the FAITH gospel presentation.

Congratulations for completing *FAITH Discipleship: Faith Reaching Out to Cults*. We hope that you will continue to grow as a disciple and as a witness by enrolling in another semester of FAITH training.

You will have 20 minutes to take the following written review.

NOTES

Session 1: Faith Reaching Out to Cults: An Orientation

Complete the three purposes of *Faith Reaching Out to Cults*.

1. To increase your understanding of historic ____________________ ____________________
2. To give you ________________________ in confronting cult members with the truth of the gospel
3. To encourage Christian ____________________ for cult members

Session 2: Defining Cults and Sects

Define a cult and a sect by checking the correct responses. A cult is a group that claims to be Christian but deviates from the traditional Christian understanding of—

❑ Christology (the doctrine of Christ) and/or theology proper (the doctrine of God);
❑ ecclesiology (the doctrine of the church) and/or eschatology (the doctrine of end times).

A sect is a group that does not deviate from the traditional Christian doctrines of the nature of God and Jesus Christ but nonetheless exhibits many sociological characteristics that are commonly associated with—

❑ governments;
❑ families;
❑ cults;
❑ colleges.

Session 3: The Church of Jesus Christ of Latter-day Saints, Part 1

Check principles you learned for witnessing to Mormons.

❑ 1. Get a clear understanding of basic biblical doctrines.
❑ 2. Get a clear understanding of basic Mormon history and doctrines.
❑ 3. Use the Bible as a bludgeon to get your point across.
❑ 4. Ask Mormon missionaries to get off your property.
❑ 5. Keep the initiative.
❑ 6. Be very patient.
❑ 7. Never turn your back on a Mormon.
❑ 8. Clearly define your terms and ask Mormons to define theirs.
❑ 9. Let the Mormon set the direction of the conversation.
❑ 10. Rely on the Holy Spirit to lead you and to change your Mormon friends.
❑ 11. Follow the FAITH Visit Outline.
❑ 12. Assure the Mormon that you accept Joseph Smith's claims as historical facts.

NOTES

Session 4: The Church of Jesus Christ of Latter-day Saints, Part 2

Identify whether each statement represents a Mormon belief (M) or a Christian belief (C).

____ 1. God is continuing to give revelation to His prophets.
____ 2. Every person who was ever born on earth was our spirit brother or spirit sister in heaven.
____ 3. Jesus Christ is God incarnate, the eternal Son of God.
____ 4. The Heavenly Father physically sired Jesus Christ in the same way all children are sired.
____ 5. Jesus' atonement provided immortality for all people but does not provide for complete salvation.
____ 6. Salvation is entirely God's work by grace through faith.
____ 7. We experience eternal life by achieving a state of exaltation or godhood in the Celestial Kingdom.
____ 8. The gospel is the good news of the death, burial, and resurrection of Jesus Christ and His complete atonement for sin for all who repent and accept Him.
____ 9. God possesses a body of flesh and bones and therefore is limited and cannot be present everywhere.
____ 10. God is spirit and does not have a body; therefore, He is not limited by space and is eternal.
____ 11. Four standard works constitute the written authority for truth.
____ 12. The Bible alone is Scripture.

Session 5: The Jehovah's Witnesses

Choose the correct answers to complete the following sentences.

1. The founder of Jehovah's Witnesses was (Charles Taze Russell, Brigham Young, Oliver Cromwell).
2. Russell was obsessed with disproving the existence of (Jesus Christ, hell, the Christian church).
3. Russell published his opinions about Jesus' second coming in an attempt to prove that Jesus Christ had returned to earth in (1874, 1968, 70).
4. The only interpretations of Scripture allowed by Jehovah's Witnesses are the ones produced by (the Governing Body of the Watchtower, Jehovah's Witness missionaries, the Gideons).
5. The only name of God accepted by Jehovah's Witnesses is (Elohim, Yahweh, Jehovah).
6. Jehovah's Witnesses believe that the Holy Spirit is merely God's (angels, ideas, invisible force) in the world.
7. Jehovah's Witnesses assert that Jesus Christ is not God but (Lucifer, Gabriel, Michael).

Session 6: The Church of Christ, Scientist

The left column lists statements Christian Scientists believe. Match them with the possible responses a FAITH Team member could make.

___ 1. Mary Baker Eddy has given me the guide to truth.
___ 2. Sin is merely an illusion.
___ 3. God is Mind, Truth, and Love.
___ 4. Angels are God's thoughts passing to humans.
___ 5. The Holy Ghost is the development of eternal life, truth, and love.
___ 6. To correctly understand the Bible, you must not interpret it literally but metaphysically.
___ 7. Only that which reflects God's nature is real.
___ 8. Don't seek medical treatment. Just realize your divinity.
___ 9. Heaven is not an actual place. Death is a transition from the illusion of life to the truth of the immortal spirit.

a. Sin is a reality. All humans are sinners.
b. Everyone must face death. Heaven is a real place that awaits those who put their faith in Jesus Christ.
c. The Holy Spirit is the third person of the Godhead.
d. The Bible is the only authoritative guide for truth and faith.
e. Some of these terms describe God's nature but are not synonyms for who He is.
f. All matter is real. God created matter.
g. The Bible is the inerrant, inspired Word of God, and its meaning is clear and understandable.
h. Sickness is real. We are never commanded in the Bible to reject medical treatment.
i. God created angels for His worship and service. They are real beings who are separate from God.

Session 7: The Unity School of Christianity

Check the biblical teachings that would be the most helpful in effectively reaching a person involved in Unity/New Thought.

❑ 1. The deity of Christ
❑ 2. The Ten Commandments
❑ 3. The nature of God
❑ 4. The biblical way of salvation
❑ 5. Christ's intent for marriage
❑ 6. Christian stewardship
❑ 7. The proper view of humankind

Session 8: The Unitarian-Universalist Association of Churches

Check guidelines for witnessing to Unitarian-Universalists.

NOTES

NOTES

- ❑ 1. Appeal to your own experience, because Unitarian-Universalists heavily rely on experience.
- ❑ 2. Discover exactly what the Unitarian-Universalist believes.
- ❑ 3. Be especially gentle, humble, and nonjudgmental.
- ❑ 4. Be prepared to use reason.
- ❑ 5. Be vague in your use of Scripture so that you don't offend them.
- ❑ 6. Be conscious of issues of equality.
- ❑ 7. Be sensitive to environmental issues.
- ❑ 8. Summarize what Unitarian-Universalists are supposed to believe.
- ❑ 9. Present arguments for God's existence.
- ❑ 10. Emphasize the danger of idolatry.
- ❑ 11. Persistently point the way to God.

Session 9: The Unification Church

Underline the answers that best describe Sun Myung Moon's teaching.

1. The Unification Church teaches that all world history is to be understood in terms of a cosmic (explosion, dualism, force).
2. God is described as (Force, Universal Prime Energy, Cosmic Force Field), which energizes a constant give-and-take interaction.
3. Eve's illicit relationship with (Satan, Adam, Noah) produced an evil bloodline through Cain.
4. The Unification Church believes that Jesus failed to redeem humanity because He never (sinned, married and produced children, taught His disciples thoroughly).
5. According to Moon, (Satan, Moon himself, Hitler) has formally apologized to God and repented of his disobedience.
6. Cosmic reconciliation is being realized through Moon's work in the world, bringing about a new age of world history called the (Second Advent, Marriage of the Lamb, Completed Testament).
7. Moon's followers acknowledge him as the (Heavenly Father, Lord of the Second Advent, Divine Ruler).
8. All people may receive the benefits of Moon's messiahship by being grafted into his (college system, Unified Vine, True Family).

Session 10: The Oneness Pentecostal Movement

Identify the following statements as true (*T*) or false (*F*).

___ 1. The origin of Oneness Pentecostal beliefs can be traced to R. E. McAlister.

___ 2. One of the largest Oneness Pentecostal organizations in North America is the United Pentecostal Church International.

___ 3. Evangelical Christians and Oneness Pentecostals agree on the biblical view of the Trinity.

___ 4. Evangelical Christians and Oneness Pentecostals agree on the inspiration and authority of the Bible.

___ 5. The Trinitarian view states that there is only one God, who exists in three separate and eternal persons—the Father, the Son, and the Holy Spirit.

___ 6. Oneness Pentecostals believe that the Godhead consists of only two persons—the Son and the Holy Spirit.

___ 7. Oneness Pentecostals baptize converts in the name of the Father, the Son, and the Holy Spirit, just as evangelical Christians do.

___ 8. Although Oneness Pentecostals do not agree with the biblical view of the Trinity, they regard a person's salvation as genuine no matter what he or she believes about the Godhead.

___ 9. Oneness Pentecostals believe that water baptism is required for salvation.

___ 10. Oneness Pentecostals believe that speaking in tongues is essential for salvation.

Session 11: The Church of Scientology, International

Underline the correct word or words in each group of choices.

1. The founder of the Church of Scientology was (Mary Baker Eddy, L. Ron Hubbard, Sun Myung Moon).
2. Before establishing the Church of Scientology, its founder was (a science-fiction writer, an astronaut, a Baptist minister).
3. Scientology teaches that negative thoughts in the mind, called (habits, sinful thoughts, engrams), cause negative traits in the personality.
4. Scientologists use an (electropsychometer, electrode, encoder) to identify negative information that needs to be removed from a person's reactive mind to allow the person to succeed.
5. When a person reaches the goal of total freedom from all engrams through therapy with an auditor, he is in a state called (E-freedom, clear, perfection).
6. The term Hubbard used to define the soul is (spirit, collective mind, thetan).
7. Scientology teaches that when a person dies, he moves down the time track through (space-time travel, reincarnation, spatial continuums).

Session 13: The International Churches of Christ

Underline the best word or phrase to complete each sentence.

1. The primary doctrinal error of the International Churches of Christ is their (view of angels, denial of Christ's virgin birth, view of salvation by works).
2. Implied guilt and (Scripture twisting, Bible study, singing) are used to manipulate members in the International Churches of Christ.
3. The moment of salvation happens when a member of an International Church of Christ (tithes, leaves his family, is baptized).
4. Disciples are encouraged to tithe. If they do not have money, they are encouraged to (make a pledge, pray, borrow money).

NOTES

NOTES

5. Members are taught that only members of (their particular church, a mainline Church of Christ, a FAITH church) are saved.
6. The International Churches of Christ target (other churches, assisted-living complexes, college campuses) to recruit new members.
7. An effective way to reach an International Church of Christ member is to offer (tea and crumpets, acceptance and ministry, free Bibles).

Session 14: The Seventh-day Adventist Church

Check the statements that represent Seventh-day Adventist doctrines.

- ❑ 1. The biblical doctrine of the Trinity is affirmed.
- ❑ 2. The unique deity of Christ is affirmed.
- ❑ 3. Seventh-day Adventists are the remnant church of the last days.
- ❑ 4. The correct day for worship is Saturday, the true Sabbath.
- ❑ 5. The day you worship is not important as long as you worship.
- ❑ 6. Worshiping on Sunday is the mark of the beast.
- ❑ 7. Jesus is weeding out false believers until He returns.
- ❑ 8. Salvation is eternally secured by grace through faith in Christ.
- ❑ 9. When Christians die, they enter an unconscious state of soul sleep.
- ❑ 10. When Christians die, they are immediately in Jesus' presence.
- ❑ 11. The unsaved suffer eternal separation from God in hell.
- ❑ 12. There is no hell. Lost people are annihilated.

Session 15: The Word of Faith Movement

Check the statements that accurately describe Word of Faith teachings.

- ❑ 1. Faith must center on God's wisdom and power.
- ❑ 2. The spoken word has supernatural power.
- ❑ 3. You must have faith in faith.
- ❑ 4. No one has seen God.
- ❑ 5. God stands ready to meet our demands.
- ❑ 6. Human beings are potential gods.
- ❑ 7. Humans are incapable of exercising divine power on their own.
- ❑ 8. Humanity's problem is ignorance.
- ❑ 9. Faith is placed in God's power to conquer evil.
- ❑ 10. God sometimes allows sickness and difficulties.
- ❑ 11. Human frailty is never God's will for believers.
- ❑ 12. The Bible must be interpreted in light of new revelations.
- ❑ 13. Individual spiritual experiences must be judged by God's Word.

Grade your written review as your Facilitator gives the answers. Each item counts one point; the highest possible score is 121. Subtract the number you missed from this total to get your score.

Highest possible score:	121
Number missed:	– ______
My score:	= ______

Verbal Review: FAITH Visit Outline

NOTES

❑ Preparation

❑ INTRODUCTION
❑ INTERESTS
❑ INVOLVEMENT
❑ Church Experience/Background
- ❑ • Ask about the person's church background.
- ❑ • Listen for clues about the person's spiritual involvement.

❑ Sunday School Testimony
- ❑ • Tell general benefits of Sunday School.
- ❑ • Tell a current personal experience.

❑ Evangelistic Testimony
- ❑ • Tell a little of your preconversion experience.
- ❑ • Say: "I had a life-changing experience."
- ❑ • Tell recent benefits of your conversion.

❑ INQUIRY
❑ **Key Question:** In your personal opinion, what do you understand it takes for a person to go to heaven?
❑ **Possible Answers:** Faith, works, unclear, no opinion
❑ **Transition Statement:** I'd like to share with you how the Bible answers this question, if it is all right. There is a word that can be used to answer this question: FAITH (spell out on fingers).

❑ Presentation

❑ F is for FORGIVENESS
❑ We cannot have eternal life and heaven without God's forgiveness.
❑ *"In Him [meaning Jesus] we have redemption through His blood, the forgiveness of sins"—Ephesians 1:7a, NKJV.*

❑ A is for AVAILABLE
❑ Forgiveness is available. It is—

❑ AVAILABLE FOR ALL
❑ *"For God so loved the world that He gave His only begotten Son, that whoever believes in Him should not perish but have everlasting life"—John 3:16, NKJV.*

NOTES

❑ BUT NOT AUTOMATIC

❑ *"Not everyone who says to Me, 'Lord, Lord,' shall enter the kingdom of heaven"—Matthew 7:21a, NKJV.*

❑ ***I* is for IMPOSSIBLE**

❑ It is impossible for God to allow sin into heaven.

❑ **GOD IS—**

❑ • LOVE

❑ *John 3:16, NKJV*

❑ • JUST

❑ *"For judgment is without mercy"—James 2:13a, NKJV.*

❑ **MAN IS SINFUL**

❑ *"For all have sinned and fall short of the glory of God" —Romans 3:23, NKJV.*

❑ **Question:** But how can a sinful person enter heaven, where God allows no sin?

❑ ***T* is for TURN**

❑ **Question:** If you were driving down the road and someone asked you to turn, what would he or she be asking you to do? (change direction)

❑ *Turn* means *repent*.

❑ **TURN** from something—sin and self

❑ *"But unless you repent you will all likewise perish"—Luke 13:3b, NKJV.*

❑ **TURN** to Someone; trust Christ only

❑ (The Bible tells us that) *"Christ died for our sins according to the Scriptures, and that He was buried, and that He rose again the third day according to the Scriptures"—1 Corinthians 15:3b-4, NKJV.*

❑ *"If you confess with your mouth the Lord Jesus and believe in your heart that God has raised Him from the dead, you will be saved" —Romans 10:9, NKJV.*

❑ ***H* is for HEAVEN**

❑ Heaven is eternal life.

❑ **HERE**

❑ *"I have come that they may have life, and that they may have it more abundantly"—John 10:10b, NKJV.*

❑ **HEREAFTER**

❑ *"And if I go and prepare a place for you, I will come again and receive you to Myself; that where I am, there you may be also" —John 14:3, NKJV.*

❑ HOW

❑ How can a person have God's forgiveness, heaven and eternal life, and Jesus as personal Savior and Lord?

❑ Explain based on leaflet picture, FAITH (Forsaking All, I Trust Him), Romans 10:9.

❑ Invitation

❑ INQUIRE

❑ Understanding what we have shared, would you like to receive this forgiveness by trusting in Christ as your personal Savior and Lord?

❑ INVITE

❑ • Pray to accept Christ.

❑ • Pray for commitment/recommitment.

❑ • Invite to join Sunday School.

❑ INSURE

❑ • Use A *Step of Faith* to insure decision.

❑ • Personal Acceptance

❑ • Sunday School Enrollment

❑ • Public Confession

Grade your verbal review. Each item counts one point; the highest possible score is 67. Subtract the number you missed from this total to get your score.

Highest possible score: 67

Number missed: – ______

My score: = ______

NOTES

NOTES

Visitation Time

Do It

1. Your visitation schedule may be altered tonight. Allow for any schedule changes your church has agreed on.
2. Encourage Learners to make the gospel presentation by themselves.
3. Urge your Team members to continue FAITH training next semester and to continue using the FAITH Visit Outline to witness.
4. Encourage Teams to return for a special Celebration Time.

Celebration Time

Share It

1. Ask a Team member to take the lead in sharing reports.
2. Hear reports and testimonies.
3. Complete Evaluation Cards.
4. Complete Participation Cards.
5. Update visitation forms with the results of visits.
6. Allow time for testimonies about what this semester of FAITH has meant to participants and to the persons they have visited.

Home Study Assignments

Home Study Assignments reinforce this session by helping you apply what you have learned.

Your Discipleship Journey

Journaling activities in Your Discipleship Journey are an important part of your development as a Great Commission Christian through FAITH training.

1. Read the following Scriptures and record the instruction the apostle Paul gave for living in the last days.

   2 Timothy 3:10-17: ______________________________

   ____

   ____

   ____

   ____

   2 Timothy 4:1-5: ______________________________

   ____

   ____

   ____

2. Many cults hold biblically inaccurate views of the second coming. What should a believer's position be in the last days, according to 2 Thessalonians 2:13-17?

   ____

   ____

   ____

   ____

   ____

3. As we engage in spiritual warfare against false teaching, what should our attitude be, and what precautions should we take, according to Jude 20-25?

____

____

____

____

Growing as a Life Witness

Growing as a Life Witness reminds you of your responsibility to witness and minister to others during the week.

1. Talk or meet with your accountability partner and share ways you have cultivated a lost person or have witnessed or ministered on occasions other than FAITH visits.
2. Discuss your responses to activities in Your Discipleship Journey. Share your plans for future participation in FAITH training.
3. Pray for lost persons by name and for each other.

Prayer Concerns	Answers to Prayer
____________________	____________________
____________________	____________________
____________________	____________________
____________________	____________________
____________________	____________________

Your Weekly Sunday School Leadership Meeting

A FAITH participant is an important member of Sunday School. Encourage Team members who are elected Sunday School workers to attend this weekly meeting. Use this section to record ways your FAITH Team influences the work of your Sunday School class or department. Use the information to report during weekly Sunday School leadership meetings. Identify actions that need to be taken through Sunday School as a result of prayer concerns, needs identified, visits made by the Team, and decisions made by the persons visited. Also identify ways you can disciple others in your Sunday School class or department and in your church.

1. Highlight needs/reports affecting your class/department or age group.

____

____

2. Pray for your teacher and department director.

3. What are ways the department/class can celebrate the Holy Spirit's work through members who have participated in FAITH training?

____

____

4. What actions can be taken to encourage members and leaders to prepare for the next semester of FAITH training?

____

____

5. How does preparation for Sunday need to consider persons who might attend because they received a witness by members during the week?

____

____

For Further Growth

For Further Growth may include additional reading or activities that will enhance your growth as a disciple and a discipler of others. These assignments are intended to be long-term projects and do not have to be completed during this semester of study.

1. Periodically review the material in this course to stay fresh in your battle for the truth.
2. Participate in a group study of *Fresh Encounter* by Henry T. Blackaby and Claude V. King (LifeWay, 1993) to understand God's pattern for personal revival.
3. Continue serving in the FAITH ministry by reaching the lost and by training Christians to reach others for Christ.

FAITH AT WORK

I always wanted to share my faith but did not know how. Nervous around people, I had a hard time just carrying on a conversation with a friend, much less going into a home and sharing the good news. So I prayed for two years about my desire to share my faith.

One night at church I heard about the FAITH strategy. Through it people learned to share with others the good new of Jesus Christ. I asked God to use me to witness to others. I started FAITH two years ago and have not stopped.

I went out every week with the Team to witness, but I also wanted to tell my loved ones about Jesus because I wanted my whole family to be in heaven with me. I shared with my mom, who was already a Christian. I shared with my dad, who was not a believer but later accepted Christ as his personal Savior and Lord. I shared with my nephew, whom I was keeping during the summer, and he was saved. Not a week goes by when God doesn't show me someone looking for something, and that something is Jesus.

My most recent witnessing experience was with a young neighbor who had just graduated from high school. My husband and I invited him over for supper one night. He did not attend church and showed no signs of salvation. We gave him a graduation gift. Then I told him I wanted to share a greater gift with him, and I presented the FAITH gospel presentation. In response he said that he knew he was not saved and wanted to accept Jesus, but he was not ready.

Since then the young man has been attending church and shows strong signs of conviction. However, what touched my heart most was a letter he wrote to me and my husband explaining that he would never forget the expressions on our faces when he told us that he would go to hell if he died that night. He said that was the first time in his life anyone had shown enough interest in him to share the gospel with him. He said that no one had ever cared enough about him to worry about where he would spend eternity.

That is what keeps me going. People may know that you care, but do you care enough to share the gospel with them? FAITH and Jesus showed me how.

Catherine Laffoon
Eastside Baptist Church
Paragould, Arkansas

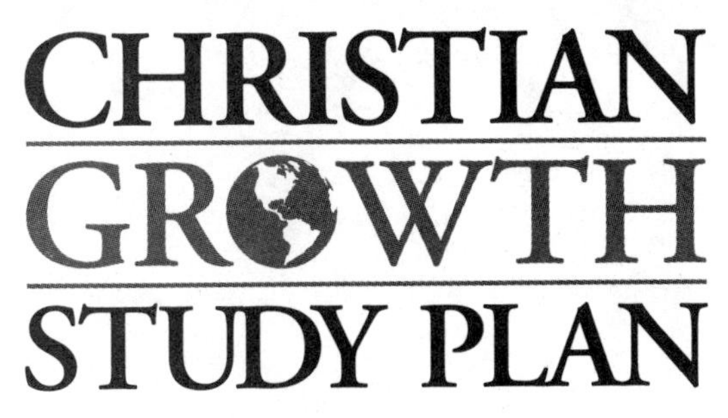

Preparing Christians to Serve

In the Christian Growth Study Plan (formerly the Church Study Course), *Faith Reaching Out to Cults* is a resource for course credit in the subject area Evangelism in the Christian Growth category of diploma plans. To receive credit, read the book; complete the learning activities; attend group sessions; show your work to your pastor, a staff member, or a church leader; then complete the following information. This page may be duplicated. Send the completed page to:

Christian Growth Study Plan, MSN 117
127 Ninth Avenue, North
Nashville, TN 37234-0117
Fax (615) 251-5067

For information about the Christian Growth Study Plan, refer to the current *Christian Growth Study Plan Catalog*. Your church office may have a copy. If not, request a free copy from the Christian Growth Study Plan office, (615) 251-2525.

Faith Reaching Out to Cults
COURSE NUMBER: CG-0607

PARTICIPANT INFORMATION

Social Security Number (USA ONLY)	Personal CGSP Number*	Date of Birth (MONTH, DAY, YEAR)
Name (First, Middle, Last)	Home Phone	
Address (Street, Route, or P.O. Box)	City, State, or Province	Zip/Postal Code

CHURCH INFORMATION

Church Name		
Address (Street, Route, or P.O. Box)	City, State, or Province	Zip/Postal Code

CHANGE REQUEST ONLY

☐ Former Name		
☐ Former Address	City, State, or Province	Zip/Postal Code
☐ Former Church	City, State, or Province	Zip/Postal Code

Signature of Pastor, Conference Leader, or Other Church Leader	Date

*New participants are requested but not required to give SS# and date of birth. Existing participants, please give CGSP# when using SS# for the first time. Thereafter, only one ID# is required. **Mail to:** Christian Growth Study Plan, 127 Ninth Ave., North, Nashville, TN 37234-0117. Fax: (615)251-5067

Rev. 6-99

Your Faith
Is for Living and Sharing

FAITH Discipleship: Sharing a Living Faith

Sharing a Living Faith is a FAITH Discipleship course that will set you on a course of growth as a Great Commission witness.

Develop a Biblical Belief System

Anchor your faith in the Word of God so that you will be confident of what you believe and why you believe it.

Become a More Effective Witness

Learn how to explain what you believe when you have opportunities to share in-depth with someone or when you are asked difficult questions like the following.

- How do I know the Bible is true?
- Does God exist?
- Is Jesus really God's Son?
- Who is the Holy Spirit?
- Why does evil exist?
- Why does God allow suffering?
- What does it mean to be lost?
- What does it mean to be saved?
- Why do I need the church?
- Are Bible study and prayer important?
- How can I find strength for daily living?
- What is the purpose of life?
- How can I overcome spiritual obstacles?

Strengthen Your Skills as a Team Leader

Practice sharing your faith, disciple your Team members, and interact with new Sunday School members who are won to faith in Christ.

The following resources are provided for FAITH churches.

- *FAITH Discipleship: Sharing a Living Faith, Journal,* item 0-7673-9345-7, $9.95
- *FAITH Discipleship: Sharing a Living Faith, Facilitator Guide,* item 0-7673-9334-1, $15.95
- *FAITH Discipleship: Sharing a Living Faith, Training Pack,* item 0-6330-0300-X, $149.95

To order, write to LifeWay Church Resources Customer Service; 127 Ninth Avenue, North; Nashville, TN 37234-0113; fax (615) 251-5933; call toll free (800) 458-2772; or email *customerservice@lifeway.com*.

FAITH DISCIPLESHIP
Journal
FAITH
Reaching Out to World Religions